# BABYMAKING

## THE TECHNOLOGY AND ETHICS

SUSAN DOWNIE

THE BODLEY HEAD
LONDON

Efforts were made to contact all possible holders of copyright material, and failure to include acknowledgement here is no indication of intent to avoid such acknowledgement. Any omissions notified to the publishers will be included in future editions.

A CIP catalogue record for this book is available from the British Library

ISBN 0–370–31136–1
0–370–31137–X (Pbk)



Printed in Great Britain for
The Bodley Head Ltd,
32 Bedford Square,
London WC1B 3EL
by The Alden Press,
Oxford

*First published in 1988*

# CONTENTS

# LIST OF PHOTOGRAPHS

# PREFACE

The overriding aim in writing *Babymaking* has been to stimulate public debate on this controversial and important issue. Assisted reproduction is advancing at such an extraordinary rate today that it is difficult for the public to keep up. But because it directly affects so many people—an estimated 35–105 million people, or one in six couples worldwide—and because it questions our most basic everyday ethics it is important that the community should take an active part in the decision-making process which in several countries has already led to legislation.

The ethical, religious, political, financial and psychological implications of the new babymaking techniques are extremely complex and emotional, and the public should be made aware of them. It is hard to turn the clock back on science and if we are to regulate and control high-tech babymaking it requires immediate attention. The doctors and scientists are encouraging public participation. Contrary to popular opinion they are not shut away in laboratories behind locked doors; they are publicly asking for the community to give them guidelines, to tell them how far they should be allowed to go.

As a medical journalist in Australia in the mid-1980s I had covered some of the main events—and ethical arguments—in the new era of babymaking. I was present when the world's first test-tube quads were born in Melbourne, when fertility drug quads were born in Sydney, when Sydney's first test-tube baby was born and when the world's first frozen embryo boy was born in Melbourne, and I started to take a particular interest in the technology, ethics and politics of the new reproductive technologies.

The idea for this book was conceived over dinner in a Bangkok hotel with two test-tube baby pioneers from opposite sides of the world—Alan Trounson from Melbourne and Barry Bavister from Wisconsin—who have both encouraged and supported me enormously in the 13 months since then. They talked about the early days of *in vitro* fertilisation (IVF), how Robert Edwards hurtled up the motorway to Oldham, where Patrick Steptoe extracted eggs from women then tried to fertilise them in the laboratory, and they described how Bavister and Edwards sat up all night waiting for a sperm to penetrate an egg on a laboratory dish. They recalled the hoaxes, including the British gynaecologist who jumped up at a conference and said three test-tube babies had already been born before Steptoe and Edwards's first, and the American magazine that carried a front-cover photograph of what was said to be the first human egg fertilised in the laboratory—it turned out to be an air bubble. Trounson told how he accidentally discovered a new technique for freezing embryos.

I realised that to write a comprehensive book, coverage would have to be worldwide. Over the next year I attended a series of international conferences in the US and Europe, and visited assisted reproduction centres in Asia, the US and Europe. In between I interviewed physicians, scientists, lawyers, ethicists, patients, surrogates, politicians, feminists and Right to Life activists from 27 different countries. I visited IVF centres to see how they are run, what sort of people run them, and how they think, all of which was important in discussing the ethics of babymaking. The picture that emerged was a fascinating one.

I am indebted to Alan Trounson (Melbourne) for reading the first manuscript so meticulously, also to Howard Jones (Virginia) and Carl Wood (Melbourne) for their comments, corrections and criticisms of the manuscript, and to those who read various chapters: Ian Johnston (a special thanks) and David de Kretser (Melbourne), John Tyler (Sydney), Cappy Rothman (Los Angeles) and the late Patrick Steptoe. Thanks to Luca Gianaroli and Lidia Diandalleri (Bologna), Alan Ferrier

(New York) and Mary English (Philadelphia) for showing me various medical and laboratory procedures; and to Michael Ah Moye and Sam Abdalla (London) for so patiently answering my never-ending list of questions on gynaecology. Thanks also to the Office of Technology Assessment in Washington and the WHO Human Reproduction Unit in Geneva for allowing me access to panel discussions and co-operation in talking with committee members; and to the libraries of the American Medical Association, the Californian Medical Association, the *San Francisco Chronicle*, the *Straits Times* (Singapore) and the Royal Society of Medicine (London) that supplied a continuous stream of material. My thanks to the other 240 people who gave me their time and the numerous others who sent papers and clippings. And a special thanks to Rina Paas (Hobart) and Carol Walker (Scotland) for their 'man-in-the-street' assessment of the manuscript.

S. J. D. January 1988

# AUTHOR'S NOTE

At the end of the book is a glossary on the technical terms of babymaking. Terms in the glossary are italicised when they first appear in the text. *He* is used rather than *he/she* or *it* when discussing babies and children. Although not all people seeking infertility treatment are married, *husband* and *wife* and *couple* are assumed to include *boyfriend* and *girlfriend* and those in *de facto* relationships. Mr is only used to identify a person holding the position of medical surgeon. Unless stated otherwise, all prices are in the currency of the country being discussed. All quotations not referenced have been made in personal communications or correspondence with the author.

# CHRONOLOGY

1790 First reported birth from artificial insemination with husband's sperm, in Britain
1890 First reported birth using donor sperm in artificial insemination, in the US
1878 First reported attempts to fertilise mammalian eggs outside the body
1944 John Rock claimed to have fertilised human eggs *in vitro*
1959 First test-tube (IVF) animals—rabbits—born in the US
1959 Daniele Petrucci showed a film of what he said were human IVF embryos
1963 Japanese girl agreed to be a paid surrogate for an infertile couple
Early 1960s Laparoscopy introduced to the UK and US by Patrick Steptoe
March 1968 Robert Edwards and Barry Bavister fertilised the first human egg *in vitro*
April 1968 Steptoe and Edwards teamed up to work on IVF
Late 1970 The Melbourne IVF team was set up by Carl Wood
Early 1973 Melbourne team achieved two early IVF pregnancies
April 1975 First known surrogacy advertisement appeared in a US newspaper. Baby born September 1977
July 1978 First IVF baby, Louise Brown, born in Oldham, England
January 1979 Second IVF baby, Alistair Montgomery, born in Glasgow, Scotland

May 1979 US Health Department approved IVF and embryo research in principle

June 1980 Australia's first and world's third IVF baby, Candice Reed, born in Melbourne

November 1980 America's first contracted surrogate, Elizabeth Kane, gave birth

December 1981 America's first IVF baby, Elizabeth Carr, born in Norfolk, Virginia

May 1982 Victorian Government set up the Waller Committee

July 1982 British Government set up the Warnock Committee

January 1984 First surrogate embryo transfer baby born in California

January 1984 First IVF quads born in Melbourne

January 1984 First donor embryo baby born in Melbourne

March 1984 First frozen embryo baby, Zoe Leyland, born in Melbourne

June 1984 Rios couple killed, leaving two 'orphan' embryos frozen in Melbourne

June 1984 Britain's Warnock Committee third and final report released

August 1984 Victoria's Waller Committee's final report released

November 1984 Victorian Government legislated on IVF, surrogacy and embryo research

November 1984 First donor egg baby born in Melbourne

January 1985 'Baby Cotton', Britain's first commercial surrogate baby, born

March 1985 Sweden's new law on artificial insemination came into force

Spring 1985 'Geep' (sheep/goat) chimera born at UC Davis, California

May 1985 First GIFT baby born to Scottish woman treated in Texas

June 1985 British Government legislated against commercial surrogacy

November 1985 West Germany's Benda Committee report released

July 1986 First frozen egg babies (twins) born, in South Australia
September 1986 American Fertility Society released guidelines on new reproductive technologies
December 1986 French National Ethics Committee report released
March 1987 New Jersey court ruled William Stern could keep 'Baby M'
August 1987 Fertility drug septuplets born in Liverpool, England
October 1987 Surrogate grandmother gave birth to her daughter's IVF triplets in Johannesburg
December 1987 Victorian Government decided to allow Rios embryos to be used anonymously
December 1987 European Parliament considered recommendations on reproductive technologies
December 1987 British Government released white paper on IVF and embryo research
January 1988 1,000th IVF baby born to the Steptoe-Edwards team, Cambridge
March 1988 IVF pioneer Patrick Steptoe died
April 1988 British Government legislated to give DI children legal status

# I
# WHAT'S ALL THE FUSS ABOUT?

'In the beginning, God created the universe . . . and man,'
*Genesis 1–2*

In 1968, Robert Edwards created an embryo, and a whole new world of science fiction came true. The British scientist's laboratory fertilisation of a human egg was relatively simple in principle but it created an ethical, moral, legal and political debate never before seen in medicine. This was partly because it involved handling early human life, partly because people saw it leading to cloning, gene manipulation and sex selection, and perhaps even 'birth' without a womb, all of which were at the time labelled 'bad'. Ten years after the birth of his first test-tube baby in 1978, the controversy it caused is far from solved; if anything, it is more complicated.

Embryologist Robert Edwards and gynaecologist Patrick Steptoe realised that the work they were doing in the cramped laboratory at Oldham Hospital in the north of England in the 1960s would be controversial, but they underestimated the public and media interest and criticism of their 'brave new world' technology. Almost 20 years after they first reported *in vitro fertilisation* (IVF) of a human egg (in *Nature*, February 1969), IVF is an established, although not very successful, technique for overcoming infertility. Along with heart and liver transplants, it is also one of the most controversial practices in modern medicine.

The 'test-tube baby technique' is no longer a matter of just mixing wife's egg and husband's sperm in a laboratory dish. Variations on a simple theme have led scientists to devise ways of freezing, injecting, biopsying, splitting, selecting and inadvertently destroying eggs and embryos, all of which have sent doctors, lawyers, ethicists and politicians in a merry dance to find ways of controlling the high-tech baby business.

Committees have been set up all over the world to consider twentieth-century babymaking, dozens of conferences have been held on the subject and tons of newsprint devoted to the controversy. Some physicians and scientists have been ostracised, had their laboratory equipment destroyed, been threatened with jail sentences, received death threats and been prevented from entering their laboratories by armed guards. Many infertile patients have willingly been scientific guinea pigs or mortgaged their houses to pay for treatment. One 46-year-old woman from Thailand went to Chicago for treatment three times and returned without a baby, after spending almost one million baht—$US38,000 or the equivalent of about 18 years' wages for the average Thai worker. Others have gone through heart-wrenching court battles to keep the babies they have borne. There was even a court case in the US over 'kidnapped' embryos.

So what's all the fuss about?

Several principles are being debated. One of the most fundamental is whether having children is a right. The United Nations Declaration of Human Rights speaks of the 'right to marry and found a family'. The Catholic Church believes a child is 'the supreme gift' from the Creator, not a right. Lori Andrews, research fellow with the American Bar Association and a women's activist, believes women not only have the right to reproduce but should be allowed to have children by whatever alternative methods are available, without judgement on whether they are fit to be parents. Boston lawyer Nancy Gertner agrees, and says women have the right to become pregnant and to carry the pregnancy regardless of race, colour, religious creed, age, national origin, marital status, sexual preference, genotype or disability. She believes the law should maximise reproductive choice and suggests that those who interfere should be sued for damages.

Whether we are doing the right thing by creating substitutes for natural functions depends on people's religious, cultural and social outlook. Buddhists, for example, have no objection to women being artificially inseminated with another man's sperm, while orthodox Catholics regard it as adultery, and strict Moslems are not allowed to masturbate and therefore cannot produce sperm for artificial conception.

Then there is the question of whether reproductive technologies such as IVF can be justified, financially and morally. Some people argue that there is no need for babymaking assistance in overcrowded countries. China, for example, with a population of more than one billion and very strict birth controls, already has two IVF centres and a third planned. With a population of 800 million India is also terribly overpopulated but has at least three IVF centres. If declining population growth was the only criterion for allowing IVF centres, the only two Asian countries to have them would be Singapore and Japan. Instead there are at least 17 centres in the region.

Sadly, in all populations, however overcrowded, there is a proportion of people who want children and find they cannot have them. Should they be denied the option of having a family of their own just because their fellow citizens have children?

One ethical question often overlooked is the cost of infertility services such as IVF, especially in developing countries, in relation to other medical needs. IVF is now offered in several countries that might be considered to have higher medical priorities, including India, Thailand, Malaysia, Argentina, Chile, Colombia and Nigeria.

However, the questionable distribution of resources is not limited to developing countries. Possibly one billion dollars a year is spent on infertility in the US, while 20 per cent of American children live in poverty, and by the time they start school more than 40 per cent have not been immunised against even one of the five preventable childhood diseases.

Other people complain that vast amounts of money are spent on infertility treatment that only benefits a small proportion of the population. But an estimated 15 per cent of the world's couples of childbearing age are involuntarily infertile, giving a total of 35–105 million people. As Dr Patrick Rowe, director of the World Health Organisation's Infertility Task Force, said, 'Fifty million people is a lot of people to ignore.'

To most people these issues are academic, but one of the

most controversial aspects of assisted reproduction is whether it is morally right to begin life outside the body, what moral and legal status the laboratory-created embryo should have, and how far scientists should be allowed to go.

The Catholic Church believes an embryo is a human being, to be respected and treated as a person from the moment of conception, and his rights as a person must be recognised, including the right of every innocent human being to life.[1] Many of the modern babymaking techniques are therefore condemned by the Church. The Catholic Church and many other organisations also condemn medical research involving embryos, yet this work may lead to cures for infertility, certain blood disorders, genetic diseases and maybe cancer, as well as giving a better understanding of how the heart, brain and other organs are formed.

The only embryo procedures acceptable to the Catholic Church are prenatal diagnosis if it is done without the intention of abortion, and therapies aimed at improving the health of that particular embryo. This excludes research into therapies aimed at improving the health of other and future embryos and indeed improvements to the human race as a whole.

It could be argued that this is the equivalent of saying we will not continue to treat AIDS patients with a certain drug or therapy because it is not helping this particular patient, even though it may lead to a successful treatment or cure for future AIDS patients. The only difference between the embryo and the AIDS patient is that the embryo cannot say whether or not it wants the therapy, and the decision is made by the mother or by both parents.

One fear often expressed is that one form of babymaking will lead to another, each less acceptable than the previous—the beginning of the 'slippery slope'. First came artificial insemination, then IVF using the husband's sperm and the wife's eggs. Now, a childless couple can use donor sperm, eggs or embryos. If more than one egg is fertilised in the laboratory it can be frozen and used later. A surrogate mother can be inseminated with a man's sperm using her egg and deliver the baby, or she may conceive, then have the embryo removed and transferred to another woman, or carry a laboratory-conceived embryo.

If we thought creating human life in a test-tube sounded futuristic 10 years ago, consider some of the prospects for the next 10 years: embryo sexing, embryo surgery, cross-species fertilisation, artificial wombs and even male pregnancy. Many people fear that science will be taken to extremes, that scientists will manipulate genes and create a super-race.

It is true that scientists will probably soon have the ability to correct genetic abnormalities in embryos. And one day they may be able to replace genes in eggs and sperm before fertilisation so all subsequent offspring have that gene. The new gene could be for growth hormone—and scientists have already done it to produce 'super-mice' and extra-large sheep—or for brown eyes or brown hair or whatever features parents want their children to have. Few people are concerned about farmers having larger than normal sheep, but many are worried that the same technology may be used to create super-humans.

Scientists have successfully crossed a sheep and a goat, to produce a 'geep', by fusing the embryo of a sheep with the embryo of a goat. This type of science raises fears that human sperm may one day be used to fertilise the egg of another species, such as a baboon, or that a human egg will be fertilised with the sperm of a different mammal, known as cross-species fertilisation, although presently this is not possible.

With the technique of *amniocentesis* it is possible to tell a pregnant woman whether her baby is a boy or girl. Scientists will soon be able routinely to sex embryos in the laboratory to eliminate sex-linked diseases such as *haemophilia*, but many people are concerned that the technology will be used to 'order' boy or girl babies. If sexing was left to humans, rather than nature, we would end up with about 20 per cent more men than women, such is the preference for male babies.

The new birthing methods have also brought into question some common definitions; for example, does adultery include giving sperm to another woman through artificial insemination? Is a woman who carries an embryo for just five days a surrogate mother? When does fertilisation take place? What is the difference between an embryo and a pre-embryo? Are twins conceived or born at the same time? Is a woman still a virgin if she has artificial insemination but not intercourse?

Then there is concern about the legal complications that the new reproductive technologies have brought with them. Much-publicised legal battles such as the Rios 'orphan' embryos in Australia, the Baby Cotton surrogacy case in Britain and the Baby M controversy in the US highlighted the fact that the law was not prepared for reproduction 1980s-style.

When the American Rios millionaire couple were killed in a plane crash in 1983, they left no children but two frozen embryos in a laboratory in Australia. Did they belong to the Rios estate, the laboratory or the state? The Rios case raised broader questions: who would have the right to a frozen embryo in a divorce case? Could a couple sue a laboratory for accidentally destroying an embryo intended for a pregnancy?

One of the most controversial issues has been deciding who are the legal parents of a child born to a surrogate mother who received a donor egg and donor sperm then gave the child to an infertile couple? Such a child would have six 'parents', or participants.

Should a woman be allowed to become pregnant with her husband's sperm, stored in a sperm bank, after his death? What happens if a surrogate mother changes her mind and wants to keep the child she has delivered for another couple? Does surrogacy come under contract law? If a woman can produce eggs but not carry a baby and she asks her mother to be the surrogate, is the resultant baby the woman's child or her sister?

Human embryos can spend their first week of life in a laboratory test tube or petri dish and a baby born at 20 weeks may survive in a humidicrib—and the gap is narrowing all the time. If an expectant woman dies between the first and 20th week of pregnancy it might be possible one day for doctors to transfer the embryo or foetus to a non-human primate such as a baboon to save the life of the baby, but should it be allowed?

In 1984, American psychiatrist and lawyer Dr Judianne Densen-Gerber sent a questionnaire to more than 1,000 political, religious and professional leaders worldwide in order to draft legislation for Michigan state. In it she posed some futuristic, thought-provoking questions. Should a surrogate mother be allowed business-related tax deductions, and if so, is the uterus a depreciable asset? If a man is implanted with an embryo and has a baby, is he the mother or father, or both? If it were possible to gestate a human baby in a machine, should people be allowed to own, operate and receive compensation for such machines?

Just because science makes these technologies possible, it does not mean we have to use them. If scientists are able to create life entirely in an incubator, without a human womb, we don't have to allow it. Technically it is possible to have cows carrying babies, but is it ethical? Men in maternity wear is a distinct possibility in the future, but does that mean we should give men equal maternal rights? I say 'we' deliberately because this is something the public has to decide on, not just the doctors, lawyers and politicians.

Male pregnancy and artificial uteri are a long way from reality, but if other research is allowed to continue unchecked they will almost certainly become an extension of, or at least a side-line of, babymaking in the twenty-first century.

The question is, at what point do we stop science? Should we ever have allowed scientists to fertilise human eggs outside the body? If we had not, we would be denying tens of thousands of couples the chance to have desperately wanted children with a procedure that is relatively safe—at least to the parents, if not the embryos. And scientists would have been denied an enormous understanding of where, how and why embryos grow and implant in the human body which in the near future will help prevent ectopic pregnancies and miscarriages in all pregnancies, not just in infertile patients.

If we accept that IVF is an established practice, should we be grateful and just stop at 'the simple case'—not allow any other procedures such as egg and embryo donation or *embryo flushing*? What would we be missing out on if we stopped all further work?

Scientists are already part-way through research that will enable them to fertilise an egg with 'weak' sperm, select against sex-linked diseases such as haemophilia, test an embryo for genetic abnormalities such as *Lesch-Nyhan disease*, and terminate one abnormal foetus in a twin pregnancy. All of these will improve the chances of both fertile and infertile couples having healthy children. If we allow scientists to finish their current work but not start any new embryo research, we may be denying ourselves understanding of, and probably treatments for, cancer and other disorders in the future.

Then there is the future, the real science fiction. In the 1960s the pioneering Australian gynaecologist Professor Carl Wood tried to develop an artificial fallopian tube. In 1987 Italian gynaecologist Professor Carlo Flamigni and his team announced it had limited success in sustaining a human uterus outside the body. The survival of premature babies is improving and the time embryos can be grown in the laboratory is increasing. As the gap between the two narrows, many people, including American reproductive scientist Gary Hodgen, believe an artificial womb will be a reality within 25 years.

The sheep and cattle industry has been splitting embryos on a commercial basis for several years. Both Wood's and Hodgen's teams have the ability to do the same with human embryos, and they believe there would be sound medical reasons for doing so, but they want approval from the public before proceeding.

The one aspect of all this scientific wizardry that concerns people most is cloning, or asexual reproduction. Will it be a reality in the next decade? And what of male pregnancy? Although it is extremely dangerous, women have been known to carry a child outside the uterus. Many transsexuals (men who have surgically become women) in America and Australia have applied to have an IVF child. As equality of the sexes improves and more women take on male tasks the ultimate in equality is yet unobtainable—for men to have children. Could men of the future be medically primed to carry a child? And if so, should we allow it?

Where do we draw the line? That's what the fuss is all about.

# 2
# THE INFERTILE COUPLE

'My infertility is a blow to my self-esteem, a violation of my privacy, an assault on my sexuality, a final exam on my ability to cope, an affront to my sense of justice, a painful reminder that nothing can be taken for granted. My infertility is a break in the continuity of life. It is above all, a wound—to my body, to my psyche, to my soul.' *M.A. Jorgenson in a letter to* Resolve, *an American infertility magazine*[1]

Hippocrates, the grandfather of medicine, once proclaimed that winds from the north caused infertility, as well as epilepsy and constipation, and, he said, the southern winds could result in infertility, as well as dysentery and haemorrhoids! Many things have changed in the medical field since 400 BC, and bringing children into the world by artificial means is one of the more recent advances of medicine. For many infertile couples, the dream of a child can now be a reality. Yet, in many cases, what causes infertility is still one of the mysteries of medicine.

The inability to have children is not a twentieth-century phenomenon—there are several Biblical references to women unable to conceive, including Rachel who cried, 'Give me sons, or I shall die.'[2] But infertility is on the increase among young people in developing countries. Some authorities say it has increased threefold in the past 20 years.[3]

The ability to have children is taken for granted. Once a couple marry they are expected by society and religion 'to be fruitful and multiply' within a year or two. No one questions that they will not. It may not have even occurred to the couple themselves that one or both of them may not be able to carry out what is taken as a natural extension of marriage. Many couples—and probably an increasing number in Western countries—choose not to have children, but for those who want to, the realisation that the marriage is barren because one or both of them is infertile is a devastating experience.

Fertility, or the ability to reproduce, is a highly valued part of people's existence and an important part of evolution. It allows the human race to continue and at the same time brings great joy to millions of parents, their relatives and friends, and the community. In many societies children are a sign of the couple's wealth, while failure to produce children can lead to social disgrace and divorce. There are practical issues at stake too: children care for their parents in old age and in some cultures pray for them after their death. And having children enables the family name and inheritance to continue.

By far the majority of couples are fertile. More than 90 per cent of couples have a pregnancy within one year of trying and 96 per cent within two years.[4] Built into fertility is a process of natural selection. The majority of the reproductive cells, the eggs and sperm, that are defective die before they meet, and most foetuses with abnormalities naturally abort. An estimated 45 per cent of all pregnancies are lost before the woman even knows she is pregnant and about 15 per cent of recognised pregnancies end in miscarriage.[5]

The World Health Organisation (WHO) definition of infertility is regular, unprotected intercourse for one year without a pregnancy. But there are several flaws in this. A pregnancy that ends in a miscarriage, without a child being born, is no consolation to a couple wanting a child, and repeated miscarriage should therefore be included in the definition of infertility. Twelve months is considered by many doctors and others concerned in reproduction to be too short a time for a diagnosis. And the lack of a child after even two years does not mean a couple is unable to have children at a later date. In rare cases it may be a lack of understanding; for example, a report in the *China Daily News* in October 1986 revealed that some couples were childless because they did not know how to make babies.

Blakiston's *Medical Dictionary* defines infertility as 'involuntary reduction in reproductive ability', and demographers define it as the incapacity to produce a live child, both of which are more realistic. It is important to recognise that some people have a '*reduction* in ability' to reproduce, without being totally infertile. What is called 'infertility' may often turn out to be 'subfertility', which means a couple cannot have a child at a particular time, maybe because of drugs, stress or other environmental factors, but are still capable of producing one later on. In fact, studies show that 20–35 per cent of couples in Western countries who have unexplained infertility become pregnant without treatment, often while waiting for treatment or preparing for adoption.[6]

There is also the question of whether a person has primary or secondary infertility. Primary infertility means they have never produced a child, and secondary that they have become infertile after having at least one child, often because of a later infection. The majority of infertile people in Western countries have never had a child—studies by the WHO and others have found 70–80 per cent of those going to an infertility clinic had primary infertility—but in Africa the reverse is true, partly because of the high incidence of infection after childbirth.[7]

Rolled together, subfertility, primary and secondary infertility all come under the heading of 'infertility'.

It is only recently that male infertility has become a recognised and treatable problem. Once a taboo subject—men were meant to be infallible when it came to fertility—it is now almost fashionable to discuss the problem in Western countries, although in many societies the stigma still remains. And feminists are delighted because after centuries of blaming women for barren marriages, doctors and the public are increasingly turning their attention to men.

Doctors are also studying hormones, which are one of the most important elements of reproduction. Without them there can be no baby. They must be delivered in the right amounts at the right time—in men and women—from long before conception until after childbirth. Anatomists of antiquity thought that the *pituitary gland* (behind the eyes) secreted mucus to cool the blood and that the *thyroid gland* (in the front of the neck) lubricated the larynx. Even today scientists are still unravelling the complex action and interaction of hormones produced by these glands. And, unlike their forebears, medical experts today are also looking more intensely at the role of environmental factors such as stress and chemicals.

## HOW COMMON IS INFERTILITY?

A major government survey in Australia in November 1986 found that one-third of those questioned said they, their spouse, a member of their family or a friend had a fertility problem. Just over half said they did not know anyone with a problem, 20 per cent said a friend did, 7 per cent said someone in their family did and 5 per cent said either they or their partner had a fertility problem. Another 15 per cent did not answer the question and the researchers commented that it was possible that some of them did have a problem but chose not to identify themselves.[8]

It is now recognised, and supported by several studies including those by the WHO, that up to 15 per cent of couples worldwide are involuntarily infertile, giving a total of between 35 and 105 million people of reproductive age who want, but cannot have, children. Studies show 5–10 per cent of couples in Western countries fall into this category but the percentage is much higher in developing countries.[9]

No one knows the exact numbers, but the huge difference (35–105 million) is because of variation between countries, the fact that it is an estimate—there have not been enough good studies to give a more accurate account—and the sheer numbers involved. The variation is 70 million, which could be the difference between someone estimating the incidence of infertility in China to be 15 per cent and someone else estimating it to be 8 per cent.

It is important, when someone quotes a figure, to check which country they are talking about and who is included as 'infertile'. Said IVF pioneer, Professor Robert Edwards, who now runs one of the most successful infertility clinics in the world, 'We must be careful to note the area and the community when assessing the data.' The most commonly repeated mistake in America and Britain is to say, 'One in six couples are infertile,' which is true in Africa and other developing countries but not in the US, where it is one in 12 couples (or 8.4 per cent), according to the US Office of Technology Assessment and other authorities.[10]

A major study in Bristol, in the west of England, in 1985 concluded that one in six couples seeks medical help to conceive.[11] As there have been no other studies of this size, it is the one usually quoted. However, Bristol is not representative of Britain as a whole because it has a higher than average standard of living, and those seeking medical help are not necessarily infertile. Most UK authorities assume the rate is about the same as in the US and generally say 5–10 per cent of couples of childbearing age are involuntarily infertile. On the other hand, some experts believe the Bristol study could be the tip of an iceberg because some infertile couples may not declare themselves and others may divorce or find new partners.

The incidence varies enormously between countries. Some surveys have found rates of 2–5 per cent in Canada, France and India and others show it is as high as 50 per cent in some areas of Africa. It also varies markedly between groups within a country, for example studies show it is 3 per cent in some parts of Zaire and 40 per cent in other parts.[12]

Sometimes differences can be seen in distinct groups or races, especially in Africa, and a 1976 survey in the US found that twice as many black women as white had not achieved a pregnancy in the previous year.[13] This does not mean infertility is race-related, but it is more a reflection of access to, knowledge of, and use of health care and the prevalence of sexually transmitted diseases (STDs) which can cause infertility in men and women.

Infertility affects women in Africa at a much younger age than in other areas, partly because of the practice in many areas of girls marrying in their teens. Women in Third World countries, especially in Africa, are more likely to experience secondary infertility due to poor hygiene at the time of childbirth, abortion or miscarriage.

Couples in Western countries are more eager to seek a diagnosis and almost half those in a WHO study of 25 countries had waited less than two years before approaching a specialist, whereas more than two-thirds in developing countries had waited more than two and a half years, and 28 per cent of those in the east Mediterranean had waited at least eight years before seeking treatment.[14]

Generally, female infertility accounts for 50–70 per cent of all infertility and male infertility for 20–30 per cent. Another 10–20 per cent is unexplained infertility, which means doctors cannot find out why the couple do not have a pregnancy.[15] The figure for women is possibly an overestimate as men are less likely to be examined and because the woman is often blamed when the couple have unexplained infertility. The proportion of male and female infertility also varies enormously between countries.

In the WHO study, almost half the infertility in men worldwide had no known cause. In some cases the man's infertility may have a recognisable cause but it is not detected by a particular clinic because of a lack of diagnostic skills and equipment, especially in developing countries.

Whether the incidence of infertility is increasing or decreasing varies between countries and among groups within countries. It rose among young American women between 1965 and 1975, along with a rise in the incidence of gonorrhoea, but at the same time infertility fell among older women in the US.[16] There has also been a fall in many developing countries since the introduction of penicillin campaigns to prevent and treat STDs in the 1940s and 50s. In Zaire, for example, childlessness fell between 1955 and 1975 in nine provinces, in one region from 20 to 4 per cent.[17]

Studies show that statistically some people are more likely than others to be infertile. In the US it is those who are older, black, have no previous children, and have received less than a high-school education.[13]

## 'WHY ME?' – COMING TO TERMS WITH INFERTILITY

In many Asian, Mediterranean and Middle East countries it is unthinkable for the man to be responsible for the lack of children. Traditionally, masculinity means proving one can father children, preferably many. So the woman is usually blamed and sometimes discarded for a better 'breeder' when she fails to deliver a baby – then may fall pregnant to her next partner. Unable to face the humiliation of infertility in their own country, many couples go to the US, Europe and Australia for specialist treatment that includes surgery, artificial insemination and *in vitro* fertilisation. Because of the stigma of male infertility Moslem women in Western countries sometimes get pregnant by another man without their husbands knowing, and there are women—in the East and West—who go through fertility tests without telling their husbands, hoping the problem is theirs, not his.

When a couple is first diagnosed as infertile, they analyse the reasons and question whether they are to blame. Barbara Menning, founder and director of Resolve, the non-profit-making organisation set up in the US to help infertile couples, says the first reaction is surprise, followed by denial ('This can't happen to me!'), then anger. Later, they experience isolation, because many infertile couples keep their problem to themselves, and guilt which often involves analysing the past and asking whether it is because of premarital or extramarital sex, birth control, abortion, STDs, masturbation, homosexual acts and even sexual pleasure itself.[18]

Infertile couples tell how they suffer frustration and isolation because they feel they cannot tell anyone, not even their best friend. They bottle up their emotions until finally they cannot cope. They burst into tears over the most trivial incidents—a spilt cup of coffee, a flippant comment from a shop assistant or even when they miss a bus.

Kay Oke, an infertility counsellor at the Royal Women's Hospital, Melbourne, explained part of the reason:

> Infertility is embarrassing because it is a sex problem—because they cannot perform sexually. It is a topic people find hard to talk about, they hide from themselves, from friends and relatives. But when they get the courage to talk about it they find others in the same position. Often they don't know anyone else who is infertile because no one mentions it, but for all they know the person they sit next to at work may be infertile.
>
> The possibility that they will never conceive hangs in the air as an unspoken and hideous threat. The reality of infertility is taken in slowly, often with a growing sense of emptiness in life and purposelessness. One woman

> described it: 'There's just this big hole inside me, gradually taking over and I can't do anything to stop it'. People describe mystifying, irrational waves of intense feeling, of anger, depression, hurt and sadness. These well up unexpectedly and may evoke guilt and confusion or a sense of failure at not coping. Isolation and aloneness are common experiences.[19]

When all possibility of pregnancy has faded, the couple suffer grief, which Barbara Menning and others say is akin to the death of a loved one. She quotes one Resolve member as saying:

> Death before life ... before we even knew our child, because he never existed. The hardest part of this death is that it is the death of a dream. There are no solid memories, no pictures, no things to remember. You can't remember your child's blond hair, or brown eyes, or his favourite toys or the way he laughed, or the way it felt to be pregnant with him. He never existed.

Menning commented:

> Society has elaborate rituals to comfort the bereaved in death. Infertility is different. There is no funeral, no wake, no grave to lay flowers upon. Family and friends may never even know. The infertile couple often comes to this point of grief alone.[18]

Psychologist Patricia Mahlstedt, of Houston, Texas, described the effect on the infertile:

> They become critical of themselves, disillusioned, and angry . . . Internal rage may be repressed because there is no one to blame. It may manifest as depression, or it may build until it eventually is unleashed on the physician, the spouse, family, friends and God. Many patients feel a tremendous sense of guilt for being infertile, for upsetting their spouses and for disappointing their families ... Some couples believe that divorce would be more socially acceptable.
>
> Both the diagnosis and the treatment of infertility have a profound impact on people's lives. It is a process which invades one's body, one's personality, one's job, and one's mind. Diagnoses are often vague and inconclusive, and treatment is painful, intrusive and time-consuming. Com-

> mon emotional responses are depression due to multiple losses and prolonged stress; anger at the confusion, ambiguity and unfairness of it all; and intense guilt.[20]

Chairman of the British National Association for the Childless (NAC), Barbara Mostyn, who is also a counsellor at a London infertility clinic and the mother of two adopted children, says infertility is like a prison sentence:

> It feels like being given an indefinite prison sentence for a crime you didn't commit . . . The label infertile makes us feel very lonely; and very different . . . It isn't long before we react just like the innocent prisoner and become very, very angry at the injustice of it all. We get angry at medicine for failing us; all those intricate heart, kidney and corneal transplants and they can't get one *sperm*, out of millions, together with one *egg!* And the research scientists, who can manipulate the unseen atom, can't seem to help . . . Marriages are put under intense strain. Irritation builds up as communication breaks down . . . We get angry at friends who reproduce like rabbits . . . And similar to the innocent prisoner, we begin to devalue ourselves, self doubt and worse yet, guilt sets in.[21]

She says most people question whether they are being punished for previous experiences:

> Was it diet, Mum never was clued in to health foods? What about the eight years at dancing school? Or was it the tight jeans we all wore? You couldn't be teenagers and wear boxer shorts in the seventies. Was it the wild, single years—late nights, smoking, drinking and a bit of pot? Should one have so many relationships? Was it my parents' divorce? A friend's death? Should I have used the Pill, coil, cap, jelly, condom?
>
> All sorts of painful experiences are relived. The guilt feelings experienced by women who've had abortions or given up a child for adoption in years past and now want a child cannot be imagined. Such strong guilt feelings lead even the most rational and logical type of person to look for mystical meanings. Am I being punished—for my selfishness: for being horrible to my parents? For my

> materialism? For my competitiveness and unco-operativeness? Is it retribution from God? These strong feelings of guilt lead us to lose our own self-esteem and feelings of worthiness; we even begin to think we are so unworthy that we are unfit to be parents. Sadly, this leads also to destructive behaviour—alcoholism, promiscuity, divorce and in extreme cases, suicide.[21]

Although some people may find it financially easier than others to handle infertility, the emotional effect cuts across all social classes. Mostyn commented:

> In the infertility clinic setting I've met foreign diplomats, doctors, super salesmen, TV producers, barristers and research scientists—people one usually associates with being confident and assertive. But if you walked down that hallway during clinic time you might be forgiven for thinking you'd walked in to a dole-queue waiting room. The despondent, dejected look, the beaten-down expressions on faces are a sad sight to behold.[22]

These are impressions based on many years of counselling and treating the infertile. What of the patients themselves? Some express the frustration and humiliation: 'I felt I couldn't do even the most simple thing, getting pregnant.' And the loss of control: 'We resent the fact that we have no control over the most essential part of our bodies and our lives.' Others feel guilty that their infertility means their partner is childless: 'I thought my husband would be better off without me, that I should let him go so he could marry someone else and have children'; even suicidal: 'I really must make his life a misery. I even considered suicide, so my husband would be free to marry someone else and at least one of us would be happy.' Some find they act in uncharacteristic ways: 'I am experiencing feelings that are very foreign to me. I find myself *hating* the pregnant women I see at school, in the grocery store, and even in church. I have never had such intense negative feelings towards others, and I despise myself for having them.'[21,22,23]

As men and women are different, infertility affects them in different ways and for different reasons. Women, for example, not only miss out on a child, but also on pregnancy and childbirth, regarded as emotionally fulfilling and rewarding experiences. Infertility sometimes means an end to the hereditary line and men seem to find this harder to accept than women. It is often said that men are less emotional about infertility than women but they find different ways of coping with it, as Patricia Mahlstedt said, 'Perhaps he simply does not express his feelings as openly, as often, or as intensely as his wife.' She quotes one man as saying: 'I am most upset over what it is doing to her both physically and emotionally. As a result, when I do feel like crying about not having a child, I don't, because I'm afraid my crying would make her feel worse. And she believes I'm not upset. I'm playing a game and we are both losing.'[20]

Men often find the fertility tests frustrating and humiliating, especially as they have to masturbate or have intercourse at a doctor–designated time. Sometimes they put off or even refuse to submit to a sperm analysis, preferring to put the blame on the woman. In *Coping with Childlessness*, Diane and Peter Houghton (Peter is also founder and director of the National Association for the Childless) quote one woman who underestimated her husband's reaction when he was asked to submit a semen sample to the local hospital: 'This caused more problems than I ever imagined. My husband just would not return with a specimen and when I returned the doctor completely washed his hands of me saying he wasn't going to give me any fertility tests without checking my husband first.'[24]

Dr Luca Gianaroli, who runs an infertility clinic in Bologna, Italy, says men often refuse a sperm test, saying they are OK. Some ask that their wives leave the room, then tell him they know they are not infertile because they have fathered other children!

Men and women react differently to the news that they are infertile, and the process of acceptance is different. Women are more likely to talk about their problem than their husbands, according to H.J. Brand of South Africa. In a report to the 1987 World Congress for Sexology in Heidelberg, he said that a husband is often willing to discuss the problem with his wife only, whereas the wife prefers to discuss it with outsiders. His study found that the intensity of disappointment at the moment of realisation that the marriage might stay childless is significantly greater for the woman than the man. And the women reported a greater personality change after the diagnosis of infertility. Increased jealousy was the main one.[25]

In a study of patients attending the *in vitro* fertilisation (IVF) clinic at the University of Pennsylvania Hospital in 1983–4, 49 per cent of women and 15 per cent of men said their infertility was the most upsetting experience in their lives. Both men and women felt infertility was more stressful than death. But twice as many men said environmental situations (including work) were more upsetting experiences than infertility.[26]

It is often suggested that infertile people are neurotic, uptight and highly strung, but in fact psychiatrist Dr Cécile Ernst, of the University of Zurich, says research on infertile couples shows their education and socio-economic status are above average and their marriages extraordinarily stable. 'Allowing for the stress of infertility and its treatment, they appear in psychological tests and psychiatric interviews very similar to controls.'[27]

Childless couples have to cope with other people's reactions and expectations, as well as their own feelings. The loss of a child to them is also the loss of grandchildren and nieces and nephews to other family members. The reaction of parents varies from consolation to complete annihilation. The Houghtons relate how a mother said to her daughter, 'If you don't do something about it, I'm going to advertise for some grandchildren!'[28]

Some couples accept their childlessness after professional counselling and/or with the support of family and friends. Others refuse to accept their infertility and continue trying different treatments for up to 15 years. An American study found that 64 per cent of infertile couples bought dogs during their years of infertility and according to Geraldine Gage, Professor of Family Social Science at the University of Minnesota, 'In the absence of a child they can, to some extent, meet their needs with a pet.'[29]

Infertile people often devote themselves to careers and become heavily involved in sports, hobbies or recreations such as travel. As a result they are often accused of being ambitious and materialistic, when they are simply seeking substitute pleasures. Sometimes they cope with their loss by helping others and becoming involved in community services but this is not always a total outlet for their pent-up affections that would otherwise have been expended on a child. The Houghtons said, 'The childless, like those with children, wish to *give* love. The involuntary childless are deprived of the chance to give deeply committed love for a child. Most others take such an experience for granted, and may be completely unaware of the terrible deprivation felt by the childless.' They quote one woman as saying:

> I'm afraid. I've got all this love, maternal love, just waiting to be wanted and used up in me – I don't think it will ever be wanted or used. What am I going to do with it? Is it going to become anger and bitterness, or unresolved and hidden because I daren't talk about it because people will think I'm stupid or awkward to have around? It's really hard to feel your role as a person is redundant at 30. *Who is going to use my love–who needs it?*[30]

Once a couple has accepted their infertility and decided to adopt or remain childless, it is not uncommon for a pregnancy to occur, and many experts believe this is because fertility improves when a stressful situation, such as infertility itself or infertility treatment, is removed. Mary English, IVF nurse co-ordinator at the Pennsylvania Hospital in Philadelphia—the oldest hospital in the US—tells how one woman became so frantic while undergoing her first hormonal treatment that she threw her husband's clothes out of the window to 'let off steam' and became pregnant immediately afterwards.

And there are examples from patients themselves: 'She tried and tried and the moment she said "so be it", she was pregnant'; 'Having adopted a baby helped me get pregnant'; 'As soon as we decided that was it, no more treatment—bingo! I was pregnant'; and '[We] had been trying for a baby for 11 years and to be honest had given up hope. I got a job with good prospects. Financially we became able to buy our own house. We moved in and discussed adoption. The lady duly called from the agency. That night we were both on an all-time high, at last we thought we had a chance of becoming a family and for the first time in years we began to relax with each other—a month later I was pregnant.'[21,22,23]

Dr Bernard Sandler, founder-director of the Infertility Clinic at the Manchester Jewish Hospital, Britain, gives numerous examples of pregnancy occurring after the release of stress:

> A patient phones for an appointment and conception occurs before the consultation; or conception occurs after a semen analysis, even before the results are known; after a simple vaginal examination; after general reassurance; after deciding to adopt. Sharman reported several hundred cases in which conception occurred after merely passing a sound into the uterus. The only common factor in all these antecedent events is relief from tension.[21]

Sometimes the stress of the treatment itself may be a barrier to conception and some couples achieve a pregnancy when they take a break from treatment.

## OPTIONS FOR THE INFERTILE

There are really only three options for infertile couples: treatment, adoption and acceptance.

Treatments today include drugs, surgery, artificial insemination and IVF. Past remedies have included drinking various potions, having sex in certain positions and women have even been advised to stand on their heads after intercourse. One (unconfirmed) report is of an ancient fertility rite that involves the infertile couple being hit with a dried pig's bladder. This bizarre English practice is said to have been performed seven times in the last 11 years, with happy results each time.

Some couples put their faith in clairvoyance, palmistry, hypnosis and acupuncture. Many women in Italy have become pregnant after Milan faithhealer Virginia Doniselli passed her hands over them, including those who had not conceived after 12 years of trying. One British woman who became pregnant after four years of conventional treatments says her husband stopped drinking Coca Cola and was put on a carrot diet to improve his sperm and she is sure that helped. Another woman tried fertility drugs, IVF, the Billings method, aerobics, stir-fried vegetables, tender loving care, low-fat diet, cough mixture, hair analysis and God. She finally conceived and said the fertility drugs, psychological factors and the Billings method played major roles.

The traditional alternative to childlessness is adoption,

which has been used in various forms since Biblical times. In the past, it was common for other members of the family or community to take on the care of a child if the mother became ill, died, had too many children or could not cope. More recently, the usual source of adoptive babies has been single women who become unintentionally pregnant and cannot, for social or financial reasons, keep the baby. But today there is far more acceptance of single mothers, abortion is more freely available and many governments give financial assistance to single mothers, so the incentive to keep the baby is greater.

With only 4 per cent of pregnant teenagers in the US giving their babies for adoption, there is a shortage of healthy, white babies in countries such as the US and UK, and some American adoption agencies have five-to-seven-year waiting lists for such babies. However, there is no shortage of older children, or black or handicapped babies to adopt.

The adoption process is demanding. As one British couple said, 'Pressure was put upon us to say that we would accept a disturbed child, teenager, physically/mentally handicapped child. You will have to have nerves of steel and be totally unemotional. One wrong word and that's it, I'm afraid.' Adopting children from developing countries is becoming more popular but it usually means adopting a child rather than a baby. It is expensive because the couple must usually go to the country to collect the child. This practice is sometimes criticised because it takes the child out of his country and culture, but one mother who had seen at first hand her child's poverty-stricken 'home', said, 'We didn't find that roots or cultural identity mattered. Just being able to live.'[21]

Some couples who cannot have a child of their own prefer to be childless than to adopt, and others accept that their childlessness is God's desire. They believe that if they are patient and accepting, they will be rewarded, either with a baby or in other ways, and they are happy to put their trust in their religion. Often it may take a couple many years to accept that they will not have children to give them enjoyment in early days and to look after them when they are old. Once they accept their childlessness, many enjoy the benefits.

One British couple regarded some writings on childlessness

as 'very depressing and obsessional and inward looking'. They went on:

> We have *happily* resigned ourselves to not having children and have realised all our advantages in life, not least our happy marriage and the support of our relatives and friends. What is the point of wasting the best part of your life being totally obsessed with a 'problem' which it is not your lot in life to have. We all could have been born in the Sudan, or in a Victorian slum, and died aged about two. Instead we live in a healthy, beautiful country with endless opportunities for enjoying and fulfilling ourselves, of which having children is only one.[22]

# 3
# MALE INFERTILITY

The possibility that the male partner may be infertile—and reluctance to admit it—often causes tension between couples, more so than when the woman is the cause of a barren marriage. The diagnosis can cause profound psychological problems: some men have even committed suicide. Sometimes men who have an active sex life suddenly find they cannot get an erection after being told they have a low sperm count. Many people find it hard to understand how a man can be sexually aroused and sexually active when he is infertile. They often confuse sexuality with fertility, and virility with the ability to fertilise an egg.

Recognition of male infertility has been slow. In the 1940s and early 1950s scientists realised not all men had the same quality of sperm and that most with low sperm counts did not father children. Other discoveries followed but it was a long time before male infertility reached the public's attention. Even 10 years ago 'male problems' were rarely talked about. Now there are scores of male infertility clinics around the world and more physicians, known as *andrologists*, and surgeons are specialising in male reproduction.

It appears that men are gradually becoming less fertile, thanks largely to twentieth-century living. Studies suggest that the number of sperm produced by fertile men is decreasing over the decades, and pollution, radiation and population stress have been blamed for this.[1]

In 20–30 per cent of infertile couples there is a male problem, but the proportion varies between countries, for example, from 30 per cent in Indonesia to only 12 per cent in Mexico.[2] In the

US, a 1962 survey found 15 per cent of infertility was due to the man; a 1979 study showed it was 18 per cent and it is now about 30 per cent, which is more a reflection of increased ability to diagnose male infertility rather than a doubling of incidence. In addition to the 30 per cent who are infertile, another 15 per cent are probably subfertile[3] which means there are almost 1.3 million American men who cannot father a child and an additional 700,000 who are subfertile.

Generally a man doesn't know he is infertile until it is time to start a family, because there are few outward signs. Despite enormous advances in the understanding of male infertility, diagnosis is much harder, and treatment much less successful than with women. Dr Gordon Baker of Prince Henry's Hospital, Melbourne, has studied male infertility extensively for more than 20 years and reported recently that 13 per cent of infertile men in Melbourne clinics are irreversibly sterile, about 6 per cent have potentially treatable conditions and the majority have reduced fertility which does not preclude conception but lowers the chance of a pregnancy.[4]

Between 50 and 75 per cent of all male infertility has no known cause, even in the best clinics in the world. However, when a cause is identified it can be anything from a congenital defect to a lifestyle – smoking, drinking alchohol and being over-weight may influence sperm production, as well as certain medications and too many hot baths.

Before describing the causes and cures of male infertility, it is necessary to look at what happens in normal male reproduction.

## NORMAL MALE REPRODUCTION

Reproduction depends on the ability of *sperm* to meet and fertilise a female *egg* and the union of these two *gametes* (sex cells) to develop into an embryo, a *foetus*, then a healthy baby.

By far the greatest proportion of male infertility—maybe 90 per cent—is due to too few or poor-quality sperm. Men who produce no sperm in their semen are said to have *azoospermia*, and those who produce too few have *oligospermia*. *Sperm* are produced all day, every day from puberty till the

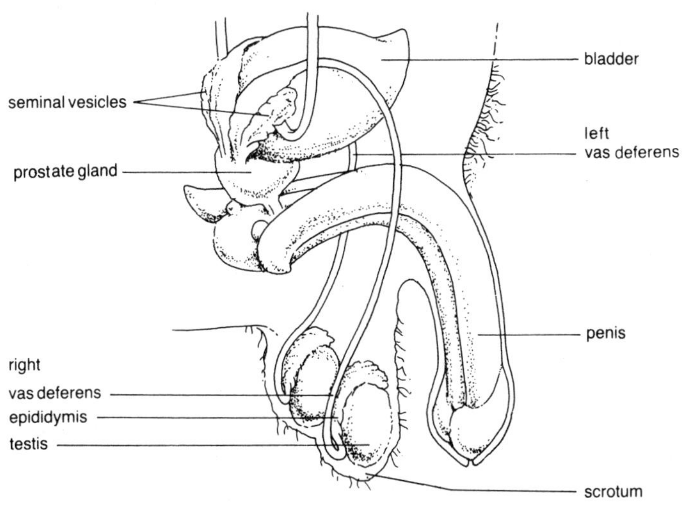


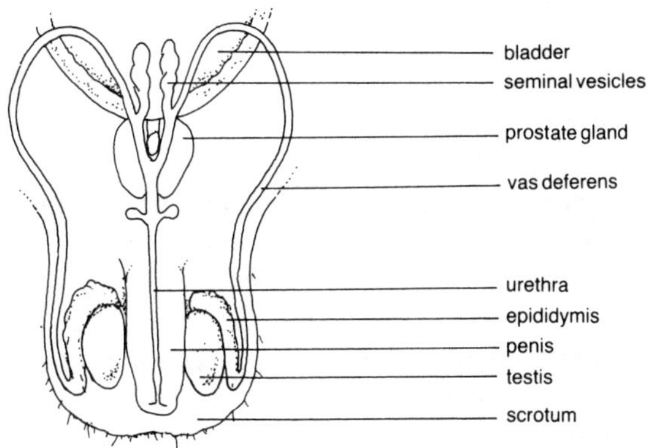


1 MALE REPRODUCTIVE SYSTEM
Sperm are continuously produced in the testes, then pass through the epididymis, vas deferens and prostate gland to the base of the penis where they are mixed with fluids from the prostate and the seminal vesicles to make up semen ready for ejaculation.

late seventies and some men, including a US Congressman, have fathered children in their eighties. Sperm begin their life as cells in the *testes* and every minute about 50,000 of these cells divide and turn into sperm which resemble tadpoles with heads, necks and slender whip-like tails.

They spend the next 12–14 days (or three to 17 days depending on how often the man ejaculates) travelling through the five-metre-long *epididymis* which is only one-hundredth of an inch wide and looks like a tangled ball of string, so tightly coiled it is the size of a thimble. As the sperm move through the epididymis (see diagram 1) they acquire their ability to swim.

They then pass into the *vas deferens*, the duct which carries them through the *prostate gland* to the base of the penis. Here they are joined by prostate and other seminal vesicle fluids which make up the *semen*.

Each ejaculation produces about one and a half teaspoons of semen which contain 100–800 million sperm. But all these sperm make up less than 5 per cent of the semen, the rest is accessory gland secretions and water. The whole process, from cell to ejaculate, takes about three months.

When sperm are ejaculated into the woman's vagina (see diagram 2) during intercourse, most are killed off by acidic vaginal fluid. It has been estimated that only one out of every 2,000 sperm survive. Those that do have to find their way through often hostile cervical mucus into the uterus then begin an uphill battle to reach a recently released egg in one of the fallopian tubes. This takes anything from a few minutes to several hours. They then attempt to penetrate the egg's outer shell to fertilise it. Sperm can survive a few days in the cervical mucus which is why *fertilisation* can still take place a few days after intercourse; however, eggs cannot be fertilised beyond about 24 hours after ovulation so the period for fertilisation is limited.

For pregnancy to occur the timing has to be right, the sperm must reach and fertilise an egg and the resultant embryo must implant in the uterus. An average fertile couple having unprotected intercourse have a 15–20 per cent chance of preganancy each month and about half of them will have to wait about five months for their first pregnancy. Generally it takes less time for subsequent pregnancies.

## TESTING MALE FERTILITY

Infertility in men may be detected by a physical examination, sperm analysis, blood tests to determine the level of hormones, X-rays to look for blockages in the reproductive tract, a biopsy to examine the sperm-producing cells and CAT (computerized axial tomography) scanning. Other methods include micro-photographics, ultrasound, laser movements and occasionally a technique using eggs surgically removed from women.

The first and most important test is to analyse how many sperm are present in each ejaculate (sperm count), how active they are (motility) and what they look like (morphology). This is generally done by examining a drop of sperm on a slide under a microscope.

One of the most important features is sperm count. A man must produce several hundred million sperm in order to give a single sperm the chance to fertilise an egg and the lower the sperm count the lower the chance. A low sperm count does not mean a lack of virility, nor does it mean no fertility—simply that the chances of conception are lower than normal.

Motility and morphology are judged by how well sperm swim and how they look. Unless they have nicely rounded heads and strong lashing tails and can swim well they are unlikely to reach and penetrate an egg. Seen under a microscope, some may have damaged or badly formed heads or tails. Healthy sperm dart across the slide like champion swimmers. Others wriggle their way across more slowly, swim in circles or crooked lines. Some do somersaults and others tend to sit in one spot and quiver.

Alternative techniques for analysing sperm, not yet widely used, include making a video of the sperms' movement to measure their velocity and motility, and time-lapse photography which enables the distance they travel in a given time to be calculated.

Sperm can then be further analysed by *post-coital*, swim-up or hamster egg tests. In the first, mucus is removed from the woman's cervix six to 12 hours after intercourse to see how many sperm have reached the cervix and how well they swim. In the other two, semen is collected by masturbation or in a special condom after intercourse. For the swim-up test, sperm swim through a culture solution in a test-tube. The better the swimmers, the better the chance of pregnancy, and sperm that reach the top of the solution are removed and analysed.

Alternatively, they are placed in a laboratory dish with hamster eggs that have had their outer shell chemically removed. In theory, sperm capable of penetrating these eggs are capable of fertilising human eggs, but this test is time-consuming and only about 85 per cent accurate. It has also raised concern about crossing human sperm with hamster eggs, but in fact the resulting conceptus does not develop beyond the two-cell stage.

Obtaining sperm for the post-coital test also involves the woman. When male fertility is under question, some men find it hard to perform to a clinical request. Texas psychologist Patricia Mahlstedt gives an example of the difficulties by quoting one of her patients:

> My wife was scheduled to have a post-coital test late one afternoon. Because of our work schedules and a 30-mile distance between our home and the doctor's office, we met at a motel close to the doctor's office to have sex. At first, I could not maintain an erection, and when I finally achieved that, I could not ejaculate. We tried everything we knew, and after no success, we dressed, checked out, and went home where we tried unsuccessfully again. This whole charade was so humiliating and painful for me that I could not imagine attempting such a thing again.'[5]

## IMPROVING SPERM

Sometimes sperm numbers and quality can be boosted by drugs, including the male hormone *testosterone*. Some doctors prescribe vitamin B. Research at the University of Texas has shown that large doses of vitamin C improve sperm motility and count (although other researchers are doubtful); and some patients self-prescribe a diet of carrots which are high in vitamin A. A man's sperm count and motility can also be improved if he stops smoking, drinking and taking drugs. Professor Robert Winston, who runs the infertility clinic at Hammersmith Hospital, London, says evidence suggests men may improve their sperm count by having sex more often,[6] and early research by David de Kretser, Professor of Anatomy at Monash University, Melbourne, shows that frequent ejaculation (twice a day in his study group) improves sperm quality for the small percentage of men with low motility and low viability of sperm.[7]

According to preliminary studies from Philadelphia, US, infertile men with low sperm count and motility can father a child if the couple have intercourse a second time 30 minutes after the first. Of the first six couples who tried the double intercourse technique, five conceived. This is largely anecdotal and has not been substantiated.

Another practice is to use the split-ejaculate method. Semen in the first part of an ejaculate contains the highest concentration of sperm, and sperm of higher motility. Some fertility experts suggest that when having intercourse during the most fertile time of the woman's cycle (see next chapter) a man should withdraw his penis after the first few spurts of the ejaculation so it is not diluted by subsequent spurts. This has led to pregnancies in couples who could not previously conceive. Alternatively, the first part of the ejaculate can be collected and used for artificial insemination (see Chapter 5).

Overall, though, few of these methods improve conception.

## POSSIBLE CAUSES AND TREATMENTS OF MALE INFERTILITY

According to a WHO 28-country study, 49 per cent of infertile men have no demonstrable cause of infertility, 13 per cent have *varicoceles*, 11 per cent have testicular failure, 7 per cent have male accessory gland infection, 18 per cent have other causes and only 2 per cent of male infertility is due to congenital abnormalities.[8] These are worldwide figures collected from 34 centres, the majority of them in developing countries, and they differ from region to region. The proportion of men overall with varicoceles, for example, was 13 per cent, compared with about 40 per cent in infertile men in the US. Gordon Baker believes 75 per cent of male infertility in Western countries is unexplained, a figure considerably higher than the WHO's.[9] And a WHO-sponsored study in the Soviet Union found 27 per cent of infertile men had accessory gland infection, compared with the average 7 per cent.[10]

The following are some of the known and possible causes and treatments for male infertility. They fall into two categories – poor sperm, which is dealt with first, and no sperm which may be due to paraplegia, impotence, a vasectomy or congenital problems.

## VARICOCELES

Varicoceles are swollen veins in the testes, often referred to as resembling a 'bag of worms'. They are the most common diagnosable problem associated with infertility in men but whether they actually cause infertility is debatable. In Western countries, varicoceles are present in 10–15 per cent of all men but not all these men are infertile. They are also found in 40 per cent of infertile men.

Surgery to tie off the affected vein has traditionally been regarded as one of the few treatable forms of male infertility, with reports of 40–60 per cent of men going on to father children.

However, recent evidence suggests that treatment for varicoceles may have no effect at all and the pregnancies that occur after surgery would have resulted whether or not the man was treated. A study by Baker, reported in the *British Medical Journal* in 1985, could find no improvement in semen quality or fertilisation rate after treatment. From a group of 650 men with varicoceles, about 30 per cent produced a pregnancy in the first year and 45 per cent within two years, whether or not they had the operation. The *BMJ* report concluded that, ironically, the men with varicoceles produced higher pregnancy rates than those without.[11]

An alternative non-surgical treatment for varicoceles is to pass a *catheter* through the affected vein with a tissue adhesive, cyanoacrylate, which acts like superglue and blocks the vein. A success rate of 90 per cent has been reported but the method is not widely used.[12]

## INFECTION

Several infections can reduce fertility or cause infertility by affecting glands, sperm and the immune system. They include tuberculosis, mumps, typhoid, influenza, smallpox and brucellosis, all of which are now uncommon in Western countries, where sexually transmitted diseases (STDs) are more common.

*STDs* can affect sperm quality and in severe cases cause a blockage in the reproductive tract. Untreated STD infections can result in permanent infertility. In Western countries, STDs account for probably a fifth of male and female infertility and are by far the most preventable cause. The main culprits are *gonorrhoea* and *chlamydia*.

*Mumps* contracted during or after puberty can cause infertility by damaging the testes, but it is rare. About 20 per cent of males who are infected develop inflammation of the testes and most recover without permanent damage. However, a Swedish study showed that for those who have inflammation in both testes the chances of fathering a child is almost halved. Other studies show about a quarter of the teenagers or men who contract mumps are rendered infertile.[13]

*Tuberculosis* (TB) is now rare in the Western world but it is still responsible for infertility in many developing countries. The virus can result in scarring and blockage in the epididymis and the vas.

*Malaria* or any similar infection can indirectly lower sperm count temporarily because the high fever that results may overheat the testes.

*Leprosy* is rare in Western countries but still frequent in Africa and Asia. Studies in Malaysia and India suggest the lepromatous form of leprosy produces sperm antibodies (see following). A US study found the testes in 28 per cent of infected men had shrunk, and a 33-year study in the Philippines found 40 per cent fewer births among men who had contracted lepromatous.[13]

*Microfilaria* is a parasitic worm that may be responsible for a proportion of infertility in Africa. Dr Donatien Mavoungou, Director of Human Reproduction in Franceville, Gabon, and a member of the WHO task force on infertility, reported recently that the areas of Central Africa with the highest incidence of infertility correspond with the areas where the worm is found. He believes the worm is picked up on the hands and feet and enters the bloodstream and that it is responsible for reduced testosterone production and epididymal blockages.

*Prostate gland* infections may also be responsible for temporarily reducing fertility, and preliminary studies in Melbourne suggest chronic low-grade infection may be an important cause of infertility. Bacteria invade the gland and cause infections which affect sperm count and motility. Prostatic infections are difficult to treat, even with antibiotics, although research in Europe and America shows that long-term treatment with antibiotics produces good results. Once the bacteria have been eradicated, sperm production returns to normal.

Sometimes obstructions in the vas can be treated by microsurgery with stitches so thin they can barely be seen with the naked eye. The scarred area is cut away and the two 'clean' ends rejoined. But in the majority of cases the results are poor and some experts report that only 5–10 per cent result in a pregnancy. Two exceptions are when it is done by a very experienced surgeon, and when the blockage is at the tail of the epididymis.

If surgery has failed, the latest technique involves removing sperm from above the blockage by microsurgery and then using them to fertilise the wife's egg in the laboratory as part of *in vitro* fertilisation (IVF). The technique was developed by an Australian team including IVF expert Alan Trounson, biologist Peter Temple-Smith and microsurgeon Graeme Southwick and resulted in the first such birth in Melbourne in March 1985. The boy was nicknamed the 'epididymis baby' because sperm had been removed from his father's epididymis after a vasectomy reversal failed. While giving hope to some infertile men, the technique is still experimental, although several teams worldwide are working on it.

A similar method was used in the US by urologist Jacob Rajfer of the University of California Harbor Medical Centre to withdraw sperm from the vas of a Los Angeles paraplegic. His wife was artificially inseminated with the sperm and gave birth to a boy in December 1985.

## ENVIRONMENTAL FACTORS

Where you live and work, how much you eat, drink and smoke and whether you are generally happy can all have some effect on fertility. Alcohol is unlikely to be the sole cause of childlessness, nor is being overweight, but both may contribute to decreased sperm production. In general, a healthy lifestyle with little stress produces healthy sperm, and this includes avoiding heat and chemicals at work as well as recreational and medical drugs. Some aspects of male infertility can be prevented and the following should be avoided for the sake of fertility.

*Occupational hazards* such as exposure to toxic chemicals, heat, noise and vibrations may affect fertility as well as sexual behaviour by causing reduced sperm production, depressed libido and impotence. Sperm count often returns to normal after the hazard is removed but long-term exposure can cause irreversible damage.

People in agriculture, laboratory work, the oil, chemical and atomic industries, pulp and paper manufacturing and textile work are the most likely to be exposed to substances that may affect reproduction, according to a 1985 study by the US Office of Technology Assessment.[14]

The OTA report listed a number of agents said to be linked

with, but not conclusively responsible for, impairment of reproductive function: metals such as lead, manganese, mercury, cadmium and arsenic; agricultural chemicals including DDT, 2,4,5–T, dioxin and Agent Orange; organic solvents; anaesthetic agents; chemicals used in rubber manufacturing; X-rays and gamma rays; non-ionising radiation from laser, ultrasound, video display terminals and magnetic fields. It also listed heat, cold, high altitudes, noise, and vibration; tobacco and alcohol; ingestion of certain drugs; over-exertion and stress. The report said only four health hazards—ionizing radiation, lead, DBCP and ethylene oxide—are regulated 'in part' because of their effect on reproduction.

Other studies have shown that jobs specifically relevant to sperm production include those involving unusual amounts of vibration such as operating a pneumatic drill. And car-, bus-or truck-parking attendants are likely to be exposed to lead-containing exhaust fumes.

*Chemicals* and pesticides are often linked with infertility although few comprehensive studies have been done. The pesticide DBCP was found in a Californian study to affect sperm count, motility and morphology and hormone levels among men employed in a pesticide factory. The herbicide TCDD, found in 2,4,5–T and Agent Orange, has been linked with infertility, and is claimed by Vietnam veterans to cause sterility, although this has not been scientifically proven.

*Lead* is known to adversely affect sperm count, motility and morphology in animal experiments. According to a report by Jane Henderson of Deakin University, Australia, the effects of lead on the human reproductive system were documented by the Greeks 20 centuries ago and it has been speculated that lead, used by the Romans as a sweetener in food and wine, caused a reduction in fertility and thus the gradual decline of the Roman Empire. She says studies have found a higher incidence of abnormal sperm in men employed at a battery storage plant, reduced testosterone and libido among men at a lead smelter and immature sperm in men working at a battery factory.[15]

*Radiation* impairs sperm production but the effect may only be temporary. A 1975 study found that technicians exposed to microwaves had reduced libido, sperm count and motility. Others show that pregnancy is less frequent when men work in a high voltage substation. High doses of radiation used in cancer treatment are known to produce infertility both in patients and hospital staff if precautions are not taken.

*Heat* around the testes can temporarily reduce or stop sperm production. The testes hang in the *scrotum* so they stay about two degrees Celsius cooler than body temperature. The effect of increased testicular temperature on sperm has been known since the 1920s when Chicago pathologist Carl Moore wrapped wool around the scrotum of rams, which then produced poorer quality sperm.

Studies show that in the tropics conception is less frequent in the hot season. Infertile or subfertile men are often told not to have hot baths or saunas. One form of contraception in Japan in the past was hot baths for men. Men who sit for a long time, such as taxi and truck drivers, are thought to be more at risk than someone moving around a shop, office or factory, as are men who wear jock straps and tight underwear, compared with boxer shorts. Very tight jeans may have the same effect if the scrotum becomes overheated, while low sperm counts have been found in men confined to wheelchairs. All this is anecdotal evidence that links heat with infertility, but it is so far unproven.

Some men with elevated testicular temperature are being prescribed a testicular hypothermia device (THD), a cotton jock strap kept constantly moist by a slow trickle of water from a small reservoir worn on a belt under the man's shirt. As the moisture evaporates, it cools the testes. The THD was developed by Adrian Zorgniotti, Professor of Urology at New York University, as an alternative to varicocele surgery. He claims it results in a 50 per cent pregnancy rate. However, as Baker showed, 45 per cent of men with varicoceles achieve a pregnancy without treatment. Nevertheless, the device may be useful in preventing infertility in certain men who have occupational exposure to heat, such as foundry and furnace workers. Dr John Tyler, of the Human Reproduction Unit at

Sydney's Westmead Hospital, believes it may also help men with unexplained infertility and reports that his first patient's sperm improved five-fold in the first 28 weeks he wore the device.[16]

*Stress* may be far more influential in infertility than doctors are prepared to admit. There is ample anecdotal evidence that stress can affect fertility but how much has not been proven. Infertility and its treatment certainly causes enormous stress and it may be a vicious circle: stress causes infertility which causes stress which prolongs the infertility. A detailed psychological evaluation of 200 IVF couples by the University of Pennsylvania in 1983–84 found 16 per cent of the women and 18 per cent of the men had 'psychological dysfunction'. About half had clinical symptoms of emotional disorders and the other half had personality disorders.[17] Men in life-and-death situations have been known to stop producing sperm, including those on death row and hanged criminals. And there is reason to think that milder forms of stress may have milder disturbances in sperm production.

*Exercise* in excess can reduce sperm production. This is generally only seen in super-athletes who are pushing their bodies to extremes. Sperm production returns to normal when the athlete returns to a normal level of exercise.

*Obesity* or just being overweight is thought to reduce fertility. Fatty tissue metabolises steroid hormones and obese people have abnormal hormone levels that could affect sperm. Another theory is that fat thighs and flabby lower abdomen may prevent proper circulation of air around the scrotum, so that the temperature of the testes remains higher than normal, damaging sperm-producing cells.

*Cigarettes* may reduce sperm count and motility, although how is not fully understood. Some studies show that cigarette smokers have reduced sperm count, fewer mobile sperm and more abnormal sperm than non-smokers, but others show no difference. Sperm quality has been shown to improve in many infertile men when they stop smoking. However, the link between smoking and infertility is more anecdotal than scientific.

Dr Mary Sexton of the University of Maryland showed recently that smoking reduces sperm count and motility, and she believes if a couple are planning a pregnancy they should both give up smoking. Dr Anne Conway at Prince Alfred Hospital, Sydney, found the average sperm count of smokers was half that of non-smokers. However, studies by other researchers have failed to find a link.

Robert Winston of Hammersmith Hospital believes smoking can cause a 'catastrophic' drop in sperm numbers and quality, especially if a man has borderline sperm, although other men may not be affected at all. He says giving up smoking may be the best treatment for someone with low sperm count who smokes more than eight–ten cigarettes a day. He tells how a man with 11 years infertility lost more than 12lbs (5.5kg) and cut back to four cigarettes a day, and shortly afterwards his wife became pregnant.[18] Again, this is anecdotal evidence, not proof.

*Alcohol* in large amounts is definitely responsible for many cases of impotence. End-stage alcoholism is known to damage the sperm-producing cells in the testes and reduce sperm count. Alcohol can also cut the production of testosterone, leading to shrinkage of the testes. Three months after consumption is cut, sperm production usually returns to normal. Moderate drinking has not been shown to affect fertility, although it may in men with borderline sperm counts. If alcohol damages the liver it may result in increased levels of the female hormone estrogen which can affect sex drive and performance.

*Drugs* used socially or recreationally can affect sperm production. Central nervous system depressants including barbiturates, heroin and other narcotics can cause impotence and ejaculation problems. The effect of cocaine and heroin on sperm is not certain, but marijuana (cannabis) has been proved to decrease both sperm count and sperm motility and to produce more abnormal sperm. Carl Wood, Professor of

Obstetrics and Gynaecology at Monash University, Melbourne, believes marijuana may inhibit ejaculation.

*Medication* prescribed by doctors can affect the quality and quantity of sperm produced. A decrease in the amount of semen in an ejaculate has been linked with certain psychiatric drugs. Antidepressants, tranquillizers, antihypertensives and pick-me-ups have all been shown to depress sperm production and in some cases cause impotence or interfere with ejaculation. Other culprits include drugs used to treat malaria, bladder infections, inflammation of the colon and some blood disorders. Chemotherapy for cancer damages sperm-producing cells and for this reason men are often advised to have some sperm frozen and stored (see Chapter 5) before treatment if they want to attempt a pregnancy later.

## INJURIES

*Physical injury*, such as a kick or a football in the groin, can damage the testes or epididymis and put them out of action temporarily or permanently or affect sperm motility as they pass through the reproductive tract. It is very rare that trauma causes such damage, but when it does it means the end of sperm production. More common is an injury that leads to a blockage in the epididymis, which may be corrected with microsurgery, although the success rate is low. Very occasionally a surgical misadventure can result in a blocked duct, for example if the duct is cut during a hernia or hydrocele repair.

*Torsion* usually occurs during puberty when one testicle or the cord supplying blood to it twists inside the scrotum. It can be extremely painful and dangerous. The testicle swells because the blood cannot escape and if the vessels rupture, the internal bleeding can damage the sperm-producing cells. Damage starts within a few hours and the degree depends on how bad the torsion is, and how quickly it is operated on. If the delay is too long the testicle may die and have to be removed, but this is rare.

## HORMONAL PROBLEMS

A disruption to the balance of hormones in men is rare and can rarely be treated. The pituitary, a tiny gland behind the bridge of the nose, controls the three main hormones: the two female hormones *follicle–stimulating hormone* (FSH) and *luteinising hormone* (LH) which stimulate the testes to produce the male hormone testosterone which in turn stimulates the testes to produce sperm. In Kallman's syndrome, a rare genetic disorder, the pituitary does not release FSH and LH and no testosterone is produced.

*Prolactin*, which stimulates milk production in women, is also found in men and unusually high levels often indicate a tiny tumour is growing on the pituitary. This reduces production of LH and FSH, and therefore testosterone, leading in extreme cases to impotence and shrinkage of the testes. The tumour can be successfully removed by surgery or controlled with bromocriptine, the drug used to treat patients with Parkinson's disease.

## IMMUNOLOGICAL PROBLEMS

About 3–8 per cent of men produce antibodies to their own sperm. The reason is not known but it often happens when there is a blocked duct or the man has had a vasectomy. Sperm are still produced but since they have nowhere to go they are reabsorbed through the walls of the duct into the bloodstream. They are then recognised by the body as 'foreign' and destroyed. Sometimes after the obstruction is cleared the antibodies disappear but often a man has antibodies for the rest of his life. They cause sperm to bind together, or clump, which reduces the number of sperm available for fertilisation, or they bind to the sperm, preventing penetration of an egg.

Generally, sperm antibodies can be picked up with a quick antiglobulin reaction test. The usual treatment is reasonably high doses of corticosteroids for several months with 50 per cent success in restoring sperm quality. A test developed recently by American andrologist Dr Nancy Alexander of the Jones Institute, Virginia, separates sperm that are heavily coated with antibodies from those marginally affected or antibody-free. The sperm without antibodies can then be removed and used in artificial insemination.

## CONGENITAL PROBLEMS

Very occasionally men are born with *hypospadias*, where the urethra opens above or beneath the penis rather than at the end. This can be corrected surgically.

Men born with Klinefelter's syndrome have small, undeveloped testicles that do not produce sperm. It is a rare problem caused by a chromosome abnormality that occurs during development in the womb.

A congenital blockage in the epididymis is rare but there is evidence that the incidence is higher in men whose mothers took the synthetic hormone *DES* (diethyl stilboestrol) during pregnancy to prevent miscarriage.

Very few men are born without a vas but a recent development to overcome this rare problem is an artificial vas which is implanted under the skin and attached to the epididymis using microsurgery. It is made of goretex tubing, an artificial material used to reconstruct blood vessels (and also used for running suits and weatherproof clothing that breathes). Sperm collect in the bag and can be drawn out with a needle by a nurse or the man's wife and then used to inseminate the wife artificially. It is done twice a week to encourage a continuous flow of fresh sperm. The technique has been tried by three teams in Britain but so far with little success.

## UNDESCENDED TESTES

*Undescended testes*, or cryptorchism, causes an increase in temperature in the testes and leads to permanent damage if it is untreated in early childhood, so that the man produces no sperm in his semen. It also increases the risk of testicular cancer by 20–30 times in adulthood. In the foetus the testes are in the abdomen, below the kidneys. Just before birth they move down through the groin to the scrotum, where they remain until death. In about 1 per cent of boys, one or both testes do not descend within the first year and remain in the body, at the slightly higher temperature. Cryptorchism is usually detected early and corrected with surgery, in most countries before the boy reaches the age of three.

However, some experts say the operation has more cosmetic than medical benefit. They believe there is probably something else wrong with the testes because after the operation many still do not produce good sperm. Although it is rare to find adults with cryptorchism in Western countries, some experts say about 15 per cent of infertile men had the problem as an infant.

## PROBLEMS WITH INTERCOURSE

About 3 per cent of male infertility is due to problems with intercourse, known as sexual dysfunction—some experts report up to 10 per cent. A man is unable to deposit sperm in the cervix if he suffers from impotence, premature ejaculation or failure to ejaculate, which may be due to surgery, medication and physical or psychological problems. Ironically, the stress of trying to conceive is sometimes the cause of the problem. As two experts reported recently: 'It may occur following the discovery of azoospermia (zero sperm count) or as a result of the demands for sexual performance during an infertility investigation,' such as a post-coital test. Attempting to conceive at a certain time turns 'making love' into 'making a baby'. 'Under these conditions, it is not surprising that a husband might have doubts that he will be able to perform once he has experienced his first episode of sexual dysfunction.'[19]

Failure to ejaculate into the cervix may be because a man is unable to penetrate his partner deeply enough, for example if either of them are excessively overweight.

Impotence is not, strictly speaking, infertility, since the definition of infertility is unprotected intercourse and one cannot have intercourse without an erection. Nevertheless, it is a reason for childlessness. Roughly half the cases of impotence are due to psychological and half to physical problems including diabetes, pelvic surgery, trauma, vascular disease, hormone and neurological problems, the use of certain drugs, alcohol and smoking.

Treatments for impotence include counselling, surgery to damaged blood vessels, hormones that are injected into the penis to cause an erection and penile implants.

## VASECTOMY

Although *vasectomy* is deliberate sterility and may not be regarded as true infertility, it is a barrier to a wanted pregnancy and it has to be reversed in order for a couple to have children. Vasectomy reversal is only asked for by 1–5 per cent of men who have been sterilised, but demand is growing with an increase in second marriages and the desire for a second family.

Vasectomy involves cutting and sealing the vas to stop sperm entering the ejaculatory ducts so a man still ejaculates semen but it contains no sperm. Sydney surgeon Earl Owen did the first successful microsurgery vasectomy reversal in the early 1970s. At about the same time, Sherman Silber introduced the technique in the US and it is now used routinely with a much higher success rate than conventional surgery.

## PARAPLEGIA

A man who is paralysed in the lower half of his body cannot get an erection naturally. However, he can with a new technique known as *electro-ejaculation.* A probe is placed in the rectum and sends electric pulses to penile nerves which causes an ejaculation. The man's semen is collected and used to artificially inseminate his wife. The technique may also be used for patients whose nerves become damaged after surgery or cancer of the testes. An alternative is an electric vibrator that stimulates the penis.

It is important that doctors investigate men thoroughly and that men realise it takes two for a conception to occur. Although masturbating for doctors can be humiliating and frustrating, no loving man should subject his wife or girlfriend to drugs and surgery until he has undergone a full semen analysis, which is cheap, instant and far less strenuous than testing infertility in his partner.

# 4
# FEMALE INFERTILITY

The female reproductive life stretches between *menarche*, the beginning of menstruation at about the age of 12, and *menopause*, at about 45, and peaks between 18 and 30. Girls as young as eight have become pregnant and in September 1987 55-year-old Cathleen Campbell became the oldest woman in Britain to have a baby—her seventh. The older a woman is, the more the risk there is that her eggs will be defective and the higher the chance of a miscarriage. There is no doubt that the risk of infertility increases with age, although the exact relationship is not certain. There is considerable debate over when women should start to worry about their childbearing ability, especially as many in Western countries now delay having children until their thirties. It is generally thought that after 35 safe, easy conception decreases, although a recent French study strongly suggests it may be around 30.[1]

For those infertile women who wish to have children, treatment has been available far longer than it has for men, and more women can be treated successfully than their partners. The most important breakthroughs for female infertility came in the early 1960s with the introduction of 'fertility drugs' and in the early 1970s with the introduction of microsurgery for gynaecological operations.

## NORMAL FEMALE REPRODUCTION

A surprising number of women do not know how their childbearing ability can be impaired. Many women are more concerned with their outward appearances than their inside workings, an attitude that can be equated with making sure the car is washed and polished but never lifting the bonnet to check the engine.

Egg production in a female starts a few weeks after the embryo implants in the uterus, and a baby girl is born with between 400,000 and two million eggs in her ovaries. Most are never released. Normally in a lifetime about 400 will be lost in monthly menstruation. And on average only two, three or four will end up as children. What determines which of these many eggs will be released is a mystery.

It takes an estimated three months for an egg to mature and be released, and if it is fertilised, another nine months to develop into a newborn baby. Many of the processes *en route* can go wrong.

Eggs are the largest cells in the female body (a sperm is one of the smallest in the male) and they are contained in the two *ovaries*, round glands that sit behind the bladder in a pair (see diagram 2). As well as maturing and releasing eggs, the ovaries secrete hormones necessary to start and sustain a pregnancy.

The *fallopian tubes*, which stretch from the ovaries to the uterus, are about as thin as a guitar string and are lined with thousands of tiny and very delicate hairs which propel egg and sperm along the tube—in opposite directions at the same time! At one end of each tube is the *fimbria* which flares out like a flower in blossom to pick up the egg after it leaves the ovary. The other end leads directly into the *uterus*, or *womb*, which is where a fertilised egg, or embryo, will imbed itself during the pregnancy.

What determines the age a girl starts her first period is unknown. The 'signal station' that receives and transmits messages to stop and start hormones is the *pituitary gland* (behind the bridge of the nose) which is in turn controlled by a higher station in the brain, the *hypothalamus*.

In a normal 28-day cycle the pituitary starts releasing larger amounts of the two female hormones follicle-stimulating hormone (FSH) and luteinising hormone (LH). FSH stimulates the *follicle*, the fluid-filled sac that contains the egg, and LH gives follicular maturation a final boost just before the egg

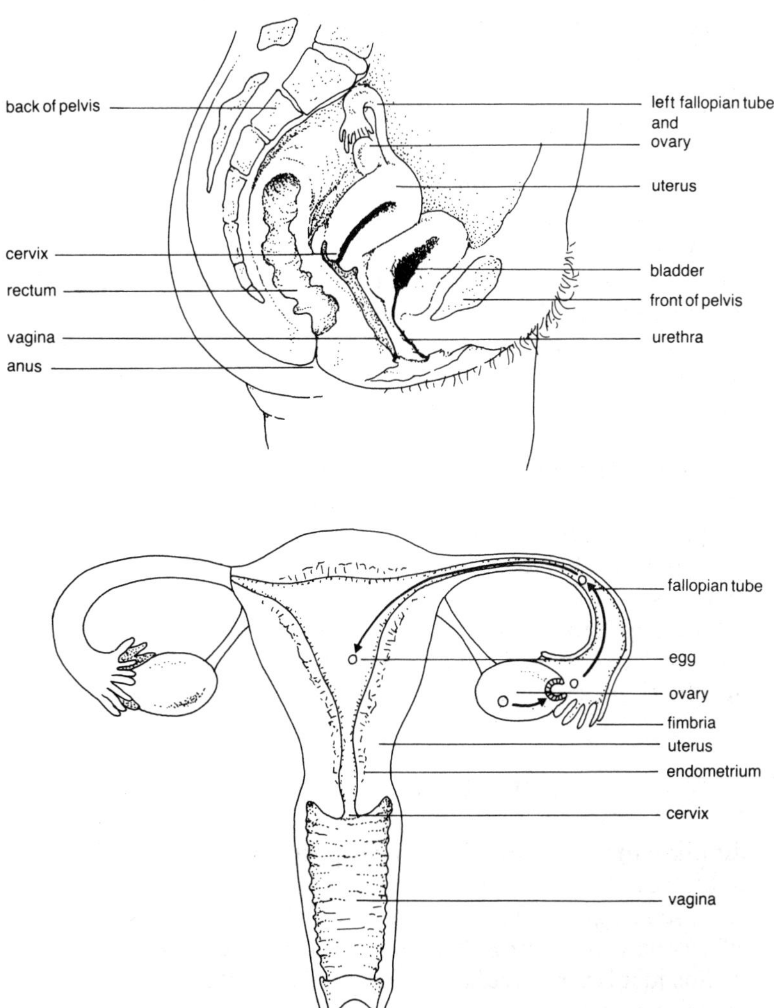


2 FEMALE REPRODUCTIVE SYSTEM
During each cycle one egg is released by the ovary, caught by the fimbria and transported down the fallopian tube to the uterus. If it has been fertilised, the embryo imbeds there; if not, the endometrium breaks down and is shed in a menstrual bleed.

bursts out of the follicle in *ovulation*. If the egg is not fertilised the lining of the uterus, the *endometrium*, bleeds, breaks down and is passed out as a menstrual period.

As the eggs mature and prepare for ovulation, the follicle increases in size from not much bigger than a full-stop to about the size of a cherry, and produces *estrogen* and *progesterone*, the hormones needed by the uterus to prepare for the arrival of an embryo. If sperm have managed to pass through the *cervix*, the neck of the womb at the top of the vagina, and enter the fallopian tube where the egg is, fertilisation usually takes place several hours after ovulation when the egg has travelled about a third of the way down the tube towards the uterus. The embryo stays in the tube for about three days, reaches the uterus on day three or four and starts to burrow into the endometrium on day seven or eight. Implantation is complete by day 14 and this is the beginning of a pregnancy.

This is in an ideal world, where everything goes as nature planned, but for millions of infertile couples around the world it is just a dream.

An egg can encounter many obstacles on its way to the uterus. And even when it manages to meet a sperm and is fertilised, the embryo may not successfully implant in the uterus.

## TESTING FEMALE FERTILITY

Unlike men, women often suspect they have a problem, which can be tested by a number of methods, and often several are used to give a clear diagnosis. Ovulation can be detected by a woman recording her body temperature which usually drops just before ovulation and goes up just after. The uterus, ovaries and cervix can be tested by examining a tiny piece of tissue in the laboratory, known as a *biopsy*. A common procedure is a *dilation and curettage*, better known as *D&C*, which involves dilating the cervix and passing an instrument through to the uterus where a sample of the endometrium can be scraped out and analysed—as can a sample of *cervical mucus*.

Levels of the hormones LH, FSH, estrogen, progesterone and prolactin (the milk producing hormone) can sometimes indicate whether ovulation is taking place. Tests of the cervical

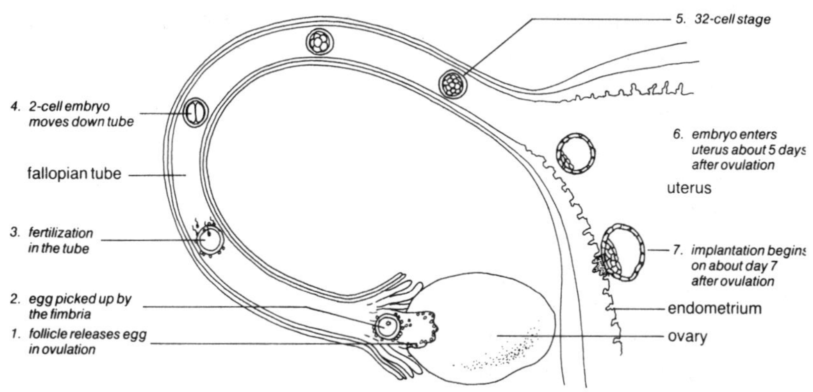


3 FROM EGG TO EMBRYO
Natural fertilisation takes place in a fallopian tube a few hours after ovulation and the embryo moves down the tube, dividing from a two- to multi-cell embryo as it enters the uterus where ideally it implants in the endometrium and a pregnancy begins.

mucus may find it is too thick for the sperm to pass through to the uterus or that antibodies are present. A biopsy of the ovaries may reveal a cyst and a uterine biopsy will tell whether the lining of the uterus is preparing to receive the embryo. Investigating the tubes requires laparoscopy, ultrasound or hysterosalpingogram.

*Laparoscopy* uses a *laparoscope*, a long, thin metal instrument with a light and magnifying glass on the end which is used to examine the uterus, tubes and ovaries. It is inserted through the woman's abdominal wall, usually at the belly-button so the scar is less obvious, into the pelvis which is inflated with gas, like a balloon, to allow the instrument to be moved around. Laparoscopy requires a general anaesthetic, the woman may have abdominal pain afterwards and in rare cases the bowel is damaged.

*Hysterosalpingogram* (HSG) involves injecting into the uterus and tubes a special dye that shows up on an X-ray screen. From this the doctor can see whether the uterus and tubes are the normal shape and whether the tubes are blocked. Some women find HSC painful, but only for the 20 minutes while the dye is in the genital tract, and it carries a small risk of introducing an infection into the uterus or tubes when the dye is injected.

*Ultrasound* also gives a picture of the position and shape of the tubes and uterus as well as ovaries. High-frequency sound waves, too rapid to be heard, are directed on to the body and echoes bounce back when they hit an organ. When the sounds are converted to electrical signals the shape and position of the organ appears on a TV-like screen and any tumours, adhesions, fibroids or other abnormalities can be seen. However, the procedure needs an experienced technician and an expensive machine—which are not available at all hospitals—and generally a woman needs a full bladder which is uncomfortable, although this is not necessary with vaginal ultrasound.

All these tests will show hormonal or physical abnormalities. What causes these problems and how they are treated will be discussed next.

## CAUSES AND TREATMENTS OF FEMALE INFERTILITY

The reasons for infertility in a woman can be influenced by her age, whether she has had a previous pregnancy and what part of the world she lives in. Often the causes are not known and in 30–40 per cent of women there may be more than one problem.

### OVULATION FAILURE

Failure of the ovaries to release an egg is a common cause of infertility in women and may be due to several reasons. An extremely rare but obvious one is that both ovaries are not present, either because the woman was born without them or had them surgically removed, possibly because of cancer. If one ovary is absent and there is nothing wrong with the other it will continue to function and an egg will be released each month.

If one or both ovaries are present but not ovulating, it could be because of a temporary shutdown due to a traumatic experience or the effects of certain drugs. Or it could be a physical problem: the ovaries may be too small or immature, or the woman may reach menopause early. The problem may be hormonal, in which case the ovaries can be 'kicked' into action with hormones, or 'fertility drugs'. This produces ovulation in about 75 per cent of women and results in a pregnancy 35–40 per cent of the time.

Gynaecologist Professor Robert Winston of Hammersmith Hospital, London, estimates that in the Western world 70 per cent of ovulation failure in women is due to hormonal or chemical problems in the body; 10–15 per cent to a functional problem, where the ovaries do not work in a particular cycle; and 10–15 per cent is because the ovaries are physically damaged, abnormal from birth or absent.[2]

He estimates a complete shutdown by the ovaries only happens in 5 per cent of cases, but ovaries that appear to have failed may suddenly start ovulating again. In some cases the follicle fails to burst or the egg may not escape. And a very traumatic emotional upset—such as bad depression, imprisonment, physical ill-treatment or severe shock—can cause the hypothalamus to stop sending out hormone-producing messages for a time. Occasionally women find it hard to get pregnant after coming off the contraceptive pill but drugs can be used to trigger the ovaries into action.

Fertility drugs stimulate the ovaries to release an egg in a process known as *superovulation*, or ovulation induction. The most common drug is *clomiphene* which jolts the ovaries into developing several follicles and releasing one or more eggs. About 80 per cent of the women treated ovulate and 40 per cent become pregnant. However, some women experience side effects and the chance of a multiple pregnancy is higher than normal.

When clomiphene fails, doctors often turn to HMG, a more expensive and much more powerful drug. Unless strictly monitored it is potentially dangerous as it can overstimulate the ovaries, resulting in a multiple pregnancy and occasionally hyperstimulation syndrome which may require hospital treatment. HMG stands for *human menopausal gonadotrophin* (hormone). Originally it was extracted from the pituitaries of dead women and the glands from 10 corpses were needed for one treatment. Today it is derived from the urine of post-menopausal women, most commonly nuns in Italy and Spain. Soon recombinant DNA technology may be used to produce a synthetic HMG. An alternative is HCG, *human chorionic gonadotrophin*, which is produced by the *chorion*, the outer membranes of a foetus which are shed in the urine of a pregnant woman.

Other fertility drugs include pure FSH, tamoxifen, cyclofenil and *GnRH analog*, a relatively new drug that does not produce hyperstimulation. It is a synthetic variation of GnRH, gonadotrophin-releasing hormone, which is produced by the hypothalamus and tells the pituitary to release FSH and LH in a proper ratio.

When used in ovulation stimulation the GnRH analog is delivered by a tiny pump, about the size of a cigarette packet, which is worn by the woman, either strapped around her waist or pinned to her bra. The liquid drug is held in a plastic reservoir and pumped into the blood stream via a tiny tube and a needle inserted under the skin.

Sometimes the quality of eggs may be substandard. Any tissue of the body that is subjected to higher than normal doses of chemicals or drugs can be damaged or altered, and the single cell egg is no exception. PCBs (polychlorinated biphenyls), used widely in batteries, transformers and lubricants in the 1970s, have been shown to damage severely the eggs of large sea birds that have eaten fish containing traces of them. Recently, Dr Wilfred Feichtinger of the Institute for Reproductive Endocrinology in Vienna, Austria, and Professor Heinz Bohnet of the Institute for Hormone and Fertility Disorders in Hamburg, West Germany, found 'quite high' concentrations of PCBs in follicular fluid removed from infertile women. Bohnet believes the chemicals found their way there via the food chain, as they do with birds. 'If a woman has endocrine [hormone] problems and there are high concentrations of pollutants,' he said in a BBC interview, 'they may inhibit development of the egg.' The study found that the women with the highest concentrations of pollutants—mainly PCBs and DDT—had fewer eggs. However, the pollutants did not seem to affect the fertilisation rates, nor the early development of the embryo.[3]

There are several other causes of ovulation failure that require treatment other than fertility drugs:

*Endometriosis* occurs when some of the lining of the uterus is flushed through the tubes to other parts of the pelvic cavity including the outside of the uterus, bowel, bladder, ovaries and tubes, where it implants then grows and bleeds as if it were in the uterus, resulting in adhesions and scarring. The reason is unknown and the exact relationship between endometriosis and infertility is controversial, but it is assumed that it prevents conception and implantation.

Studies suggest 10–15 per cent or more of all women in Western countries have endometriosis, although only half of them are infertile. It has been suggested that some women may have a hereditary predisposition to endometriosis. The condition can occur at any age but women over 30 are more at risk. Because many women today delay childbearing, some experts predict an increase in the number of cases. The problem often improves during pregnancy and after the menopause. Endometriosis is common in Europe and America but rare in African countries and this is probably because most Western women have 13 periods a year whereas those in less affluent societies are often either pregnant or breastfeeding and therefore have fewer periods.

The most common symptoms are pain, especially during intercourse and menstruation, and heavy and irregular bleeding. A recent study by the Research Centre for Maternal and Child Health Care in Moscow found that 72 per cent of women with endometriosis complained of pain and all experienced exhaustion or weakness and irritability during menstruation, 20 per cent experienced vomiting and nausea, and some had headaches and complained of tremors in their hands and/or feet.[4]

Endometriosis can sometimes be diagnosed by a medical history, physical examination—the doctor may find lumps or thickening of internal tissues—and biopsy. The best diagnostic tool is the laparoscope, through which the doctor may find patches of endometrium, and in advanced cases adhesions and cysts.

The Moscow study suggests endometriosis may be linked to infections, other gynaecological problems and abortions. After eliminating all other possible causes of infertility, researchers found the incidence of previous infectious and viral diseases—including chronic tonsillitis, influenza, pneumonia and infectious hepatitis—was two to three times higher among women with mild endometriosis than in the general population.

The misplaced endometrium can generally be treated with drugs or surgery. Mild cases are often controlled by contraceptive-type drugs, the natural hormone progesterone or anti-estrogen drugs. The most widely used since the 1970s is danazol, a synthetic derivative of testosterone. After 5–10 months' treatment the tissue dies in 50 per cent of cases. A similiar drug, gestrinone, was introduced in 1982 and is claimed to have fewer side effects. For minimal and mild endometriosis, the pregnancy rate after danazol and gestrinone treatment is 60–70 per cent, although it varies between clinics. However, 10–20 per cent of women on these drugs can experience fluid retention, weight gain, acne, unwanted hair growth, hair loss, voice changes, breast changes, hot flushes, depressed libido, inflammation of the vagina and a dry vagina during intercourse.[5] And up to 50 per cent of women need repeat treatment in the following 10 years.

Recently, gestrinone has been developed as a subcutaneous (under-the-skin) implant. A tiny plastic hormone-filled capsule is injected into the buttocks under local anaesthetic and it slowly and continuously releases the drug. Researchers at the WHO collaborating centre for human reproduction in Brazil are now developing a gestrinone vaginal ring which is inserted in the vagina where it slowly releases the drug which is absorbed into the bloodstream through the wall of the vagina.

The French-designed 'abortion pill' RU486 has 'enormous' potential as a treatment for endometriosis, according to Dr Gary Hodgen, scientific director of the Jones Institute, Virginia.

When drugs fail or when the condition is too advanced, endometriosis can be treated by surgery. The adhesions are cut or burnt away in open surgery, laparoscopy or laser, with 80 per cent of the women achieving a pregnancy. Open surgery is technically difficult but the pregnancy rate is about 60 per cent within a year; laparoscope offers mixed results and, although laser is widely used in the US, it is still considered experimental in Britain. Some experts say there is an increased risk of an ectopic pregnancy after endometriosis treatment. Those who have been unsuccessful with drugs and surgery can consider IVF which at the Jones Institute has a pregnancy rate of 25–35 per cent for women with minimal and mild endometriosis, although a disappointing result for severe cases.

*Polycystic ovarian disease* meaning many (poly) cysts of the ovaries, is one of the most common causes of ovulation failure. The exact cause of PCO is not known, although it seems that in sufferers, messages between the hypothalamus and pituitary are distorted. Consequently, follicles develop each month but do not burst and instead turn into cysts. In time, the ovaries can fill with a mass of cysts and swell to three times their normal size. They produce male hormones which indirectly suppress ovulation and often result in excess hair growth on the face, breasts and thighs. PCO is frequently linked to obesity and a recent study by Thai researchers concluded that women with PCO had higher body weight, blood pressure and a higher proportion of low-density lipo proteins (LDLs), which increase the risk of heart disease.[6]

Generally PCO starts in the teens and is established by the time a woman reaches the age of 20. It is difficult to diagnose but hormone tests and a laparoscopy usually confirm the disease. PCO is treated with drugs which force the follicles to burst.

The condition was discovered by Irvine Stein and Michael Leventhal in the 1930s. To their surprise, whenever they removed a piece of ovary to study it, the women began ovulating. It is assumed that the removal of a piece of the ovaries tones down the amount of hormones released and now wedge resection has become a standard method for treating PCO in open surgery, when treatment with stimulation drugs has failed.

Laparoscopy is used more often now to cut out a small piece of the ovaries and recently laser has been used experimentally, either in open surgery or directed down a laparoscope. Those who use it say it leaves far less scarring and bleeding than conventional wedge resection and can be done in half an hour at outpatients, compared with several days in hospital with open surgery. Surgeons in America are enthusiastic about lasers but their colleagues in Britain are more reserved. Gynaecologist Mr Keith Edmonds of Chelsea Hospital for Women, London, says it may be valuable for certain cases of PCO but the numbers are 'minuscule'.

*Hyperprolactinemia* means 'too much prolactin condition'. Prolactin is the 'milk hormone' that normally is elevated when a mother is breastfeeding, and high levels suppress ovulation so it is a natural contraceptive during lactation. However, about one in 25 infertile women have hyperprolactinemia. The progressive symptoms are head-aches, dry vagina during intercourse, sporadic and eventually no periods, and finally breasts may start to leak milk.

David London, Professor of Medicine at Birmingham University, England, says elevated prolactin is far more common than doctors are aware of and until recently it was responsible for a large proportion of 'unexplained infertility'. He believes 20 per cent of the women who present themselves to a gynaecologist with a menstrual problem have hyperprolactinemia.[7]

Normally, the hypothalamus tells the pituitary to block production of prolactin, unless a woman is breastfeeding. If the message is interrupted the pituitary starts prolactin production and this can be triggered by stress, drugs and infections (particularly encephalitis, inflammation of the brain) which are usually temporary and easily remedied; an underactive thyroid gland which can be stimulated into action with drugs; and in rare cases, a tiny tumour on the hypothalamus which can be treated with drugs, irradiation or surgery.

However, about half the cases of hyperprolactinemia are due to a small tumour on the pituitary and this blocks the 'do not produce prolactin' message. Often it is too small to be picked up by X-ray or CAT scan (computerised axial tomography), though a recently revised blood test has improved the chances of accurate diagnosis.

Women wanting to get pregnant can be given daily doses of bromocriptin to suppress the tumour, resulting in normal menstruation in 80 per cent of cases, though the tumour often returns when the treatment is stopped. Two new drugs, known as dopamine agonists, are being used experimentally in America and Europe. They are said to be longer-lasting and to have fewer side effects. The drugs present no increased risk of abnormalities in babies, even when taken during pregnancy, but there is a slightly higher than normal chance of twins.

When drugs are ineffective, or in the rare cases where a woman is intolerant to them, the tumour can be simply and successfully removed by surgery, although some women are being given surgery when medication is all they need.

## TUBAL DAMAGE

Fallopian tubes can be damaged by trauma in the pelvic region such as surgery or a ruptured appendix, but in most cases the harm is done after a pelvic infection. In most cases this is because of scarring or adhesions inside or outside the tubes. It is not unusual for the tubes to be 'glued' to other tissue including the uterus, ovaries, bowel and bladder, because of adhesions. Sperm, eggs and embryos may be prevented from passing through the tubes because the pathway is distorted or damaged. The muscle wall or the tiny hairs that line the tubes may also be damaged. When this happens, even if the tubes are open, they are no longer able to transport the egg or embryo.

Tubal damage is the primary cause of infertility in women worldwide, according to studies by the WHO. The highest incidence is in Africa where it accounts for 85 per cent of all female infertility. The causes of tubal damage vary from region to region. In Europe and North America, STDs are the main culprits but in Greece it is backstreet abortions. In Nigeria one of the main causes is infection after childbirth and in other African countries it is infection after circumcision in teenage girls. The sexually transmitted disease (STD) chlamydia is the major cause of tubal damage in Western countries.

Africa warrants special mention, because the incidence and

causes of infertility there are different from the rest of the world. The proportion of women with blocked tubes is almost three times higher than anywhere else and infection-induced infertility is twice as high, while pelvic infection is responsible for up to a third of gynaecological admissions to hospital. About half the infections are contracted after childbirth and the rest after abortion and STDs. One of the main problems is lack of resources and understanding which are compounded by centuries-old traditions such as female circumcision, infibulation and the practice in some areas of pouring near-boiling water into the genital tract after delivery. It is not uncommon in Africa for a man to have six or seven wives, the youngest often half his age, and he may spread STDs among them all. One traditional belief in the province of Sierra Leone is that a man will be cured of an infection if he has intercourse with a virgin, but this can render a young girl infertile after her first sexual encounter.

Donatien Mavoungou, who runs the human reproduction unit in Franceville, Gabon, recently reported cases of tubal blockage in 13–15-year-old African girls. He found the average age of the first sexual contact was 12½, and the average age of starting menstruation was 14½, so that some girls become infertile before they are fertile. 'It is common for women in this population to commence sexual activity prior to menarche and it is possible and indeed probable that young women could contract STD prior to menarche and become infertile,' he said.[8]

A number of events can leave the tubes damaged. Sometimes it is caused by endometriosis, as we have seen. Other causes are listed below in their order of frequency.

*Pelvic Inflammatory Disease* (*PID*) is by far the most common cause. In some countries it is the principal cause of sterility and in Sierra Leone and Gabon, in Africa, it accounts for at least 80 per cent of all female infertility.

PID occurs when microorganisms such as bacteria get into the pelvic region and cause inflammation of the tubes resulting in scarring and sometimes blockage, almost always in both tubes. It can happen after contracting an STD, after a contraceptive IUD is inserted or if the woman becomes infected after spontaneous or elective abortion, childbirth or surgery. Studies in the US and Scandinavia show that 20 per cent of PID is linked with delivery, abortion or curettage (scraping of the uterus, as in D&C). A study in Uganda found that one-third of the women hospitalised with PID had gonorrhoea and one-fifth had PID due to infection after delivery and abortion.[9]

World-famous PID expert Professor Lars Westrom of Lund University, Sweden, says 1 per cent of all women in Western societies aged 15–34 have at least one episode of PID and 2 per cent of those aged 15–24.[10]

In the US an estimated one million women a year have PID and of them 300,000 are hospitalised, costing an estimated 2.5 billion dollars a year in treatment. As Louis Keith, Professor of Gynaecology at the Northwestern University, Chicago, said, 'It affects millions and costs billions.' Those most at risk of PID are sexually active women under 25, those who have taken on a new partner in the previous two months and women who do not use barrier contraceptives.

More than one in seven women can be left infertile after an episode of PID, but about half of them may never know they have had an infection, according to Westrom who has spent more than 20 years researching PID. He established that 13 per cent of women end up with blocked tubes after one episode of PID, but after two infections 35 per cent have tubal occlusion and the figure goes up to 75 per cent after three episodes.[10]

PID can cause chronic pain in some women while others have no symptoms, or ignore them or attribute them to another problem. Symptoms include fever, abdominal pain, painful intercourse, burning on urination, spot bleeding after intercourse and between periods, genital itching and vaginal discharge. It is often wrongly diagnosed as appendicitis, ectopic pregnancy or endometriosis. Scientists are hoping to develop a blood test that may pick up specific chemicals released by a pelvic infection for more accurate diagnosis.

The risk of an ectopic pregnancy is increased sixfold after one or more episodes of PID and the risk is more than eight times higher than it was in 1930.[11] Other consequences are recurrent infection, chronic pain, infertility and death.

There are a number of causes of PID, including:

*Sexually transmitted diseases.* The number of women rendered infertile by STDs has increased with promiscuity and extra-marital relationships. The more sexual partners, the greater the chance of catching an STD, leading to an infection, maybe scarring and possibly blocked tubes. Chlamydia and gonorrhoea are the two main sexually transmitted micro-organisms causing infertility. Others include herpes, genital warts, trichomoniasis and anaerobic infections.

Chlamydia is now more common than gonorrhoea. In most cases a woman does not know she has been infected, even though her tubes may be damaged beyond repair. The microorganism is carried on the head and tail of sperm from a man who is infected, or it may be picked up by sperm as they pass through an infected cervix. Chlamydia is a very delicate microorganism and difficult to culture in a laboratory. A new instant test was released in the US and Britain in 1985 but is only 85 per cent successful. Chlamydia is treated with the antibiotic tetracyclin.

Gonorrhoea is caused by the gonococcus bacteria that lives in warm, moist parts of the body including the genital tract, rectum and throat and is spread though sexual contact. A woman has a 50 per cent chance of contracting it from an infected man. In the US in 1985 more than 920,000 cases were reported to the Centers for Disease Control. Generally, symptoms last ten days to two weeks but almost half the cases are asymptomatic, making detection and treatment difficult, and 10–20 per cent of women who have untreated gonorrhoea develop PID. A gonorrhoea test is almost 100 per cent accurate and is based on a laboratory culture from a cervical swab. Gonorrhoea is treated with penicillin and occasionally anti-biotics, and researchers at Stanford University, California, are working on a vaccine against it.

*Inter-uterine devices* (IUDs) have been blamed for PID more often than they should. There are two theories; that because the IUD is rigid and foreign it irritates the uterus, causing inflammation and a breeding ground for microorganisms; and that microorganisms are passed into the uterus when the IUD is inserted, either because the device was contaminated or it picked up microorganisms from the cervix and transported them to the uterus. In the mid-1970s it was believed that bacteria moved up the string of the IUD into the uterus but this theory has since fallen into disrepute.

'PID occurs in women who do not wear IUDs as well as women who do. In fact, the vast majority of women who develop PID do not wear IUDs and the vast majority of women who wear IUDs do not get PID. The risk of infection must be placed in perspective by recognising that the major causes of PID are sexually transmitted microorganisms,' said Louis Keith.

IUDs are used by more than 60 million women worldwide, the majority in developing countries where hygiene is substandard and PID prevalent. PID could be reduced if gynaecologists tested for the presence of microorganisms before inserting an IUD, though it is standard practice worldwide not to. A new antiseptic-coated IUD has been developed to reduce infection at the time of insertion. An antiseptic, chlorohexidine, is released for up to two weeks after the IUD is inserted and kills all microorganisms that enter the upper genital tract, including gonorrhoea, chlamydia and trichomoniasis. Dr Willem van Os of Elizabeth's Hospital, Haarlem, the Netherlands, reported to the 12th World Congress on Fertility and Sterility, in Singapore in 1986, that it appears to be 99 per cent effective in preventing PID.

*Induced abortions* occasionally lead to pelvic infection and subsequent tubal damage in Western countries. However, infection after termination is quite common in developing countries, and in countries where abortion is illegal and backstreet operations are usually done by untrained practitioners under less than hygienic conditions. One Malaysian study found signs of infection in 22 per cent of women hospitalised after their abortion.[12]

According to a Swedish study, women with chlamydia infections are at least five times more likely to develop PID within four weeks of an induced abortion than those without chlamydia.[12]

Spontaneous abortion can occasionally result in infection if the abortion is incomplete because the tissue that remains in the uterus is a breeding ground for bacteria. But the chances of infection are far less than after an induced abortion, as shown in a Bangladesh study of more than 1,000 women admitted to hospital because of incomplete abortion: 10 per cent who had had induced abortions developed pelvic infections compared with only 1 per cent of the women who had had spontaneous abortions.[12]

Dr Basil Tarlatzis of the Department of Obstetrics and Gynaecology at the Aristotelian University, Thessalonika, Greece, believes post-abortion infection is one of the biggest gynaecological problems in his country. About 40 per cent of infertility in Greece is due to tubal damage, and poorly performed illegal abortion is largely to blame because until abortion became legal in 1980 all except rare cases were backstreet operations. Today there are an estimated 300,000 abortions a year in Greece, and this high rate is mainly due to the low use of contraceptives. 'A popular way of family planning is abortion,' said Tarlatzis. He thinks the need for abortion could be dramatically reduced and that by failing to encourage contraceptive use doctors are partly to blame for tubal damage caused by abortions.

*Childbirth* weakens the body's immune system, making it more susceptible to infections, and the uterus and tubes are particularly vulnerable for the first few weeks. Delivery also opens the cervix up and removes the plug of mucus that usually prevents microorganisms from entering the uterus.

Some experts estimate that in Western countries 15 per cent of tubal infection may be due to postpartum (post-delivery) infection, often because an STD is present or microorganisms are transmitted on hands or instruments not adequately sterilised. One US study showed that women who have chlamydia during pregnancy are two and a half times more likely to develop postpartum infection. In developing countries the problem is often inflated by poor hygiene, unskilled midwives and lack of facilities.

A high proportion of women in Africa are infertile after having one or more children, and post-abortion and postpartum infections are second only to gonorrhoea as a cause. According to the *Population Report* of the Johns Hopkins University, Baltimore, in several hospitals postpartum infection accounts for 14 to 30 per cent of maternal deaths, and a large proportion of the women who survive end up with secondary infertility. In an Ethiopian hospital 10 per cent of gynaecological patients had postpartum infection. In a Ugandan study about 10 per cent of hospital admissions for acute PID were due to postpartum infections. And in a recent Indian study the figure was 16 per cent.[12]

Dr Dinah Jarrett of the Princess Christian Maternity Hospital, Freetown, Sierra Leone, and a member of the WHO Infertility Task Force, says 75 per cent of deliveries in her country are at home and 90 per cent are by women who have no training. 'It is a task handed down from generation to generation so we have a cultural problem, plus basic hygiene and facility problems.' Other researchers report traditional practices that include placing specific herbs in the genital tract to encourage contractions and hasten delivery. But these too can introduce infection.

*Circumcision, infibulation* and other forms of gynaecological mutilation are still performed in some Middle Eastern and African countries. These traditions involve removing external genitals, usually the tip or all of the clitoris and sometimes the labia minora and labia majora. The vulva is then sewn or held closed with small clamps or thorns. This results in scarring and encourages infection of the genital tract. In a major report on infertility in 1976, Mark Belsey, medical officer with the WHO's human reproduction unit in Geneva, said one study claimed that 20–25 per cent of the cases of infertility in the Sudan were due to infibulation, even though the practice has been banned there since 1946. He described it as 'a radical procedure with a very high immediate risk of haemorrhage and infection [which] may frequently result in severe scarring and nearly complete obliteration of the vaginal [entrance]'.[9]

He reported that female circumcision was widely practised in areas of Africa, and in one study 84 per cent of Moslem girls in the upper classes of a Guinean school had their clitoris removed between the ages of eight and 11, as had three out of 10 Christian girls. He also said certain delivery and birth rituals may add to the risk of infection or injury. 'The practice of the Hausa of pouring near-boiling water into the genital tract following delivery may decrease the risk of some infections but may also increase the risk of burns and possible scar formation.' He said another study, in Ghana, found that more than 10 per cent of the infertile women had hardening and narrowing of the vagina, 'resulting from ritual circumcision and native treatments'.

*Personal habits* may play a part in PID but it is still an unproven and controversial area. Wearing tight jeans may be sexy, but these fashionable thigh-huggers could be encouraging the growth of bacteria. Nylon underpants may do the same by increasing temperature and moisture in the area. As Louis Keith put it, 'The microorganisms that cause PID love a warm, damp environment.' The type and timing of sex and the use of tampons may also be linked to PID.

No studies have confirmed any of these theories, but there are medical reasons why they could be responsible, according to Keith. 'Tampons change the amount of oxygen at the top of the vagina which may influence the growth of certain microorganisms that are in abundance at the time of menstruation. Skin-tight jeans and nylon underwear increase moisture and facilitate the spread of bacteria.' He also believes that having intercourse during menstruation may facilitate the microorganisms because blood is a perfect medium for them to multiply in, so abstaining from sex during menstruation may help.

The above are the infections that cause tubal damage. Other causes include surgery, appendicitis and ectopic pregnancies:

*Surgery* anywhere in the pelvic region can start an infection or inflammation, and leave scar tissue and adhesions which can block, damage or distort the tubes, even under the best conditions with the best equipment. Occasionally a D&C can cause adhesions. Damage is most likely to happen during attempts to open blocked tubes or the removal of ovarian cysts.

*Appendicitis* is occasionally responsible for scarring, especially if the appendix burst before it was removed. A simple appendectomy without rupture does not increase the chance of tubal infertility, according to a study released in 1987 by the US National Institutes of Health, the University of Washington and the Fred Hutchinson Cancer Research Center. After ruling out other factors that may cause infertility, they showed that when the appendix ruptures, the woman is five times more likely to become infertile subsequently if she has never had a pregnancy, and three times more likely if she has already had at least one pregnancy.[13]

*Ectopic pregnancy* occurs when the embryo imbeds in the fallopian tube instead of the uterus. The tiny tube swells and unless the embryo is removed, it bursts, causing massive bleeding and endangering the woman's life. If an ectopic is detected early, the tube does not have to be removed. But the chances of a second ectopic are 10 times higher because once the tube has been damaged, in the next pregnancy the embryo is more likely to become lodged in the damaged area and imbed there. Occasionally the affected tube has to be removed, but the woman can still have a normal pregnancy, provided the other tube is healthy. Ectopic pregnancies will be discussed in more detail in the following section.

Although the list of causes is long, the list of treatments for tubal damage is disappointingly short. Surgically repairing the tubes requires a general anaesthetic, one or more hours in the operating theatre and several days in hospital. There are considerable risks involved and only 40–50 per cent of women later achieve a pregnancy, although some experts have higher figures.[14] Tubal surgery involves opening the abdomen, cutting away adhesions and reshaping the tubes. There are three different techniques, depending on what part of the tube is affected.

Often the open end of the tubes near the ovaries closes and puffs up like a balloon filled with liquid, but if cuts are made at the blocked end the tubes can be reopened in an operation known as *salpingostomy*. A blocked middle area can be cut away and the two clean ends rejoined, which is similar to reversing sterilisation when the tubes have been 'tied'. If the blockage is near the opening to the uterus the damaged section can be cut off and the fresh end refitted into the uterus, although this may weaken the uterus, eliminating the possibility of a natural delivery.

Technically tubal surgery is relatively straightforward and has been made easier with the introduction of microsurgery, but often the lining of the tubes is damaged and they still do not function. The two main dangers are that surgery itself may reintroduce an infection or cause scarring, in which case the tubes may end up more damaged than before surgery, and that if the tubes are opened but residual damage is left an embryo may lodge in the damaged area and cause an ectopic pregnancy. The chances of an ectopic after tubal surgery are considerable. According to Robert Glass, Professor of Obstetrics and Gynaecology at the University of California, San Francisco, 15 per cent of women who have adhesions diagnosed by laparoscopy become pregnant without surgery.[14] Because of this, plus the possibility of an ectoptic or reinfection, some women choose not to have surgery. These women, and those whose surgery has failed, can attempt IVF, although the success rate is even lower.

## UTERINE PROBLEMS

Even if an egg is released from a follicle, fertilised in a tube and the embryo reaches the uterus, it may pass out with the next period and be lost. There are two types of problem that can stop the embryo implanting in the uterus: the woman may have a misshaped uterus or there may be abnormal growths on the lining or wall. These include fibroids, adenomyomas, polyps and adhesions. Abnormal shape and growths can sometimes be felt in a physical examination but are more likely to be diagnosed with ultrasound and hysterosalpingogram (HSG). For tumours, laparoscopy and a D&C biopsy give a better diagnosis.

*Congenital.* It is unusual for a woman to be born with an abnormal uterus and extremely rare for her to have no uterus. The abnormalities fall into two groups: unknown cause and DES.

Occasionally a woman is born with a very small, asymmetrical or double uterus, which has two sections and looks like a Y. Pregnancy can occur, and women have been known to carry twins—one in each arm of the uterus. If the formation proves a problem it can be rectified by surgery—the wall between the two arms is removed, joining them into one cavity.

*Diethyl stilboestrol (DES)* is a synthetic estrogen, given to many women, mainly in the US in the 1940s–60s, to prevent miscarriage. It was designed for women who had several consecutive unexplained miscarriages, but was grossly over-prescribed and many doctors routinely gave it to all women who had a miscarriage, even though in nature miscarriage occurs in one out of six known pregnancies in the general population. Several years later it was discovered that the daughters of women who had DES during pregnancy were born with abnormal uteri. DES daughters have an increased incidence of infertility, endometriosis, ectopic pregnancies and premature labour, as well as vaginal and cervical cancer.

*Abnormal growths* in the uterus are not uncommon and do not always cause infertility. Generally they are only treated if pregnancy is proving difficult.

*Fibroids* are fibrous growth in the uterine wall. They are one of the most common tumours—it is assumed that in Western countries about a quarter of the women aged 30–50, and a third of those over 40, develop fibroids. They grow very slowly, are almost always benign and are usually painless, although they may cause bleeding between periods and in severe cases may cause miscarriage. They distort the shape of the uterus, making it difficult for an embryo to implant. Fibroids are usually only treated if they cause pain, bleeding or pregnancy difficulties. The traditional treatment is a hysterectomy, but a less radical approach now is surgically to cut the growths out of the wall, and laser may be used in the future to do this. Because fibroids need estrogen they grow more during pregnancy or if a woman is taking estrogen supplements after the menopause. They can be successfully treated with anti-estrogens. Roughly half the women become pregnant within a year of surgical or hormonal treatment.

*Adenomyosis* is endometriosis in the muscle wall of the uterus and occurs in an estimated one in 10 women who have a uterine problem. Small patches of the endometrium imbed in muscle fibres which produces 'pockets' in the wall, leading to scarring and enlargement of the uterus. Like fibroids, these growths give the uterus an irregular shape, hampering implantation. Some experts believe changes to the supply of blood to the uterus and possible chemical changes associated with adenomyosis may also contribute to infertility.

*Polyps* are small growths on the lining of the uterus and, like fibroids, are a hazard for the implanting embryo. They may also interrupt implantation by acting like a foreign body in the uterus, in the same way that an IUD does. Their cause is uncertain but they are generally treated with a D&C.

*Adhesions* are strands of abnormal fibre that form between two organs and bind them together, like glue, into a rigid shape. They occasionally stick the walls of the uterus together and can obstruct, distort and partially block the cavity, making implantation difficult. Fibres can involve the ovaries, tubes, uterus, bladder, bowel or abdominal wall and often appear after an infection (usually PID or TB), or surgery (usually induced abortion). The WHO estimates that endometrial TB occurs in 50 per cent of the women who have tubal TB. Uterine adhesions can usually be cut away with surgery, often with a good success rate if the condition is minimal, but poor if it is advanced.

## CERVICAL PROBLEMS

A couple can be denied a child because of a cervical problem at opposite ends of the babymaking scale: either before fertilisation or before delivery. Sperm may encounter a physical barrier or unfavourable cervical mucus. And if fertilisation and implantation are successful, the pregnancy may be lost in a miscarriage because the cervix is too weak or damaged to hold the baby.

Infection or injury to the cervix can damage the cells that produce the mucus, which must be the right consistency for sperm to survive and pass through the cervix to the uterus. Damage can also lead to scarring, which may partly close the canal, preventing sperm getting through, but this is rare and a narrowed or closed cervix can usually be opened. Injury is most likely to be caused by gynaecological intervention, for example during childbirth, an abortion, removal of cervical cancer or a D&C. Any of these can also increase the chance of a miscarriage, as the weakened cervix may be unable to hold the foetus in the womb. Some gynaecologists have been critical of these 'sloppy' practices that add to the problem of childlessness.

Occasionally a woman is born with a wide or *incompetent*

*cervix*. As with an accidentally weakened cervix, it can be held closed during pregnancy with a surgical nylon stitch placed across the cervix at 12–16 weeks of pregnancy and removed just before birth, if it is a vaginal delivery.

The cervix can also produce antibodies, in which case there is an immunological problem.

## IMMUNOLOGICAL PROBLEMS

The WHO estimates that about 3 per cent of infertility is due to immunological causes. This is when the body reacts to defend itself against foreign 'invaders', and produces antibodies—just as it does when confronted with the 'flu or the AIDS virus. Sperm are foreign cells in the female genital tract and scientists do not yet know why they are not usually regarded by the body as foreign. Occasionally they are. The cervix produces antibodies which attack the sperm, killing them or rendering them incapable of getting to the tubes. Just as some men produce antibodies against their own sperm (Chapter 3), a woman can also develop *sperm antibodies*, although this is less common than in men. However, only about 20 per cent of hostile cervical mucus is accounted for by sperm antibodies—the cause of the remainder is unknown.

Occasionally the antibodies appear after particles of sperm enter the woman's bloodstream, for example, if she has a ruptured surface in the vagina, uterus or fallopian tubes. With each new ejaculation, the antibodies attack and kill the healthy sperm before they reach the eggs.

The problem generally disappears if the cervix does not come in contact with the sperm for several months, and one solution is for the couple to use a condom for six months. When they stop using it, they are sometimes rewarded with a pregnancy, although some physicians say this practice is a waste of time.

There are several other treatments, but all have disappointingly poor results. Drugs have been tried, including antibiotics, steroids and prednisone, which is used to prevent rejection after kidney and heart transplants. Artificially injecting sperm into the uterus by-passes the trouble-spot, although sperm may encounter antibodies in the uterus.

## PROBLEMS AFTER FERTILISATION

To be able to conceive is a triumph for infertile couples, but it is only half the story, and the end result in the quest for children must be a live birth. More emphasis is needed to understand and prevent the three problems that can occur after fertilisation: failure of the embryo to implant, ectopic pregnancy and miscarriage.

*Implantation failure* is by far the main reason for the difference between the number of eggs fertilised and babies born. London gynaecologist Keith Edmonds has estimated that in nature about 60 per cent of embryos never develop—they fail to implant in the uterus or are lost in spontaneous abortions, 45 per cent of them before the woman even knows she is pregnant.[15]

As discussed, the embryo may not bed down in the lining of the uterus because of obstructions, such as fibroids, or because the uterus is distorted. It may also be because of an imbalance of hormones which have to be present in the right amounts at the right time for implantation. How, where and why an embryo implants is one of the mysteries of reproduction, although *in vitro* fertilisation now allows scientists to study the development of the embryo outside the body.

*Ectopic pregnancy* is extremely dangerous. It occurs when the embryo implants somewhere other than in the uterus. In about 95 per cent of cases it is in the fallopian tube, but the embryo can also attach itself to the ovaries or cervix.

The condition was first described in AD 936, but the first successful operation was not until 1759. Today the operation is similar to appendix removal. Traditionally the embryo and the whole tube were excised, but with recent conservative surgery the tube can sometimes be left in place. However, the chances of a second ectopic are very high because the tube is damaged. The ectopic is now frequently removed by laparoscopy or chemically, and American surgeons who use laser say it can be removed with minimal damage to the tubes or the delicate cells lining it.

About one in 250 pregnancies is an ectopic, and the proportion is increasing. One of the main reasons is the increase in STDs causing pelvic inflammatory disease—it is at the scar sites that the embryo lodges and begins to grow. In 1975 Lars Westrom of Sweden found that the chances of an ectopic were one in 24 if a woman had had PID.[10]

*Miscarriage* or spontaneous abortion, is quite common in all pregnancies and higher in countries with substandard hygiene, poor nutrition and a high rate of disease. However, about 50 per cent of miscarriages before the 12th week are because of chromosome abnormalities in the embryo—nature's way of eliminating childhood disorders. The majority of other miscarriages are caused by infections and the consequences of unskilled abortion or gynaecological practices, and occasionally by immunological, hormonal or psychological disorders. Of the viruses and bacterial infections, probably the best known in Western countries is rubella (German measles). Those common in developing countries include syphilis, malaria and toxoplasmosis, while in Africa and Asia the filaria worm is also thought to be a cause. In Western countries infections are usually treated, but that is not always the case in developing countries where viral and bacterial diseases are prevalent.

It is well known that the rate of spontaneous abortion is higher in groups of malnourished women in poorer regions. However, even in a country of plenty, diet should not be ignored if a woman is at risk of a miscarriage. Cigarette and marijuana smoking and alcohol consumption are increasingly being linked with spontaneous abortions, although as yet there is not much evidence to support the theory. Exposure to lead poisoning, radiation, anaesthetics, certain pesticides and high levels of noise are reported to jeopardise a pregnancy; and diabetes, thyroid problems, kidney disease and extremely high blood pressure are known to, although these are more rare causes.

## STRESS AS A CAUSE OF INFERTILITY

How much stress and trauma are responsible for infertility in women is controversial and not fully understood. Stress is not a proven cause of infertility, but it almost certainly upsets the fine balance of hormones needed for conception and embryo implantation. It is known that the hypothalamus is easily upset by certain drugs such as tranquillizers and mood modifiers, and many experts believe it is also sensitive to stress.

When the body is under extreme physical and emotional stress reproductive organs slow down, and in some cases shut down completely. This is nature's way of saying that under certain circumstances a person is not capable of carrying and supporting a foetus. It certainly does not happen to everyone under stress—women who are raped, and obviously suffer enormous physical and emotional stress, actually have a higher pregnancy rate than normal. One theory is that the rape stimulates ovulation, leading to speculation that stress may in certain circumstances improve conception. However, it has been shown that women in jail and concentration camps develop the 'shut down' mechanism. Females who have severe anorexia nervosa usually find their periods stop, and it is not uncommon in professional and Olympic-standard sportswomen. Menstruation usually returns to normal when the woman returns to a normal lifestyle: when she leaves jail, eats properly or reduces training.

When there is no physical reason for infertility the anxiety and frustration of childlessness and its treatments may reduce fertility, although many experts dispute this. However, it is well known that women who have tried for many years to conceive succeed soon after they give up trying or decide to adopt, and one woman in California fell pregnant 17 days after a surrogate mother, whom she and her husband had contracted to have a child for them, became pregnant. As Robert Winston commented, 'The speed that people get pregnant when an emotional situation is resolved makes one feel that perhaps, after all, we are sometimes the cause of our own problems.'[16]

Dr Bernard Sandler of the Infertility Clinic at the Manchester Jewish Hospital, England, believes stress may provoke infertility in as many as 25 per cent of cases.[17] However, not everyone agrees with him. Swiss psychiatrist Dr Cécile Ernst of the University of Zurich says, 'The suggestion that psychological problems are, as a rule, the primary cause of infertility is not well founded.' Others think it is unlikely to be the primary cause, but may *reduce* fertility.

After reviewing many studies, British psychologists Robert Edelman and Kevin Connolly of the universities of Surrey and Sheffield respectively, concluded, 'There appears to be little to support the suggestion that psychological factors play a part in causing infertility,' but said the question remains unanswered. They believe it is possible that depression, anxiety and fear may influence hormones and reduce the chance of conception, but 'whether psychological factors can actually cause infertility is difficult to gauge'.[18]

## THE INCIDENCE OF FEMALE INFERTILITY

The incidence of female infertility varies between, and within, countries, as does male infertility, depending on the availability of specialists and the levels of diagnostic skills, the motivation of the couples to attend the clinic and their ability to pay for treatment. In parts of Africa—particularly Gabon, Sudan, Cameroon and Zaire—20–40 per cent of the women over 50 are childless. Yet, in other regions of the same countries the incidence is 3–6 per cent, which is comparable to rates in the US, Canada and India for women over 50.[9]

Endometriosis is common in Britain, the US and Australia but almost unheard of in Africa. And *hirsutism*, a hormonal problem characterised by excessive hair growth and obesity, is very high in the USSR but extremely rare in Western countries. Tubal damage is the main cause of female infertility in many developing countries, but in most Western countries it is ovarian failure.

The WHO 25-country study found that worldwide tubal abnormalities and ovarian failure were the prime causes of infertility: 41 per cent of infertile women who had a diagnosed condition had tubal and 38 per cent had ovarian failure. Endometriosis accounted for 6 per cent, and ovarian, uterine and cervical abnormalities for 5 per cent. Congenital abnormalities and TB were rare. No cause was found in 35 per cent of infertile women, compared with 19 per cent in women *and* men in some American studies. However, the difference is probably due to a lack of diagnostic skills in some developing countries rather than a lack of diagnosable cause. The WHO study also found that the incidence of tubal abnormalities increased, and endocrine causes decreased, with age.[19]

Not all countries have the same incidence as these world-wide figures. Studies in the US, Denmark, Israel and Singapore suggest ovarian failure accounts for about 15–25 per cent of all female infertility, tubal damage for only 15–25 per cent and endometriosis for 10–15 per cent, which is considerably higher than worldwide.[20]

To give an idea of numbers, Professor Ricardo Asch of the University of California at Irvine has calculated that 1,215,000 American women are infertile because of ovulation failure, 675,000 because of tubal damage, 180,000 have endometriosis, 135,000 have immunological problems, 90,000 have a problem with the uterus and another 90,000 have cervical problems. He estimates about 855,000 cases have no known cause.

Robert Winston reported recently that in 68 per cent of the women he saw with blocked tubes, the damage had been caused by previous surgery in the pelvic region and only about 5 per cent of tubal damage in his patients is attributable to STDs.[21] Yet Ward Cates, head of the division of STDs at the Center for Disease Control in the US, says that 20 per cent of all infertility in the US is caused by STDs.

Infertility in women is more common than in men and a large proportion of it could be prevented by reducing STDs and gynaecological procedures that lead to pelvic infections. Diagnosing female infertility is more demanding and more invasive, usually requiring internal examination. Many of the treatments are long-standing procedures that are constantly being up-dated and improved, although pregnancy rates for most of them are still only moderate.

# 5
# ARTIFICIAL INSEMINATION AND SPERM BANKS

Artificial insemination(AI) involves placing semen in the female genital tract. According to some accounts, it was first used when a farmer stole the semen of a prized stallion to impregnate his mare, and the fourteenth-century Arab tribesmen are said to have impregnated enemy mares with semen of inferior stallions. In the early 1890s researchers in Moscow developed AI for sheep, cattle and horses, and the technique is now a major part of the sheep and cattle industry worldwide. It has been practised in patients for almost 200 years and tens of thousands of children a year are born after AI.

The procedure is painless and so simple it can be done by the woman herself—some women say it is similar to inserting a tampon—but the ethical and legal consequences are far more complex, especially when sperm other than the husband's is used. While some people would like to see it stopped, others argue that as it is here, and well established, we should make provision for it, for example by setting standards of practice and defining the legal status of the sperm donor, the recipients and the children involved.

## USING HUSBAND'S SPERM (AIH)

The first recorded birth after artificial insemination with husband's sperm (AIH) was in 1790. A London couple were unable to have a natural conception because the husband had hypospadias, a defect of the urethra. The baby was conceived after the husband's sperm had been collected and placed in the mother's genital tract. The first doctor who successfully used this new technique was the British surgeon, John Hunter. Today, more than 2,000 AIH babies a year are born in Britain alone.

If the woman does not have a fertility problem, AIH can be used for five main reasons: if sperm is not being placed in the vagina during intercourse, which could be due to ejaculation problems or hypospadias; if the woman has hostile cervical mucus in which case sperm can be placed directly into the uterus; when a man's sperm count is low, but not too low to exclude a pregnancy with a little help; if he has sperm antibodies which can sometimes be removed; and after a man undergoes surgery or radiotherapy which would damage the sperm or end sperm production, in which case his sperm is frozen before and used after the treatment. Some doctors have suggested that men joining the armed forces in active combat could also have their sperm frozen in case of subsequent injury.

As mentioned in Chapter 3, AIH can also be used for paraplegics where the sperm is collected after electro-ejaculation, and in rare cases if a man has a blocked vas or epididymis by removing the sperm from the reproductive tract via a fine needle. It can also be used for prisoners on long-term sentences. In August 1985 the Italian Government, for the first time, gave permission for a prisoner to provide sperm for his wife to be inseminated. He was a terrorist serving a 14-year sentence and his wife, also a former terrorist, had been released several months earlier after a five-year jail term.

AIH is generally performed by a doctor but can also be done by the husband and wife at home, although this is less usual. At the time of ovulation, semen is collected after masturbation and within a few hours placed in the upper vagina or the cervical canal with a plastic needle syringe and plunger. The few women who inseminate themselves use a common medical syringe with the needle removed, or a turkey baster which works on the same principle as a syringe and plunger and is normally used in American kitchens for basting a roasting turkey. Mail order do-it-yourself AI kits are also available in the US. After the insemination the sperm is held in place with a cervical cap. If the woman has hostile cervical mucus this is by-passed by placing treated sperm directly into the uterus, which is said to increase the chances of pregnancy.

It is further increased if the sperm are 'washed', or the best ones separated in the 'swim-up' procedure. The semen is placed in a test-tube with culture medium then placed in a centrifuge, which is not unlike a miniature spindryer that separates the sperm from the seminal fluid and culture. The washing process is repeated twice, then the sperm swim through a culture solution in a test-tube and the top layer (which contains the fastest swimmers, and presumably the healthiest sperm) is removed and placed in the woman's upper genital tract. Fifteen-30 per cent of women become pregnant after insemination has been attempted during six menstrual cycles.

On the whole, there is very little moral objection to AIH. The two exceptions come from the Catholic Church, which says the conjugal act and procreation should not be separated and forbids masturbation, and Moslems, who do not approve of masturbation. Lovemaking and babymaking need not be separated thanks to the introduction of a perforated condom that the Church does not see as a contraceptive because a tiny hole in the end of the condom means it is not a barrier to conception. The couple can have intercourse, collect the sperm in the special condom, take it to the laboratory and have it injected into the cervix or uterus.

Although Catholic and Moslem leaders have condemned AIH, many couples wanting children have ignored their rulings. The objection to masturbation has come under strong criticism. Peter Singer, Professor of Philosophy at Monash University, Melbourne, believes it is 'downright cruelty to condemn masturbation when it is the only means by which the couple can conceive a much-wanted child. Does the Vatican really know so little about conjugal love that it imagines that the only sexual expression of such love involves the insertion of the penis into the vagina? Masturbation need not be a solitary act, but can also be a form of conjugal love.'[1]

In *Medicine, Patients and the Law*, Margaret Brazier points out that if the marriage has never been consummated, the acceptance of AIH cannot prevent the wife from petitioning later to annul the marriage. She refers to a court case in Britain in 1949 and adds, 'although on policy grounds the court may refuse a decree if they consider that in having the child the wife approbated the marriage'. The child from AIH will not be illegitimate because he was conceived in marriage, albeit a non-consummated marriage.[2]

AIH can place enormous strain on the people involved. The couple have to accept that it is not nature's way. The attempt at conception is almost always done at a set time in a clinic, rather than spontaneously at home. When first asked to masturbate and produce a semen sample, it is not uncommon for men to fail to ejaculate, causing embarrassment and adding to the already mounting frustration of being infertile. There have been reports of husbands and sperm donors forced to masturbate in hospital toilet cubicles. Some centres now have masturbatroia, special rooms with a couch/bed and books, magazines and sometimes videos.

Even if the semen is collected in the perforated condom after intercourse, it has to be rushed to the laboratory to be processed, usually from a nearby hotel in the middle of the afternoon. UK infertility expert Robert Winston notes: 'Many couples find AIH so frustrating and invasive of their sex lives that they may give up after three or four months.' One study in Britain shows the drop-out rate is high: even in the familiar atmosphere of a private practice, 39 per cent of couples gave up within five inseminations or less and 60 per cent within 10 or less.[3]

But for those who do attempt again, there is one major emotional advantage over using donor sperm or adopting—the child is genetically the offspring of both partners, which is more reassuring to the parents, and more easily accepted by their friends and relatives than when donor sperm is used.

## USING DONOR SPERM (DI)

American gynaecologist Robert Dickinson is recorded as the first physician successfully to inseminate a woman with sperm from a man other than her husband, in what is now called donor insemination or DI, previously known as artificial insemination with donor sperm, or AID. The first such baby was born in 1890. This method has been practised in Sweden at least since the 1920s, although it was not used in Britain until the late 1930s. It is now used extensively and routinely in America, Australia and Europe. An estimated 100,000 DI children have been born in the US and about 10,000 in the UK, and each year it is used by more than 20,000 American couples. Donor insemination is much more successful than AIH with a 60 per cent birth rate after six insemination cycles. It has been proven that there is no increased risk of spontaneous abortion during the pregnancy or abnormalities to the children.

Like AIH, the method is used if the couple is having difficulty with intercourse or if the man has a low sperm count, if the sperm count is very low or he does not produce sperm at all, or if he carries the genes for a hereditary disease, such as haemophilia, Huntington's chorea, Tay-Sachs disease or blindness. One US expert reports that 29–40 per cent of donor insemination cases are done because the man has low sperm count, 30–66 per cent because he has no sperm and 8–30 per cent because he has a genetic problem.[4]

The insemination procedure is the same as with AIH except that in most cases the donor sperm is frozen and later thawed for the insemination. This means doctors do not have to rely on donors providing fresh semen at the woman's most fertile time. The woman's partner is often present during the insemination so that he feels part of the babymaking process, even though it is with another man's sperm. Some doctors suggest the couple have intercourse after insemination to strengthen their bond.

The main hesitation a couple may have in using donor insemination is that the resultant child is not genetically the child of the husband, yet donor insemination has advantages over adoption in that the child is at least half theirs genetically and the couple can experience conception, pregnancy and delivery.

Another concern, especially in Asian countries, is that half brothers and sisters may marry without knowing they are related through the same father. For this reason many AI centres limit the number of donations each man can make. In Britain the recommended limit is 10, in Singapore it is four. It has been estimated that there is a one in 40,000 chance of genetic incest occurring if the sperm from one donor is used six times in a city with a population of about three million. In

1984 it was reported that at least two couples in the US had been told after they were married that they were half brother and sister.

Few couples tell friends and family they had donor insemination, partly because of the lingering stigma of male infertility, although this is changing. Some experts suggest that during the pregnancy the woman be seen by a doctor who does not know, so that it is assumed from the beginning that her husband is the father. Others disagree and say there should be nothing to hide and the child should be told. One of the dangers of not telling a child is that if the marriage is going through a rough patch or the child is being troublesome, the husband may refer to the child as 'your child'. There is a strong argument that the child should be told that his social father is not his genetic father.

There is no evidence that children resulting from donor insemination are resented or less cared for by their social (but not genetic) fathers; nor that they have psychological problems. Some people have suggested that such children may suffer emotional conflicts, knowing the man they call 'Dad' is not their genetic father, but there is no evidence to suggest or refute this.

Traditionally, the majority of sperm donors have been medical students attached to a hospital with an artifical insemination programme, or friends of the physician. In Sweden donors have also been from the ranks of the military services. Generally it has been regarded as a charitable service. Today, many of the clinics in the US are private and pay their clients, anywhere from $1 to $100. Some centres, including all those in France, prefer married men who have at least one healthy child, which means the wife has given consent and that the donor is a 'proven' father. Since Sweden passed a law in 1985 which allows the child to know the name of his genetic father (the sperm donor), most of the donors are now married men with a family of their own and they donate with the consent of their wives.

How well donors are screened depends a lot on whether the programme is private or run in a government hospital or clinic. The main criteria are that the donor has a high sperm count and does not have any hereditary diseases in his family or any infections himself. Details of the donor's ethnic origin and hair, skin and eye colour plus height and weight are taken so he can be matched as closely as possible to the husband, who will become the social father of the child. And some clinics take personal details including the donor's educational qualifications and interests, such as sports and hobbies, so the couple have some idea of his character. Some parents choose to pass this description on to the child in later years. Sometimes the couple choose the donor from a catalogue of photos.

Before a test was developed to detect antibodies to the AIDS (acquired immunodeficiency syndrome) virus several women received the virus when they were inseminated with donor sperm. Donor insemination programmes in Western countries now test for the antibodies and exclude homosexual men from donating. Because antibodies may not show up for three to six months, the semen is usually stored and not used until the donor is tested again six months later. If the second test is negative, the semen is then used. This means that most donor sperm is now frozen, although unfortunately not all sperm banks use this safeguard.

To give an example of the screening process, these are some of the details of each donor taken by one well-regarded private sperm bank in California:[5] religion; education; general health including diet, exercise, vision, hearing, condition of teeth; whether he has had any surgery, is on any medication or had hepatitis, pneumonia, mononucleosis (glandular fever) or amoebic dysentery; whether he or his sexual partner has been exposed to or treated for syphilis, gonorrhoea, non-specific urethritis, chlamydia, venereal warts, herpes, AIDS or any other sexually transmitted diseases.

The clinic also looks for any environmental factors that may affect sperm, including whether the donor's mother took DES (diethyl stilbestrol) or any prescription drug during her pregnancy; whether he has ever used marijuana, cocaine, barbiturates, heroin, hallucinogens or tranquillizers; whether he smokes, drinks or wears jock-type underwear; whether he has been exposed to excess heat (saunas, hot baths, steam rooms), radiation or X-rays, 'Agent Orange' or any other herbicides, toxic chemicals, sprays, fumes, lead products, asbestos or cleaning solutions.

The clinic also wants to know his family's medical history including whether there were any genetic diseases, multiple pregnancies or infant deaths; and whether the donor's mother, father, brothers, sisters, grandparents, aunts, uncles and cousins have ever suffered from any heart diseases, blood disorder, respiratory or gastro-intestinal problem and any muscle, skin or sight disorders.

Few screenings are as thorough as this and some experts say it is too much. They point out that women receiving the sperm do not have their medical history scrutinised. Many clinics that use university students rely on the donors volunteering information on infections and hereditary diseases. Lori Andrews, of the American Bar Association, points out that some physicians maintain they need not do detailed physical examination because most of the donors are medical students and can do their own reports, 'but it stretches credulity to think that medical students will reveal to the physicians (who often are their professors) that they are engaging in sexual behaviour that puts them at high risk of venereal disease or AIDS'. She quoted a study of 168 donors at one university which found the majority had a family history of a genetic disorder but did not recognise it as being genetic, despite their medical training.[6]

## AI WITH MIXED SPERM (AIM)

AI presents a third possibility: mixing husband's and donor's sperm together for the insemination, known as artificial insemination with mixed sperm (AIM). The couple could also have intercourse after insemination with donor sperm. It is unlikely the husband's sperm will result in pregnancy, but some doctors encourage this because, as one said, 'The aura of mystery will still exist.' Others condemn it because it is not honest and therefore not fair on the child. The Swedish Government has prohibited AIM because it excludes the possibility of the genetic father being identified, although this may be possible in the future with DNA technology.

Many people not involved in infertility treatment think that AIM is a solution when the husband's sperm is not good enough and the couple is uncomfortable about using another man's sperm. They say, 'What you don't know doesn't hurt you,' and if no one can prove it was not the husband's sperm that fertilised the egg, it is easy to pretend it was. But while this may be a psychological comfort to the couple, it means they have not accepted their infertility or the relationship between the biological and social father, and for this reason many doctors are reluctant to use AIM.

Adding the husband's poor sperm to good quality donor sperm also reduces the chances of fertilisation, which is another reason AIM is not popular. However, if a couple insists on AIM and is prepared to accept a lower success rate, some doctors will oblige.

Dr E.V. Macalalag, senior urologist at the Chinese General Hospital in Manila, the Philippines, who has been using artificial insemination for more than 20 years, reported that he had achieved a 27 per cent increase in pregnancy rate by mixing donor and husband sperm. However, other urologists and infertility experts are sceptical.

Some clinics also mix the sperm of different donors so no one knows who the genetic father is, but this practice is loudly condemned by many physicians and lawyers. They say the couple requesting insemination must accept that knowing the child's genetic origin is important, for emotional and medical reasons. A child would find it much easier to accept that Mr X, the blue-eyed accountant, was his genetic father than the ambiguity of not knowing whether it was Mr X, Y or Z. Knowing the genetic father is important, and sometimes life-saving, if the child needs certain medical advice. Several governments, including those in Victoria (Australia) and Sweden, have banned the use of sperm from more than one donor, and the Council of Europe has recommended that its 21 member countries also prohibit the practice.

## SEXING SPERM

For various reasons, some people want boy or girl babies and it is possible to produce one sex or the other by fertilising an egg with so-called male or female sperm. When sperm are ejaculated half of them have an X-shaped *chromosome* in their nucleus and the other half have a Y-shaped chromosome. If the X-bearing sperm fertilises the egg, a female baby results and if it is a Y-bearing sperm a boy will be born, so there is generally a 50:50 chance that the baby will be one sex or the other. In theory, if the X and Y sperm can be separated and used in artificial insemination, the would-be parents can have a baby with the sex of their choice. However, so far, the success rate with these techniques has not been good.

Sperm with the X (female) chromosome are slightly larger, heavier and swim slightly more slowly in cervical mucus than sperm with the Y (male) chromosome. There is also thought to be a difference in surface charge between the X and Y sperm and researchers have tried to separate them with electric currents. In addition, the male sperm usually have a spot on their head which shows up under fluorescent screening. The Lawrence Livermore Laboratory in California is reported to have developed a method of sorting the fluorescent sperm at the rate of 1,000 per second.[7]

The most widely used sperm separator is the Ericsson method, invented by former American rancher Dr Ronald Ericsson, who developed the method to sex cattle sperm. He places sperm in a test-tube with graduated layers of albumin, a protein derived from human lymph. Because of gravity and the weight of their heads, sperm swim downwards and as the male sperm swim faster, in theory they will reach the bottom first. Each layer of the albumin is progressively removed and the sperm in the bottom layer are used for artificial insemination, hopefully resulting in a male baby. The process takes about four hours and Ericsson claims that in 75–80 per cent of cases it produces the desired result nine months later, although other researchers have not been able to repeat his success rate.

Ericsson set up a network of franchises from his base in San Francisco, and he has more than 55 centres around the world, including several in Asia, where the desire for male babies is strongest.

In theory, this selection of the fastest sperm is also a selection of the fittest as it culls out sperm with abnormalities.

'There has been no problems with the children having any abnormalities, or problems with the pregnancies. It's been the other way around, it has improved the pregnancy rate and reduced the abnormality rate,' he told a press conference in Bangkok when opening his franchise there in January 1987. More than 600 babies had been born after using his method, he said.[8]

Several variations of the Ericsson method are now being used, including a Thai technique that uses chicken egg yolk, rather than albumin. It was developed by Professor Vitoon Osathanondh of Bangkok's Ramathibodi Hospital who says early studies show it is 75–87 per cent effective in selecting male sperm. The big advantage of the Thai version is the cost. Ericsson's method costs a Thai couple $US280 (it costs an American couple $700) but Vitoon's egg-yolk technique costs them just $40.

Egg yolk has been used as a solution in which to freeze sperm for more than 20 years and Vitoon says it is not only less harmful to sperm than other solutions but it may in fact improve the sperm's performance. 'Egg yolk has so many good properties that make the sperm more active,' he says. 'Glycerol, which is often used, decreases sperm activity and the tails curl and they spasm. When you have egg yolk alone, the motility is increased.'

An alternative to 'swimming' the sperm through a solution is to filter them through special filter paper to separate the larger X female sperm.

It appears that male sperm also have a liking for laboratory beads specially designed to separate X and Y sperm. According to researchers in Philadelphia, when sperm are placed in a glass column with beads of gel, most of the male sperm stick to the beads and are unable to pass through the column. The researchers found this to be 95 per cent successful in separating X sperm but another found only marginal differences.[9]

The ethics of sex selection will be discussed in Chapter 13.

## SPERM BANKS

Sperm can be used immediately after collection or frozen and stored in a sperm bank to be used later, either as donor sperm or by the man himself, for example if he is undergoing surgery or chemotherapy. There are now sperm banks in most developed countries where artificial insemination is carried out: in the US, for example, there are about 20 registered sperm banks. Although the pregnancy rate may be up to 20 per cent higher with fresh sperm, many physicians prefer to use frozen specimens because the insemination can be done at any time and it allows time for the donors to be re-tested for the AIDS virus. When frozen sperm is sent to other parts of the country, it reduces the chance of half brothers or sisters accidentally marrying.

The idea and technique of freezing and storing sperm is not new. Dr Cappy Rothman, a Californian expert on male infertility who runs a private sperm bank, reports that about 200 years ago it was first noticed that sperm were inactive when they were cooled and could be revived when rewarmed. In 1866 it was suggested that a man dying on the battlefield might beget a legal heir with his semen frozen and stored at home. In 1953 it was demonstrated that frozen-thawed human sperm were capable of fertilisation. Interest in sperm banks increased after a report at the International Congress of Geneticists in September 1963 which documented normal births resulting from insemination with frozen sperm. It has been since shown that there is no greater risk that frozen-thawed human sperm will result in spontaneous abortion.

The freeze-thaw method, known as *cryopreservation*, was developed for animals in the late 1950s and has played a major part in improving cattle, sheep and goat breeds around the world—one ejaculate from a prize bull can inseminate up to 600 cows.

Semen is collected and the sperm separated. A *cryoprotectant* (which literally means freezing protectant) is added to the sperm before they are placed in tiny glass ampoules or 'straws' which are then gradually lowered into a special cylinder of liquid nitrogen at –196 degrees Celsius. No cell changes take place at this temperature and they can remain in suspended animation indefinitely, perhaps for thousands of years.

Frozen human sperm was used by several physicians in the late 1960s and one of the first private sperm banks in the US was set up by Robert Quinlan in 1971. It was designed primarily for men to deposit their sperm before being sterilised. In those days vasectomy reversal was not very successful, but if a man decided to have another child, he could collect his sperm from the bank and have his wife inseminated. In 1976 Quinlan admitted that the initial deposits had been inadvertently thawed and ruined, and faced lawsuits and financial ruin.

This raises the question of the legal status of sperm. Generally, men who deposit sperm for their own use regard it as their property and in this case sued Quinlan for loss of property. What if a man dies and his wife wants to be inseminated with the sperm? Californian lawyer Lawrence Nelson believes the wife would have no claim under US law: 'If I donated sperm to a sperm bank this afternoon and was killed, my wife would have problems laying claim to that sperm legally if she decided to be inseminated. Some courts may rule that she could have it on humane grounds even though legally she would have no claim to it.'

In an emotional and highly publicised case in 1984 a French court ruled that a 23-year-old widow could be inseminated with her husband's stored sperm after he died, but emphasised that the decision was not to be seen as a precedent. Alain Parpalaix contracted cancer of the testicles and placed some of his sperm in a bank before having chemotherapy which would damage his fertility. Two years later, on Christmas Day 1983, he died. Two days earlier he had married, and soon after his wife Corinne asked to be inseminated with the sperm of her dead husband, saying it was his wish that she have his child.

The sperm bank refused to hand over the sperm without instructions from the Ministry of Health, which replied that the whole area of AI was under review and a decision on the use of a dead man's sperm had not been reached. Corinne Parpalaix took the sperm bank to a court which ruled against her, although a higher court later ruled she could have the frozen sperm. However, she did not become pregnant after the insemination. If she had borne a child it would have been considered illegitimate, as under French law a child must be born within 300 days of its father's death for paternity to be officially recognised.

Faced with the Parpalaix case courts in other countries—and indeed other courts in France—could rule differently. Opinions vary from one extreme to the other. The Swedish Insemination Committee, which drafted legislation on AI in 1983, recommended that insemination with a deceased man's sperm should not be allowed on ethical grounds as it was considered necessary for a child to have access to both a father and mother.[10] However, the Ontario Law Reform Commission in Canada recommended in 1985 that posthumous insemination be allowed, that the mother be allowed to register her deceased husband as the father on the birth certificate, and that the child be entitled to inheritance rights.[11] And the New South Wales Law Reform Commission in Australia in 1986 recommended similar laws, 'provided that the woman is his widow and unmarried at the same time of insemination and birth'.[12]

US lawyer/psychiatrist Dr Judianne Densen-Gerber, who helped draft legislation on reproductive technologies for a Michigan senator, asks what would happen to the stored sperm in a divorce case—can the wife claim half the sperm, as she could half her husband's other property, such as a house? Can, and should, a sperm bank give a woman her husband's sperm even if he is still living? What would happen if the bank did, without knowing the couple had divorced, and the woman then sued her ex-husband for maintenance for a child who would have been born by AI after they separated?

And there are other questions. Should donors of sperm have any legal claim over their own sperm while it is still in the sperm bank? What if a man married after donating sperm and his new wife objected to his sperm being used to father children for another woman? Could he, or she, retrieve the sperm from the bank and destroy it? Does the donor legally own the sperm in the bank and can he legally retrieve it? Rothman, who is also a urologist at the University of California, Los Angeles, says it ceases to be the donor's property when he is paid for providing the sperm. However, Louis Waller, Professor of Law at Monash University, Melbourne, believes the man can withdraw his consent for the sperm to be used. 'We don't own part of the human body but we have control over it.' And the Ontario LRC made a recommendation that after donation, but before the sperm is used, the donor be entitled to say what happens to the sperm—whether it be disposed of or returned to him.[13]

It is not unreasonable for a couple to have a child by a certain donor and want a second by the same donor so the siblings are genetically identical. In countries where recipients pay for the sperm the couple could buy a number of his deposits which could be kept in storage at the bank, but what if the bank accidentally gave them to another couple? If the donor could not make any more donations, could the first couple make any claim on the deposits which they had bought, and legally owned? Waller says it would be a breach of contract and points to a case in New York in the 1970s where a jury rejected a claim for property damage but awarded damages for psychological harm after a member of the hospital staff deliberately destroyed a laboratory dish containing egg and sperm (see page 280).

Presumably a man has a right to do with his sperm as he likes and his wife or girlfriend cannot legally stop him, just as in many countries a husband or boyfriend cannot stop a woman having an abortion even if it is his own child. Shortly after she married in the 1950s, Densen-Gerber refused to allow her husband, then a fourth-year medical student, to donate sperm on the basis that she did not want his genetic material shared by other women.

> I was pregnant and I was outraged when he came home and told me he was going to donate. I said, as I married you I have the right to bear all your children and I don't expect to find your children all over the place. Maybe it was jealousy but that's how I felt. And you have to ask, does taking a vow for monogamy imply intercourse or bearing children?

Some sperm banks now insist on written consent from the donor's wife, if he has one, and those in the Australian state of Victoria are forced by law to obtain this. Failure to do so carries a penalty of one year's imprisonment.

## 'SUPER' SPERM BANKS

The possibility of using new reproductive technologies to override natural selection and create a super-race has concerned many people, especially ethicists and religious leaders. They were given more to worry about when, in 1980, Robert Graham, the famous optometrist who invented shatter-proof lenses for spectacles, announced he had set up a sperm bank for elite breeders in California. It would use the sperm of Nobel prize winners and scientists with exceptionally high IQs to inseminate women with high IQs.

The idea of a select sperm bank was advocated more than 25 years earlier by Hermann J. Muller, the 1946 physics Nobel Prize winner who was concerned about the decline in the human race. Graham set up the sperm bank in his honour with the aim of increasing, even by a small margin, the number of intelligent people in the world. The 74-year-old Graham brushed aside similarities with Hitler. 'I don't see a parallel. I'm not thinking in terms of a super-race—only of ensuring a few more creative, intelligent human beings who otherwise would not have been born.'[14] He admitted later that his dream was to have such centres dotted all over the country. Since the 1984 Los Angeles Olympics he has extended his 'Repository for Germinal Choice' to include athletes and other outstanding individuals and several other 'special' banks have been set up, including one that specialises in catering for single women and lesbian couples.

In his book written in 1970, *The Future of Man*, Graham urged the intelligentsia to have more children in order to avert a class war launched by the dregs of society against the 'haves'. He later said selective breeding would stop what he called the continual pollution of the human gene pool with too-rapid breeding by the 'non-producers' of society.

In February 1980, he announced that three women had been inseminated, and donors to the world's most exclusive men's club included three Nobel Prize winners and two other famous scientists. His 'Nobel sperm bank', as it became known, provided potential mothers with a portfolio of the famous scientists. Women who were accepted by Graham as worthy recipients were sent the sperm in liquid nitrogen containers. His donors were not paid and the only cost to recipients were the freight charges (sperm for the first birth was sent on a Greyhound bus) and a deposit that was refunded with the return of the nitrogen container. The 'Nobel bank' was said in 1984 to cost Graham $700,000 a year, but money was no object to the self-made millionaire who wanted to improve the human race.

The sperm bank recorded the donor's IQ, hereditary details, 'outstanding characteristics' and the number of children he had already fathered, which Graham said was important 'so she knows he's not an untested stud'. On the bottom of the form Graham added his own comments. One read: 'A very famous scientist. A mover and shaker. Almost a superman.' He then selected the women to be inseminated. They must be young, bright, married and preferably with an infertile husband, he said. 'We pick the cream of the crop. . . I don't want a whole flock of ordinary women.'[15]

Gathering the sperm of the elite has to be done with discretion and in 1982 the *Washington Post* described the approach of Graham's assistant:

> Paul Smith slips into the office of a well-known scientist, has a brief conversation and slips out again. He takes a walk around the block and returns only when the scientist places a rubber band on the office doorknob, signalling that the material Smith seeks is ready. Such intrigue may befit a spy, but Smith is a geneticist. He has been leaving the offices of some of the finest scientists and mathematicians in the country carrying not their latest formulae, but their sperm.[16]

Smith was sacked by Graham in 1984 after he was quoted in a magazine interview as saying, 'If they want defectives, they can go to ——.' The only sperm bank in that area, which was one of the first in the country to be run entirely by women, promptly sued him for implying their donors produced defective babies. Smith then set up a sperm bank not far from Graham's, run along similar lines and using some of Graham's donors.

The Nobel bank's first two births raised ethical questions and considerable controversy. The first baby was born to Joyce Kowaiski of Chicago who, it was later revealed, had lost custody of her two children from a previous marriage because she had been beating them. She had been convicted and sentenced for fraud which included using the names of dead children. The second birth was to a woman psychologist,

Afton Blake of Los Angeles, who wanted a baby without a husband. Both these cases raised questions about the selection of would-be parents and in particular whether single women should be allowed to use the services.

One of Graham's most outspoken supporters has been 1956 physics Nobel Prize winner, 77-year-old William Shockley who lives in Palo Alto, California. When the sperm bank opened, the Stanford University engineer, who was awarded the prize for his part in inventing the transistor, was the only Nobel winner to admit publicly that he was a sperm donor. He said it was an important cause, 'a remarkable cause', and added, 'But I want to make it clear also that I don't regard myself as a perfect human being or that ideal candidate. I'm not proposing to make supermen.'[15]

Jim Cross, Professor of Genetics at the University of Wisconsin, did not condemn the idea. 'I am not outraged. For a woman to choose a sperm donor because of his physical and intellectual traits doesn't seem very different to me from choosing a husband for the same reasons.' According to Kenneth Kidd, Professor of Genetics at Yale University, by crossing a maths genius with a maths genius, generation after generation, 'we could probably develop a strain of individuals with extremely high mathematical ability. Gradually, by selecting the "best" offspring in every generation and mating them, it could probably work in the same way that it works for race horses.'

In newspaper interviews in 1980, several other Nobel Prize winners commented on the Nobel bank. Said Sir Martin Pyle, a 1974 Nobel winner for physics, 'It is absolutely and basically wrong. The way the human race develops, if it develops at all, cannot be fiddled with.' Commented Sir Alan Hodgkin, a 1963 medicine laureate, 'The world would be a terrible place if we were all Nobel Prize winners.' And the 1962 medicine laureate, Professor Maurice Wilkins, added, 'I wouldn't like the world to think that Nobel Prize winners were setting themselves up to be wiser than other human beings.'[17]

Newspaper columnists, such as America's Charles McCabe, were condemning.

> I see no objection to a woman with an infertile husband having a child through the sperm of another man. What the child will turn out to be will be the luck of the game [but] to set out deliberately to produce children that are *superior* is quite another thing. We had a massive experiment along these lines under one Adolf Hitler, and it did not turn out all that well.[18]

Selective breeding is one concern, the child is another. What expectations will these children grow up with and what emotional problems will they experience if they don't fulfil their parents' dream of a 'super-child'? If the donor had been a great mathematician or pianist, the child would be expected to perform to a level far beyond his classmates. If he did not, the parents would be disappointed and may feel cheated. And the object of their disillusionment and resentfulness, however subtle, would be the child. If the child was not told his genetic father was a great achiever he would be confused by his parents' feelings towards him, and if he was told, the pressure on him to achieve would be greater than on his peers. As American gynaecologist and AI doctor Martin Greenberg said, 'Of course, most of the children are going to be as normal as you or me. What kind of suffering could result?'[19]

This type of selection does little to alter the intelligence of the community as a whole and it may have little effect on the individual child if he is put in the 'wrong' environment. Having a high IQ does not mean someone will be intelligent. It may mean they have the ability to be, but that potential may not be realised.

Studies show that if a child of intelligent parents is adopted out, he is more likely to be intelligent if he is in a good family than if he is with a less intelligent family. He may have the potential to be intelligent but it may not surface if he is in an environment that does not stimulate him or present him with opportunities. To put a child with a Nobel prize winner's genes into a family accused of child beating and fraud will probably not produce another Nobel prize winner.

My favourite story is of a French couple who had an exceptionally bright child after the wife had received donor sperm. Everyone who met the child was struck by how intelligent she was. Curious, the couple went back to the doctors who did the insemination and asked if the donor had been an academic or mathematical genius. They checked and found he was a wood-cutter![20]

# 6

# DI: THE SOCIAL, LEGAL AND RELIGIOUS ISSUES

The main medical concerns with donor insemination are that the donors are thoroughly screened and the couple properly counselled. Most of the objections come from religious and legal quarters. There has been considerable ethical argument over whether DI children are emotionally any different to other children; whether they should be told that their social father is not their genetic father; and whether donors should remain anonymous.

## RELIGIOUS OBJECTIONS TO DI

As with AIH, strict Catholics, Jews and Moslems will not be recipients or donors because it involves masturbation. In addition, Catholics and Moslems object to donor insemination because they regard it as adultery.

The adultery argument is difficult to understand, as the definition of adultery is 'sexual unfaithfulness'. Donor insemination does not involve sex and it is done with the blessing of the husband. Dame Mary Warnock, who chaired the British Government's committee on human fertilisation and embryology, says it is a ridiculous argument.

> You would think adultery is a physical (sexual) act because most people do it for pleasure rather than to produce children. There is no analogy whatsoever between adultery and DI. The motives for DI are procreation and the motives for adultery are pleasure. But the Catholics appear to think

> adultery is receiving into the uterus the semen of a man other than your husband, so whether you do this by artificial means or naturally it doesn't make any difference to them, which totally disregards any emotional, ordinary human reasons why people commit adultery.

In the Bible, Onan was ordered by his father to sleep with his brother's widow so she could have children. He slept with her but he 'spilled his seed on the ground'—one of the earliest examples of natural contraception.'[1] Is adultery the act of intercourse or the placing of sperm in the uterus? If his brother had been alive, would Onan have been absolved of adultery because he 'spilled his seed', even though he had intercourse? If the answer is 'yes', married people who wish to have an affair can do so without being accused of adultery simply by wearing a condom or 'spilling the seed'. If the answer is 'no', then donor insemination is not adultery.

In February 1985, Israel's two chief rabbis announced a ban on artificial insemination unless the recipients were married and used the husband's sperm only. Mordecai Eliahu of the Oriental Jews and Abraham Shapiro of the European Jews said the ban also prohibited Jews from providing sperm to hospitals. 'The principal reason is that the donor is anonymous and incestuous marriage and wrongful inheritance may occur,' explained Dr Joseph Schenker, Head of Obstetrics and Gynaecology at Hadassah University Hospital in Jerusalem.

In September 1987, Moslem leaders in Indonesia, the world's largest Moslem country, ruled that artificial insemination could only take place if it involved using the sperm of the legal husband. Hasan Basri, chairman of the Indonesian Ulemas (Moslem Scholars) Council also announced that the council ruled against setting up sperm banks.[2]

The much publicised 'Vatican document', released in March 1987, stated the Catholic Church's opposition to donor insemination. The practice separates lovemaking and babymaking and denies the child respect, the statement said, 'The one conceived must be the fruit of his parent's love. He cannot be desired or conceived as the product of an intervention of medical or biological techniques; that would be equivalent to reducing him to an object of scientific technology.' The statement said donor insemination is 'contrary to the unity of marriage and to the dignity of the procreation of the human person [and] the child's right to be conceived and brought into the world in marriage and from marriage; it deprives him of his filial relationship with his parental origins and can hinder the maturing of his personal identity.'[3]

Other Christian denominations are not as strict as the Catholics in their opposition to donor insemination. In Britain, the Methodist Church, for example, does not condemn it, nor condone it, although it regards it as 'a morally unsatisfactory device for obtaining children'. In a draft paper, the Methodist Marriage and Family Committee stated that donor insemination raises moral problems, 'since it involves the deliberate conception of a child by an unknown father, and intentionally breaks the bond between paternity and the nurture of the child'. It said the moral issues are not the same as in adultery or adoption. 'In the former there is deliberate unfaithfulness with a known person in a full act of sexual intercourse, in the latter a child has already been born and requires the security of a loving and caring home.'[4]

## SOCIAL AND LEGAL CONSIDERATIONS

Some of the social issues raised by donor insemination were considered by the British Government's 1982–84 Committee of Inquiry into Human Fertilisation and Embryology (known as the Warnock Committee), which said concern had been expressed that the introduction of a third party (the donor) may threaten the couple's relationship; the wife may feel the child was hers rather than her husband's; the husband may experience a sense of inadequacy; the wife may be emotionally closer to the child than the husband is; and the child may feel different from his peers.[5]

Nevertheless, it has been shown in various studies that a couple using donor insemination is far more stable and far less likely to divorce than the average couple. A recent survey in Belgium showed that of 1,200 couples who used the technique, only 11 subsequently divorced, which equals less than 1 per cent.[6] In some countries, such as the US, the average divorce rate is about one in three.

Concern that DI children will be less stable may also be unfounded. What studies there are show them to be above average in personal and intellectual development. Researchers in Japan in 1968 subjected 40 DI children aged between two and 11 to intelligence and developmental tests and found them to be above average in both. Another study, of 133 DI children, found they progressed well, with above average physical and intellectual development.[7]

It is often said that to know one's origin is important for finding one's identity and for personal development. According to Swiss psychiatrist Dr Cécile Ernst of Zurich University, this can be translated as: 'Children that do not know their biological parents are at higher risk for developing psychiatric disorders than those who do.' But, she says, there is no scientific evidence to support this. 'Adopted children grow up without their biological parents. Their psychosocial development has been thoroughly investigated and it depends on two factors: their genetic vulnerability for psychiatric disorder, which is transmitted to them by their biological parents, and the qualities of their adoptive home.'[8]

As there are few studies on DI children, she drew a comparison with adopted children, who generally do not know either of their biological parents. 'On average adoptees do not differ in their psychosocial development from non-adoptees [and] on the average they are not plagued by problems of identity. Common sense could lead one to expect that the outcome of children conceived by artificial procreation would be even better than that of adopted children, because usually at least one of the social parents is also a biological parent.' It is the quality of the care that counts more than the genetic make up of the child. Ernst says, 'Studies make it evident that the quality of emotional relationship within a family is more important than family structure.'[8]

It could be argued that donor insemination is a treatment for a social rather than a medical problem. Like other forms of assisted reproduction, such as surrogacy and *in vitro* fertilisation, it does not treat the problem of infertility, it simply side-steps it. An alternative to DI would be for the woman to conceive naturally with another man, without medical assistance, but since that is socially unacceptable, donor insemination is used to solve a social problem. However, this is not to say that because there is an alternative, childless couples should be denied donor insemination.

The legal concerns centre around the status of the child resulting from donor insemination. It is a nature versus nurture argument—should the legal father be the one who provides the hereditary material (the sperm) or the one who nurtures and cares for the child?

In most countries the husband of a married woman is presumed to be the father and he is therefore regarded as the legal father. Until recently in Britain a DI child was, strictly speaking, illegitimate and technically the husband of the woman inseminated had no parental rights and duties towards the child. As a sperm donor is usually anonymous most British couples had filled in false birth certificates, naming the husband as the father, although it was perjury. However, under an act passed in April 1988, a child born in England and Wales will be treated as the legitimate child of the mother and her husband, where the husband has consented to the insemination, and the donor has no rights or responsibilities to the child, nor any rights to trace the child. The new law was long overdue — after all, the definition of illegitimate is 'born out of wedlock' and does not distinguish between whose sperm is used.

Even so, the importance of whose sperm is used has given lawyers around the world headaches and resulted in numerous court battles. One of the earliest decisions in the US was by the Californian Supreme Court in 1958 in which the justices unanimously held that the husband was the lawful father, although he was not the natural father, and as a result he could be prosecuted for failing to support the child. Two years earlier, a judge in the state of Illinois declared that DI amounted to adultery, even if it was done with the consent of the husband.

A few years later the Californian Supreme Court ridiculed the adultery ruling by pointing out that it meant the woman was committing adultery with the doctor or donor, when the doctor may be a woman and the husband may inseminate his wife at home with a syringe. 'To consider it an act of adultery with the donor, who at the time of insemination may be a thousand miles away or may even be dead, is equally absurd,' the court said. The following year California passed a law stating that if the husband gave written consent to the insemination, the birth was legitimate if it was in a marriage or within 300 days of a marriage breakup.[9]

Today, most countries have legislation or accepted practice which mean that the husband of the woman inseminated becomes the legal father of the child and the donor has no rights or responsibilities to any offspring that may result from him donating sperm. It means the mother cannot claim financial assistance from the donor, nor is the child entitled to any of the donor's inheritance. This is now law in 15 European countries and at least 14 states in the US and several in Australia.

DI is not popular in Asian and Latin American countries, mainly because of the high Moslem and Catholic populations respectively. In Brazil and Libya it is outlawed and carries a heavy penalty for anyone involved.

In 1977, Portugal became the first country in Europe to pass legislation ensuring that the husband becomes the legal father. More than half the European countries, including Yugoslavia and Bulgaria, have since followed suit. In addition, Sweden enacted a law in 1985 giving the child the right to access to information on his genetic father when he is considered by a counsellor to be mature enough 'not to suffer harm'. The counsellor can arrange for the child to meet him, but only if the donor agrees. Under German law the donor has two years from the child's birth in which to claim he is the legal father and the woman has two years in which to ask him for financial support. After that, the social father becomes the legal father, the donor relinquishes all rights and the child has no access to the donor, or his estate. There are moves in the US to have similar rulings although the campaigners are a small minority.

## SHOULD THE DONOR BE ANONYMOUS?

Several countries have now passed laws allowing adopted children access to their birth certificate, which has the names of their genetic parents on it, and it is argued that the same should be allowed to DI children. But how many children want to know who their genetic parents are and what harm might it do? The vast majority of adoptees who have access to information do not request it. Less than 1 per cent of those in England and Wales did so in the first three years it was available and only 7 per cent have in Scotland where access has been possible for the last 50 years.[8] This small number could be expected to be less with DI children, where only one parent is not the genetic parent.

The main argument against laws that allow the child to know the donor's name is that a donor may one day open his front door to a young man saying 'Hi, Dad', 20 years after making a donation to help an infertile couple. A second argument is that the supply of donors would diminish.

In the debate leading up to the introduction of the Swedish law it was suggested that if donors were not anonymous, DI would go underground, frozen sperm would be imported or infertile couples would go abroad. However, since the new law came into force in March 1985, this has not been the case. Although the number of sperm donors has fallen there has also been a fall in the number of people requesting donor insemination and there is no shortage of donor sperm, according to Tor Sverne, the country's former ombudsman who chaired the committee that proposed the new law.

The change in law has also brought a change in the type of donor. Most are now married men with families. Sverne says doctors see this as highly desirable because the donors come from established families with a mature outlook and the consent of their spouses.

Knowing the donor's name is not just a matter of whether the child may approach the donor in the future, but it may be important medically, especially in establishing whether hereditary diseases are passed on to the child. If a child develops diabetes, for example, a doctor would want to know whether his father also had diabetes. A woman requesting oral contraception would be asked whether anyone in her (genetic) family has a history of heart disease, diabetes or breast cancer. If a social father develops heart disease, a DI son who does not know he has a different genetic father may worry unnecessarily that he is at risk too.

Having access to the donor's name may also be life-saving,

for example, if a DI child or adult needs a kidney or bone-marrow transplant and doctors can trace the donor or any of his other children, who would be half brothers or sisters. In a 1981 case in the US, the courts refused to allow the donor's name to be revealed when a DI person was in need of a bone-marrow transplant.

This sort of problem could be solved by filing all information about the donor with an independent body such as a medical council or government institution which could act as a go-between, supplying the necessary information without the patient having any contact with the donor.

Until recently, very few AI clinics around the world kept proper, long-term records of who donated and who received sperm. Records were usually buried under dust and later discarded. Others were often deliberately destroyed to eliminate the possibility of the donor being traced by the recipient or her child. When I asked one AI counsellor in England what she would do if the government passed a law today giving children access to the donor's name, she said without hesitation, 'Burn all the files.'

Nobody has the right to wipe out the genetic heritage of another person, and because of increasing awareness of this, many governments are now moving towards setting up permanent 'storage banks' for DI records. The Victorian Government in Australia passed legislation in 1984 which protects the donor's anonymity from the recipients but it also makes a provision for him to be traced in an emergency. All AI centres have to be approved by the Health Commission and they must lodge with the Commission records with details of each donor and recipient, including names. These are kept under lock and key and can only be released by the Minister for Health under special circumstances. A report with non-identifying particulars about the donor is given to the couple, and the donor is also offered a non-identifying report on the couple. In addition, he can request particulars of each child born as a result of his donation.

The Warnock Committee recommended that, on turning 18, a DI person should have legal access to basic information about the donor's ethnic origin and genetic health. It also suggested a central register of all donors in the country, where donors are number-coded to ensure anonymity and that no one person makes more than 10 donations.[10]

A report by the British Council for Science and Society pointed out that certain insurance forms require disclosure of parentage, and the insurance contract might be invalid if someone seeking insurance gave incorrect information about his genetic father. It also said that fundamentally the child has a right to know his genetic origin, just as an adopted one already does under British law.[11]

## SHOULD THE CHILD BE TOLD OF HIS ORIGINS?

One of the most important concerns is if and when the parents should tell the child that the person called 'Daddy' is not his biological father and what the child's reaction will be. Some people ask, why tell at all when it may upset the child? Many people—from child counsellors to academic lawyers—believe everyone has the fundamental right to know his origins. Telling the child he was conceived after donor insemination does not mean telling him *who* his genetic father is.

Even if a child does not have a fundamental right to know, there are strong arguments against keeping secrets within a family. It means the couple cannot discuss the insemination or their anxious attempts to get pregnant with family or friends in case these people 'let the cat out of the bag' in front of the child in later years, and they must always be on their guard against a slip of the tongue themselves. There is always a danger that the secret will come out during a family argument, either between the parents or with the child. But probably the most compelling reason is that the child is being deliberately deceived about something very fundamental.

In a personal view Dame Mary Warnock, chairman of the Warnock Committee, expressed concern that no matter how hard the parents tried to keep it a secret, the child would eventually find out, which could be more damaging than if he had been told the truth in the first place. She described as 'absolutely monstrous' the idea of withholding information from the child or mixing husband and donor sperm so it is not certain who the father is.

> The child has the right to know whether the father bringing him up is his 'real' father. I think it is crucial that he knows. I feel so terribly strongly about that, I have a great sense of genetic continuity and I hate the idea of pretence that you are genetically connected to someone when you are not. If by chance the social father turned out later on to be the carrier of some genetically transferrable disease, the child would want to know if he was at risk and you would have to tell him.
>
> Concealment is not all that easy and there is certain evidence that [DI] children do sense that there is something funny going on. They sometimes sense a certain embarrassment when grandmothers and aunts say 'I don't know where he got those funny ears from, they are not in our family,' or 'I can't think why he is so musical,' and there is a horrible silence. Children are terribly sensitive to when their parents are embarrassed or momentarily don't reply.

Despite the many arguments for telling children, the majority of couples still choose not to. According to one report, 85 per cent of couples in the US do not tell. Robert and Elizabeth Snowden of the University of Exeter who interviewed 70 DI families in Britain and published their research in *The Gift of a Child* in 1984, found almost all the couples had no intention of telling their children. Most said there was no need. Some of the reasons were that they feared the child would be distressed, he would be uncertain about his own self-identity, he would be stigmatised at school, he might think less of his father or even reject him, it might be hurtful to the father to have to tell because it would mean admitting he was infertile.[12]

The Snowdens point out that most of these are groundless fears rather than realities. They found most of the parents who did tell their children were pleased that they did, and so were the children. None of them found it a particularly traumatic experience. None of the children regretted the fact that their parents had used donor sperm and some of them honoured and respected their parents more. 'They were enjoying life and happy to be alive and realised that they owed their existence to DI. They were pleased to feel that their parents had wanted a child so badly, and that they were the child which had fulfilled their parents' wishes.'

The research showed that rather than disrupting the family relationship, it had in some cases strengthened it as the son or daughter realised the anguish the father must have experienced. The Snowdens concluded that not being honest with the child is to some extent denying him respect, and that research shows children are less upset by strange and apparently unpalatable facts than they are by any form of deception.

Most studies—and there are few—have focused on the DI child and his family, without consideration of what emotional effect donating has on men and their families. Generally, most sperm donors are still single men who often donate without full consideration of the long-term effect. A married man who donates may find that it causes friction with his partner or children at a later date. As his children grow up, possibly through adolescence, they may have confused feelings, knowing they may have several anonymous half brothers or sisters somewhere. If the donor agreed that the DI person, possibly in his teens or twenties, could meet his family, it may result in his own children experiencing conflicts after the visit, even if they agreed to the meeting beforehand. It is hoped that they would regard their father's donation as charitable but it may also open up hidden resentments. None of this has been examined.

If the parents of a DI child both died or were killed, it is conceivable that a responsible donor, possibly with his own family, might want to take over the rearing of the child. Legally he gave up all rights and responsibilities when he donated the sperm, but if the legal parents are dead, could he, or should he, have any claim to becoming the legal, as well as the genetic, father? Should he and his wife be given priority over another couple wanting to adopt the child?

Donors are generally seen by recipients as generous, caring, considerate men. Couples who tell their children often refer to him as a nice man who gave them a precious gift. One Belgian woman echoed the thoughts of many when she said: 'He must have been a very kind man, I will tell Ernst [her son] he was a nice man who helped him to exist. Maybe he donated because he knows a couple who have problems and he pities them and wants to help others. I would like to help him because I was so grateful. I found it very sad because masturbation is something very intimate but not in a hospital where everything is white and clean.' She said she would never seek him out 'because may be it would be a disillusion'.

## REGULATING DONOR INSEMINATION

In Britain as early as 1948 a report by the Church of England's Archbishop of Canterbury said donor insemination should be made a criminal offence, although it found AIH acceptable. Twenty years later DI was accepted by the Government as part of the National Health Service. The 1984 Warnock Committee went one step further and recommended the law be changed to allow the husband to be registered as the father.

This progressive acceptance of DI has come with an increase in the number of couples benefiting from the practice and a realisation that it could not be stamped out. It has been a case of if you can't beat them, join them. And that means accepting the practice and controlling it. If donor insemination were made illegal and the parties involved were forced underground, where couples inseminate themselves without counselling, medical supervision or legal guidelines, it would lead to more of a legal and social dilemma than now exists, especially as the donor would be known to the couple and more likely to see the child and perhaps want access after the birth. Without proper screening, there would be no guarantee of eliminating the possibility of passing on an infection such as AIDS or gonorrhoea, or an inherited disease.

With this in mind, the Warnock Committee recommended donor insemination only be available at licensed clinics, where the donor is anonymous and the couple give written consent. Anyone offering donor insemination without a licence should be prosecuted. Several countries have since passed legislation to this effect but, as yet, the British Government has not.

Probably the most commendable systems are those used in France and Sweden. In France all donors are married men with at least one healthy child, and those who receive sperm are encouraged to recruit donors for future couples entering the programme. Donors are limited to six specimens which are to be given within a month, after counselling and without any payment. This system means the donor is seen to be fertile and not to have a genetic disorder; the donation comes from a couple, not just the man; it is done to help childless couples, not for money; and in part it makes recipients responsible for keeping the cycle going.

The Swedish model restricts donor insemination to approved centres and allows the child to meet the donor *if* a counsellor thinks he is mature enough emotionally and *if* the donor agrees. This system serves both the interest of the child and at the same time encourages more mature donors.

As mentioned, the Victorian Government in Australia guards the donor's records, and the Warnock Committee recommended a national register of all British donors. Both are also commendable systems, for it is essential that all information on the donor be kept, including his name. However, his name need only be used in life-threatening situations. There is no reason why the necessary medical information, and if necessary the organ for a transplant, cannot be passed to the DI person via a medical director, without him meeting the donor.

## AI FOR SINGLE AND LESBIAN WOMEN

AIH can be used when the husband has a physical or genetic problem and donor insemination when he has low or no sperm count. But what if there is no husband? Should single and lesbian women be allowed to have artificial insemination? Some countries, such as Sweden, have laws that only allow AI between married or co-habiting heterosexual couples, but most other countries have no such laws. However, artificial insemination is so simple, any woman can inseminate herself with sperm provided by a willing man, and laws are unlikely to stop a single woman or lesbian couple if they really want a child.

By allowing women the right to abortion, in the historic *Roe versus Wade* case in 1973, the US Supreme Court gave women some constitutional right to make up their own minds about having children. There are no laws in the US prohibiting AI for single women and all states now allow unmarried couples to adopt children, Wayne County amended its policy to allow single women to have donor insemination after a woman threatened to sue the state university for refusing to inseminate her because she was single. Clearly, there is little to stop women in the US receiving donor insemination legally.

However, physicians and hospital ethics committees are not keen on the idea and do not encourage it. Married couples are not required to show proof of their ability to support a child financially, yet it is reported that only 10 per cent of doctors in the US will perform the service for single women without such proof.[13]

Recommendations of the Ontario Law Reform Commission, which have not yet been legislated, include approval for single women to have access to artificial reproduction methods, provided they are 'stable'. In deciding who is suitable, a physician should consider the home environment, the physical and mental health of the woman, her emotional reaction to artificial conception and her individual stability.[14]

Some physicians in Europe, the US and Australia have inseminated single and lesbian women privately but very few public centres do. One exception is the Vrije (Free) University in Brussels where the first AI baby was born to a lesbian woman in 1983. Hilda Olbrechts, who counsels and screens all patients requesting artificial insemination and *in vitro* fertilisation, takes extra precautions with single and lesbian women. 'They are always seen by a psychologist—*always*—two, three, four times. We have a very strict protocol.'

Some people may say the US physicians and the Belgium counsellor are discriminating against certain women. Others say it is in the best interest of the child and preserving 'the family'. Olbrechts explained why this strict protocol is important.

> Lesbians must be in a stable situation. They must have accepted their lesbianism. And they must be accepted as a couple in their family environment. They must be aware of the problems of educating a child without a father and must have thought it over. They must have other father figures in their neighbourhood—brothers or friends, not necessarily homosexual men. All of this is very important.

About 50 per cent of the lesbian couples who apply for AI are refused after counselling. They are told why they don't fit the criteria and they can apply again later if they have resolved some of their problems. 'We are now accepting people we rejected before,' Olbrechts said.

Single women must be psychologically sound, too, according to Olbrechts. Many are rejected because they have the wrong reasons for wanting a child.

> Most of the single women have tried to build a relationship with a man and it did not succeed so they come when they are 36 and have no relationship and no child but they always wanted a child. So more single women are refused than lesbians because they have tried it first and didn't really want a child out of a relationship.
>
> A lot of single women live isolated lives. Some hate men and we don't allow them because they will pass this feeling on to the child. They must be able to cope with males. They have to make sure the child is strong enough to cope with this. A lot come to prove they can do better than their mothers, for example if a child is abused, badly treated, left alone or has a drinking father, she says I will prove to my mother I can do better. One woman was rejected by her mother and really wanted to prove she was better, but she was not in a relationship and didn't want to lose time. She was an extreme feminist.

Many people who oppose AI for single women and lesbian couples do so because they are concerned about the environment the child will be brought up in, how he will cope with the fact that he comes from an atypical family and whether he is likely to have problems with his identity and sexuality. Supporters of the practice point out that a single woman is just as capable as a married one. Commented Professor John Leeton, who runs a private infertility clinic in Melbourne: 'Because a woman is single does not mean she cannot be a caring mother.' However, under a new law, physicians in Victoria can no longer legally offer AI to single women.

Critics of AI express concern that the practice deliberately produces 'fatherless children'. However, a child brought up by a single woman would not be greatly different from millions of other children in Western countries where single-parent families are now common. One in three marriages in the US now ends in divorce and 45 per cent of the children born in the mid-1970s will live in a one-parent family before they turn 18.[15] Even in conservative Switzerland two out of 11 children grow up with one parent or in a common-law household.[8] Although many divorces are amicable, a large proportion of these children witness ugly scenes between their parents, experience emotional trauma and are the subjects of bitter tug-of-war custody battles. On the other hand, a child born to a single parent who remains single will not be subjected to the traumas of a divorce or a split family.

Whereas the vast majority of couples have children as a matter of course—it is the expected procedure after marriage—a single woman has to defy tradition, pass stringent psychological testing and overcome medical and social opposition before she even becomes pregnant. In the following years she has to endure comments and criticisms, ensure the child has a suitable father figure and work extra hard to make sure she is not accused of doing the child an injustice by not providing a father. The child is obviously a much-wanted child and it could be argued that it makes her a better mother.

Psychiatrist Cécile Ernst believes that as long as the quality of care given to a child is good, it does not matter whether the parent is single or homosexual.

> The relationship between care-giver and child is more important than the structure of a family. There is no reason why being brought up by a responsible, stable and friendly single woman should entail more risk for the psychosocial development of a child than being brought up by a widow. There is no reason why the sexual orientation of a man or woman should have a negative influence if the person is responsible, stable and friendly and if the family is not ostracised because of his/her orientation . . . On the other hand these new treatments for infertility should not be used to promote new family structures that are not yet accepted by the majority in that community. What may be possible

> in California might in Switzerland give the child of a single woman or a homosexual couple a very uncomfortable position, and in the long run endanger his/her mental health.[8]

Girls from female-headed families are highly independent, have high self-esteem and are more highly achievement-oriented, according to a 1985 report by Drs Maureen McGuire and Nancy Alexander, then of the Oregon Health Sciences University, US. The lack of a man as head of the household seems to lead to a closer family relationship between mother and child, they said, and pointed out that an estimated 10 per cent of women in the US are lesbians. Of them 15–20 per cent are mothers and there are an estimated 1.5 million children living in families with lesbian mothers.[16]

McGuire and Alexander quote a study, published in 1983, which found children in divorced lesbian households spend more time with their fathers than those in divorced heterosexual households.

> Additionally, lesbian mothers have higher educational status and professional training, score more normally on psychological tests, and often receive more support from their co-habiting partners in child care and household duties. The daughters of lesbian mothers choose more prestigious and masculine careers and report greater popularity than their heterosexual matches.

If the definition of parenthood is babymaking by sex within marriage, AI for a lesbian would be unethical according to Dr Gerald Perkoff of the University of Missouri, US. But, he said, 'If parenthood is the love, care and nurture one gives a child, AI could be considered an ethical and moral act for a woman in a monogamous, stable, lesbian relationship.'[17]

AI for single and lesbian women raises the question of whether resulting births could in some cases be virgin births. Certainly if the woman has never had sexual intercourse, she is a virgin by definition. Yet the Catholic Church, which disapproves of AI, maintains that Jesus's was the only virgin birth. However, as the Bible was written long before AI was first practiced, this may be another example of where the new reproductive technologies have outgrown conventional definitions.

One of the few public opinion polls to question attitudes towards AI for single women was conducted in Australia in 1984. It found 62 per cent of people thought it should not be available at all to unmarried women, 16 per cent said it should be available to women living in a long-term relationship with a man and 15 per cent said it should be available to any unmarried woman who requested it. The other 7 per cent did not know.[18]

Although there is religious opposition to donor insemination, it is simple, painless and brings great joy to tens of thousands of infertile couples. But most importantly, it puts a child in a stable, loving environment apparently without him suffering psychologically. If the child's legal status and emotional stability are to be considered, there is need for legislative change in countries that do not recognise the social father as the legal father. It could be argued that if there is no law to prevent single women conceiving naturally—and there is no evidence to suggest they will not be as good at mothering as married women—there should be no law against them having a child through DI.

# 7
# SURROGATE MOTHERS

'We are caught in the middle of a major social experiment without the faintest idea how it should be conducted.' *Daniel Callahan, director, Hastings Centre, New York.*[1]

The practice of one woman bearing a child for another is almost as old as childbirth itself, but in the 1980s surrogacy has become one of the most controversial forms of babymaking. Technically simple, it is far more complicated legally and ethically. Arguments over whether it should be allowed have divided society, religious communities and the medical and legal professions.

Before the contraceptive pill, abortion and single mothers were accepted, unwanted pregnancies solved childlessness for many infertile couples, and the teenagers and young women who accidentally became pregnant were, strictly speaking, surrogate (substitute) mothers. However, from the early 1980s, the term *surrogate mother* has been used to describe a woman who deliberately becomes pregnant with the intention of delivering a baby that she will then hand over to someone else, usually—but not always—an infertile couple unable to bear their own child. Unlike adoption, a contract is signed before the baby is conceived, the surrogate becomes pregnant for a specific couple (whom she may never meet) and is paid for her services.

The emotional rewards for the surrogate and the couple are enormous when all goes as planned, but heartbreaking when it doesn't, and a small proportion of disputes have been played out in the public arena—in the courts and the media. Although the most prominent cases have been in the US and Britain, surrogacy is also practised in Canada, the rest of Europe, Asia, Australia, the Middle East and South Africa.

## WHY SURROGACY?

With the difficulties of adoption in the 1980s, many childless couples are turning to another woman to have a child for them. For most, it is a last resort after they have been unsuccessful with infertility treatments. Not only is there a long wait for healthy white babies to adopt—five to seven years in the US—but after going through various treatments many infertile couples find they are too old to adopt.

Sometimes the surrogate is a sister or close friend, but more often it is a stranger, and the arrangements are made through a lawyer or an agency which matches a prospective surrogate with a childless couple.

Generally, the surrogate is artificially inseminated with sperm from the husband—and if he is infertile, with donor sperm—although in some privately arranged cases the child has been conceived naturally. An insemination can be done by the surrogate herself, but is more often done by a physician. She then carries the baby for the full pregnancy, handing it to the couple after birth. With *in vitro* fertilisation (IVF), it is possible for an egg to be removed from the infertile wife and fertilised in the laboratory with her husband's or donor sperm, then transferred to the surrogate, who acts as a gestator, or 'incubator'. Generally, the couple officially adopt the baby soon after birth, so that they become the legal parents.

There are two medical reasons why couples would want to engage a surrogate: if there is a risk that the woman will pass on a genetic disease to the child, and if the woman is infertile. However, provided she has a healthy uterus these can generally be overcome with the use of donor eggs or embryos. If she has no ovaries and no uterus, in which case she cannot provide the genetic (egg) or gestational (pregnancy) components of childbirth, she has no alternative but to engage a surrogate or adopt. A woman might also use a surrogate when she has eggs, which can be fertilised *in vitro* and transferred to a surrogate, but not the gestational ability, for example if she has no uterus, has a uterine malformation or a medical condition such as severe hypertension or diabetes which would endanger her health or the baby's.

The American Fertility Society, in a special 1986 report on

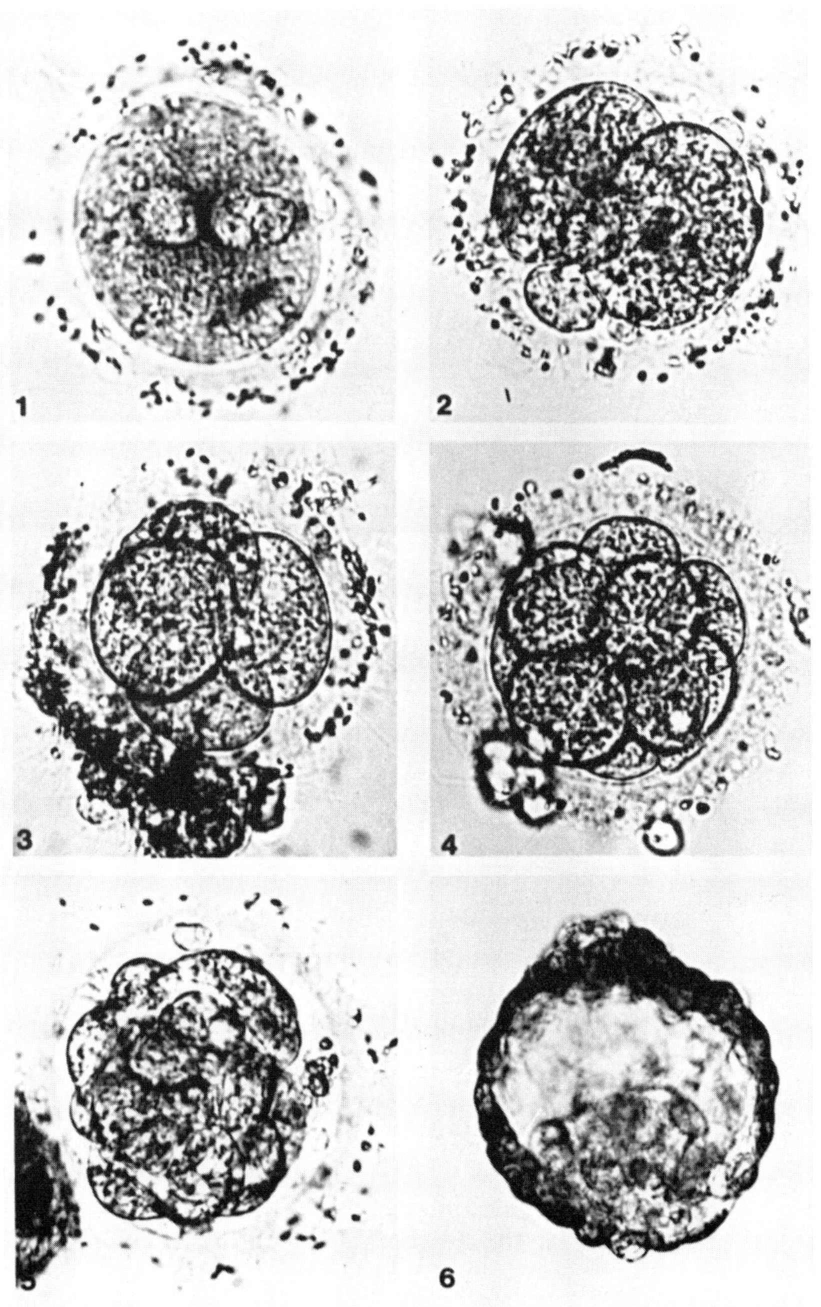


An IVF or naturally conceived embryo before it implants in the womb: 1, pronuclear 1-cell egg with the nuclei of the sperm and egg side by side before fusion takes place (day 1 after sperm is added to the egg); 2, 2-cell embryo (day 2); 3, 4-cell embryo (day 2); 4, 8-cell embryo (day 3); 5, morula or multi-cell stage (day 4); 6, blastocyst, the embryo just before implantation (day 6).

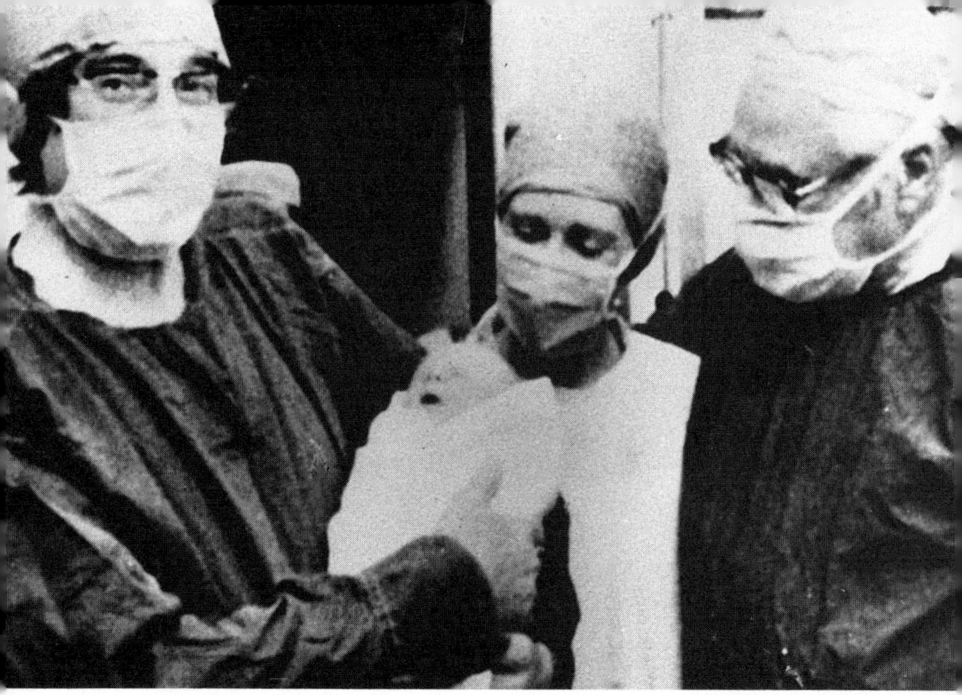

IVF pioneers Patrick Steptoe (right), Robert Edwards and Jean Purdy with the world's first test-tube baby Louise Brown minutes after she was born in England on 25 July 1978. Possibly 7,000–10,000 IVF babies have been born since then.

American IVF pioneers Howard and Georgeanna Jones with the first fifty test-tube babies born at their clinic in Norfolk, Virginia. Mothers' Day, 1985.

reproductive technologies, pointed out several reasons for surrogacy to be used. For the husband of an infertile woman, it may be the only way he can have a child who is biologically his, short of divorcing his wife and remarrying or having an adulterous union with another woman, in which case 'the use of a surrogate mother seems far less destructive of the institution of the family'. Surrogacy gives the child an opportunity he would not otherwise have—the opportunity to exist. And there are benefits for surrogates: it offers them the chance to be altruistic; some surrogates like being pregnant; some may be using the experience to help themselves overcome a previous birthing experience; and it can allow a single mother to stay at home with her existing children instead of going out to work.[2]

Surrogacy has several advantages over adoption: if the husband provides the sperm he is the natural father and if the egg comes from the wife the child is genetically hers; it is not necessary to wait several years for a baby; the couple play a part in the conception and can sometimes be involved during the pregnancy.

Using surrogate mothers to overcome childlessness is not a recent concept. The most commonly quoted Biblical example is in Genesis, where Hagar the servant girl bore a son for Abraham because his wife Sarah was infertile.[3] In another example Jacob's two wives, Rachel and Leah, each used their slave girls to bear children for Jacob and each of the girls had two babies because her mistress could not.[4]

Interestingly, Hagar despised Sarah when she was pregnant. Sarah ill-treated her surrogate, who ran away, but returned in time to give birth to a boy, Ishmael, who was then handed over to her mistress. Eventually, because of family conflicts, Hagar had to take Ishmael and leave. This is one of the earliest recorded examples of surrogacy and it was by all accounts not a happy arrangement.

It is not uncommon in certain communities—both tribal and Western—for a woman to give her baby to another woman soon after it is born. Nor is it uncommon for children to be brought up by aunts and uncles or grandparents. Unofficial adoption has existed for centuries, and commercial adoption agencies have been in operation for decades, arranging for one couple to take another's child.

So why has surrogacy 1980s-style become so controversial? Because it usually involves money, strangers and lawyers. Add to that babies, love and despair, played out in highly emotional, well-publicised court cases, and you have an instant front-page story. Unfortunately, the public's image of surrogacy is based on a handful of extreme cases that have been given international media coverage. However, of the first 600 known surrogate arrangements in the US, only three came before the courts. One of them centred around the infant known as Baby M, and the public was left with the impression that surrogacy involves a tug-of-war over a baby that ends in heartbreak. The vast majority of surrogate arrangements, however, result in joy rather than tears.

## AN OLD CONCEPT BECOMES BIG BUSINESS

Although surrogacy had existed, under another name, for a long time, it did not catch the public or media's attention until it involved money for the first time publicly. One early known case is of a Japanese girl who agreed in 1963 to have a child for an infertile couple who were prepared to pay one million yen (then about $US2,800) if she promised not to demand custody of the child, according to the *Mainichi Daily News*, a national English-language newspaper in Tokyo. The young girl was looking for a job to help pay her way through college when she heard of a wealthy married couple who wanted to have a child but could not. She agreed to be artificially inseminated and signed a contract to relinquish custody of any child that resulted.

However, it was in the US, not Asia, that surrogacy became big business. This small advertisement, which appeared in the classified section of the *San Francisco Chronicle* on 14 April, 1975, was the beginning of commercial surrogacy which is now a multi-million dollar business in the US:

> Childless husband with infertile wife wants test-tube baby. English or Northwestern European background. Indicate fee and age. All answers confidential. Write this paper, Ad No. 16297.

The ad referred to a surrogate baby as a test-tube baby.

However it, was more than three years before the world's first test-tube baby was born and it was not until some time later that the term 'surrogate' was used in the media. The West Coast Sunday-school teacher who placed the ad was of Scandinavian stock and prefered the surrogate to be of similar background. His search for a surrogate mother was not easy—local obstetricians would have no part in his plan; he flew to Sweden and Denmark but gynaecologists there told him to either leave his wife or have an affair, and seven West Coast newspapers refused to run his advertisement.

After the *Chronicle* ran the ad and a story on the man's search for what the paper called a 'human incubator', he received more than 160 offers, including some from Britain, Canada, Australia, New Zealand, Kenya and one from Bangladesh. Some offered to carry his child out of compassion, others because they liked the idea of creating life or because they enjoyed being pregnant. Some were interested in the $10,000 he said he would pay the woman and others offered their services for free.

With the help of his doctor and lawyer, the devout Methodist selected an unmarried office worker from the San Francisco Bay area as the surrogate. She was artificially inseminated and nine months later, on 6 September 1976, delivered a red-haired, blue-eyed girl. He paid $7,000 to the woman and another $3,000 for medical expenses. Soon after, his wife adopted the baby girl—as the natural father, the husband did not have to adopt his own daughter.

The first public surrogate arrangement raised little controversy, although the lawyer who organised it questioned whether the child was illegitimate. The father saw it as the male version of donor insemination:

> It isn't bizarre when you think about it. It is exactly equivalent to artificial insemination of women by anonymous donors, a standard practice when a husband has an insufficient sperm count. I see no real difference if the mother rather than the father is the anonymous donor.

He described the surrogate as 'an angel in human form, taking pity on a forlorn and helpless man'.[5]

The month after he placed his ad, an infertile Californian couple did the same, stating: 'Childless husband with infertile wife wants test-tube Caucasian baby. Indicate fee and age.' Several other ads followed, and in the mid-1970s Michigan lawyer Noel Keane started to co-ordinate surrogate mothers and childless couples through what became the first informal surrogate agency. Initially he provided his services free but later charged a $3,000 fee to find a surrogate for a couple and arranged the adoption. The surrogates were not paid because Michigan, like most American states, prohibited payment for adoption.

At least five children had been born in Michigan and several more in New York to unpaid surrogates when, in November 1979, attorney Katie Marie Brophy and infertility specialist Dr Richard Levin began running classified advertisements in Louisville newspapers offering to pay surrogates. They set up a company, Surrogate Parenting Associates, to 'institutionalise' surrogacy and claimed it was the first organisation in the world that legally arranged surrogacy for a fee. Later, law firms in other states started advertising in college newspapers.

Brophy and Levin's first client was an Illinois housewife using the pseudonym Elizabeth Kane who became the first acknowledged surrogate mother in the US to bear a child under contract. The 38-year-old mother of three was commissioned in 1980 by an anonymous Kentucky couple, using the names Richard and Emily Ransdale, who paid her 'less than $10,000' when she surrendered her parental rights to the baby five months after he was born.

Levin said at the time, 'I don't think what we're doing is any more remarkable than the first blood transfusion or the first heart transplant. But people get a little more excited when a procedure deals with reproduction or sex.' Brophy pointed out that people had been doing surrogacy privately for years, but they were wide open for abuse. 'What if the surrogate starts hounding the couple, or tries to reclaim the baby or gives birth to a child with a defect?' Surrogate Parenting Associates aimed to overcome possible problems by strictly screening the surrogates and asking both the surrogate and the commissioning couple to sign a rigid contract in which the surrogate agreed to give the baby to the couple.

To date, an estimated 800 babies have been born in the US, most of them through commercial agencies such as Keane's and Surrogate Parenting Associates. Several of the American agencies have recruited surrogates from other countries or set up agencies overseas. Californian lawyer Bill Handel established a screening service in Australia in 1984; Harriet Blankfeld's National Centre for Surrogate Parenting set up an agency in London in the same year, was responsible for Britain's first commercial surrogate birth and now accepts couples from Australian states where commercial surrogacy is outlawed; and in 1987 Noel Keane expanded his agency to Europe where he set up office in Frankfurt, West Germany. Keane is reported to be responsible for one-third of the first 500 surrogate births in the US, and to have 20 foreign couples using surrogacy.[6]

In the majority of cases, surrogacy is no longer an altruistic act between friends or relatives. It is a business—involving lawyers and psychologists, contracts and money, highly-paid go-betweens and anonymous payers. For this reason surrogacy has been called 'baby selling' and surrogates 'whores'.

## WHY SOME WOMEN BECOME SURROGATES

When Richard Levin and Katie Brophy started advertising for surrogate mothers they expected to hear from single women, unmarried mothers and people in low income groups. Instead they had enquiries from 'ladies next door', many of whom were married with children of their own. Most surrogates say they take on the job out of sympathy for infertile couples or because they regard it as the ultimate act of giving. Most also say they do it for the money although generally that is a secondary reason. Others believe it will replace a lost opportunity or experience. Sometimes it is because they had an abortion or gave up a previous baby for adoption.

For one American woman it was a way of fulfilling a personal wish. 'As a midwife I'm always talking about home birth, but with my son I ended up in a hospital. I wanted to try it again, but we can't afford another baby.' Laurie Yates, a Michigan surrogate who refused to hand over her twins after they were born in August 1987, wanted to have a baby of her own because her only child was born out of wedlock and her husband was sterile.

Sometimes the surrogate is a sister of the infertile husband or wife, and she bears a child for them from a purely altruistic motive. Other women offer to be surrogates because they have a relative or friend who is infertile and even if they cannot help them, they can help someone else in the same predicament. Elizabeth Kane, who in 1980 became the first known commercial surrogate in the US, said she became a surrogate out of 'Christian life' and 'sisterhood', and added:

> I feel I'm giving childless people new hope and I guess I'm doing it for all the infertile couples in the world. Someone has to start it. And it might as well be me. It's something I've wanted to do for years. I have two relatives and know about six couples who are infertile. I've seen their heartbreak. I've spent most of my married life worrying about not being pregnant, and whenever I've gotten pregnant I feel so guilty telling those people.

Kane said if she were younger she would be a surrogate a second time and added, 'If I did it again, I wouldn't charge the parents a nickel.'[7]

One woman from Victoria, Australia, known only as Jane, had three surrogate babies—all without payment. She had six children of her own before delivering her first surrogate baby in 1983 at the age of 35. She said she did it for friends, for love. She wanted to do something worthwhile and found the experience rewarding, especially knowing that she had brought happiness to infertile couples.

For British surrogate Kirsty Stevens (pseudonym) surrogacy was a personal challenge: 'I was ready for something new.' She enjoyed her two previous pregnancies but did not want any more children and being a surrogate would give her the best of both worlds. As she explained in her book *Surrogate Mother: One Woman's Story*:

> My body was still working well: it had proved itself fully capable of producing healthy babies without trouble. I loved being pregnant and, at 23, I was still very young. It seemed a waste not to take advantage of my child-bearing abilities . . . why not use it to help others? Why not bring some happiness to a childless couple? . . . Surrogate parenting

> was a kind and generous act . . . the ultimate gift of love . . . in the end I would be giving them their baby as a gesture of friendship.

She said that after the birth, 'I was proud of doing what I said I'd do, and I felt that we were all bound together by our feelings of love for the baby I'd borne them.'[8]

Britain's most famous surrogate, Kim Cotton, told a television audience:

> I did it for two reasons—I love my children and I wanted to help my family financially and in doing so I could create a family for someone else who couldn't have a family. It's a lovely thing to do for somebody, it's like doing a favour for somebody but the warmth of it is with you for the rest of your life. I feel I have achieved something with my life. You take from life all the time and it's like giving something back.[9]

In her book *Baby Cotton: For Love and Money*, she said:

> I couldn't imagine getting married, so much in love and wanting a family, and then finding I couldn't have one. I think it would have destroyed my life if I had discovered I was sterile . . . It was extremely important to me to feel happy about who the parents would be. I couldn't have done this for some lazy rich woman who just didn't want the annoyance of being pregnant or didn't want to interrupt her career. It had to be someone who was at the end of her tether.[10]

'This bond of love, trust and friendship is the whole essence of the surrogate relationship,' is how Sydney woman Mary Buist described her relationship with the woman who acted as a surrogate for her and her husband. 'Our surrogate mother is a known and loved friend . . . A baby by surrogate can be the most beautiful arrangement—we know.'[11]

This comment from one American surrogate is typical: 'This is the ultimate gift you can give anybody. I'm unbelievably excited.' Her friend added, 'I enjoy being pregnant and wanted to do it for somebody else who could not. I also wanted to do something unusual, to break a new frontier, I'm a Christian and my whole ethic is a Christian one.'[12] Michigan surrogate Deborah Snyder said:

> I hadn't done anything for anyone except myself and my family . . . When I used to hear the stories of childless couples, I would get an empty feeling for them. Motherhood to me is the essence of life. Without children, I don't know what I'd have to work for or go on for.[13]

Another surrogate expressed similar views:

> I feel like I'm going to be able to give the gift of life to someone. Nobody else is going to do that for these people. In a way [surrogate parenting] is like being an extension of the woman's body. I'm doing her a favour by sharing my maternal abilities.[14]

A 1983 study of potential surrogates by Detroit psychiatrist Philip Parker found three main motivations: money, a desire to be pregnant and the urge to reconcile a birth-related trauma in the past. About a third of the 125 women he interviewed had had an earlier induced abortion or gave up their baby for adoption. He concluded that statistically the average surrogate is a 25-year-old Christian, married, with at least one child and a high-school education.[15] More than half the women he interviewed were married, a fifth divorced and about a quarter single. About 57 per cent were Protestant and 42 per cent Catholic. More than half were high-school graduates and a quarter had higher education.[2]

Another study, based on detailed psychological evaluation, suggested surrogates have relatively normal personalities with slightly raised energy levels and social extroversion tendencies.[16] In a more recent study of surrogates who had started on a programme, Californian attorney William Handel found they had an average age of 27, an average of 13.6 years of education, more than half had gone beyond high school, 86 per cent were married, the group had an average of 1.9 children, a third were housewives and generally they had been raised in Christian faiths including some seen as conservative. The study did not support suggestions that surrogates are stereotypically feminine.[17]

Analysing why the women wanted to be surrogates

Handel concluded that: 'The surrogates were generally women who enjoy children, have completed their own families, and who find pregnancy a tolerable, if not wonderful, experience.' Several also had experiences with infertile couples and 28 per cent had had abortions or given up a child for adoption. While this may be a subconscious reason for wanting to be a surrogate, only one woman in Handel's study saw a connection between her previous loss and her desire to be a surrogate. The proportion of women who had an abortion might be higher than average because one condition of surrogacy is that the woman be prepared to have a termination if necessary, and those who oppose abortion would not therefore offer to be surrogates.

## BEING A SURROGATE

Surrogates frequently pay a price—emotionally and socially—for their efforts. They are often ostracised by friends and colleagues who have pre-conceived ideas about surrogacy, and some find their parents refuse to speak to them when they discover their daughter is having another man's baby. Elizabeth Kane's husband was sacked by his insurance firm because of the publicity and controversy she created, her mother would not speak to her, nor would a lot of their friends, she said:

> My pet peeve is those people who treat us like disposable wombs and disregard our long-range problems. You feel like you have to keep up a facade of cheerfulness and you can't admit you do have fears . . . When the baby first kicked I was so excited, but there was no one to really share it with.[18]

Kirsty Stevens started thinking about being a surrogate in 1982 when the concept was hardly heard of in Britain. She found a couple, then handed over her baby without involving agencies or lawyers. But she had to deceive her local doctor, neighbours and her family. She even lied to her parents-in-law and only told two friends that she was a surrogate. 'I was beginning to find it a terrible strain not to be able to tell anyone about my secret. When I was nearly three months pregnant, I decided I absolutely *had* to have someone else to talk to.'[19]

Even in the US, where surrogacy is more popular, it is still not totally accepted today.

Most agencies interview the surrogate's husband to ensure he agrees with what she is doing and that he will be supportive, but some surrogates find their partner's attitude changes after they take on their new role. One American woman tells how her fiancé left her for another woman, another said her husband could not look at her after she was inseminated, 'He calls me a whore, prostitute and rent-a-womb.' One commented, 'My husband first felt it threatened his manliness.' Another said, 'His attitude has turned against me. We're hardly having any sex at all now,' and one reported that her husband wished she had never become involved in surrogacy and that their sex life was non-existent.[12]

Others say their partners are understanding and totally supportive. Beth Scott of California remarked, 'My husband is the most generous man in the world. There was no question of jealousy or ego. He loved me and took care of me the same as during the other pregnancies.'[20] Kim Cotton said her husband was very supportive.

> You can't do it on your own, it's a family thing. If you say I'm going to be a surrogate, I don't care what you think, it's the end of your marriage. It does affect the family if you are carrying someone else's baby. It takes a very big-hearted man to be able to do that because it's not like having an affair with somebody, but room is taken up by an outsider.[9]

Most agencies only take surrogates who have at least one child of their own, yet these children may become unintentional victims of the surrogacy business. Some children have been teased and tormented by friends, others have been ashamed of what their mothers did. Surrogates must carefully consider how they will explain the pregnancy to their existing children, especially if they are young, and ensure there is no resentment.

Kim Cotton said her eldest child, aged seven, was old enough to understand, and he approved before she became pregnant.

> I explained to him that things are not perfect in this world, there are people who cannot have children. I said, Mummy and Daddy were very lucky but there are people who it doesn't work for and somebody wants me to do it for them, do you mind? He thought about it for a while then he said, just don't charge them too much money because they will need a lot of money to look after the baby.[9]

What should a surrogate tell her children when they see her go off to hospital then come home without a baby? Kirsty Stevens told her two young children that the baby died and went to heaven. They both accepted it.

## CONTRACTS AND COUNSELLORS

Technically there is nothing complicated about surrogacy. Texas midwife Carol Pavek says, 'It's simple'. She wrote to Noel Keane in 1980 after seeing him in a TV programme and said she would like to be a surrogate.

> He told me about a couple in California who wanted a child. I talked to them over the phone and they got on the bus to my house the next day. I went to the drug store and bought a syringe. They went into another room and after a little while, the wife brought me her husband's sperm in a paper cup. She stayed and talked with me while I inseminated myself. That insemination didn't work, so I went out to their home, tried again and it worked. That was May, just three months after I'd written Noel, and I was pregnant.[7]

Some surrogate agreements, especially those between sisters and friends, are done privately, without the use of lawyers or contracts. However, the majority are organised by lawyers or commercial agencies that specialise in finding and matching surrogates, and couples then take care of the medical and legal arrangements. In some countries and states, such as Britain and Victoria, commercial agents and surrogate advertising are banned but in others, such as the US, commercial surrogacy is not illegal and it flourishes.

The contract is signed by both the commissioning couple

and the surrogate and in the US a couple usually pays $25,000–50,000, about $10,000–15,000 of which goes to the surrogate and the rest on medical and legal expenses, transport costs where necessary and a fee to the agency. Some contracts differentiate between payment for a baby and payment for the pregnancy, or the service; for example, the surrogate may receive $10,000 for a live birth but only $3,000 if the baby is stillborn, and proportionally less for a miscarriage.

Most agencies put potential surrogates through a strict evaluation—usually interviews with psychologists and/or psychiatrists—to find out why they want to be surrogates and whether they will have problems coping after the birth. This should identify women who are likely to want to keep the baby and eliminate any potential problems.

It takes a special kind of woman to be a surrogate mother. According to Harriet Blankfeld who runs the National Center for Surrogate Parenting in Chevy Chase, Maryland, less than 3 per cent of the women who apply to be surrogates are accepted. She says women can only take on the role if they are really committed. 'There is nothing worse than going to a job every day that you hate, and this is a full-time job and a 24-hour-a-day job. Can you imagine the emotional pressure of living with your commitment when everyone around you is opposed to what you are doing?'[14]

Stipulations vary between agencies, but these are the conditions imposed by one in the US: the surrogate has to be married, be the mother of at least one healthy child, be medically and psychologically fit, abstain from cigarettes, alcohol and any other drugs during the pregnancy and must agree to give up her parental rights after the baby is born. Psychological fitness is based on an evaluation by two psychiatrists and a psychologist, and her husband must also pass a test. The couple must present a medical report on their health, the results of a semen analysis showing the husband is fertile, a laboratory report on their blood type and their marriage certificate. The agency arranges the contract, life insurance for the surrogate's family should she die during pregnancy or childbirth and life insurance or a will for the child should the couple die before the child is born.

Not all agencies have these arrangements; some are more

elaborate and others less so—one has a 27-page contract for the surrogate. Some allow the surrogates and couples to meet each other, others prohibit it. Several agencies keep in touch with the surrogate after the birth as part of research into the long-term effects and benefits of surrogacy, and at least one subjects its surrogate to medical and psychological evaluation after the birth.

The potential parents also need to be counselled. Katherine Wyckoff, who runs an agency in Ohio, says, 'Some of the parents are so desperate for a child they are completely vulnerable and you need to be totally scrupulous. I've had a multi-millionaire offer me a blank cheque to give him and his wife a baby.'[12]

Once surrogates and couples are accepted to the programme, it is important that they have counselling on how to cope with the physical and emotional problems they will encounter. There are practicalities such as the insemination, prenatal care, the delivery and adoption procedures, and social considerations including what and when to tell family, friends and neighbours. They must be prepared for any criticism from people who do not agree with what they are doing, and they must be aware of the emotional strain that comes with such an unusual pregnancy.

## PREGNANCY AND PARTING

Although the wife of the infertile couple has no genetic contribution to the baby if it is conceived as a result of artificial insemination, she can sometimes play an active part in the pregnancy. If the insemination is done at home, the couple can masturbate or make love to collect the semen and the wife can be with the surrogate during the insemination. She can also share the experience of the pregnancy, attend prenatal classes with the surrogate and be present during the birth. As the wife of one couple said, 'It was really neat getting to know each other. I don't feel like I'm pregnant, but I do feel like I'm expecting. It's my baby.' However, not all couples have contact with their surrogates and many are isolated from the conception and growth of what will be their child.

Some surrogates and couples become good friends during and after the pregnancy and give each other emotional support and spend time together socially. Some surrogates say they could only give their baby to a couple they liked and who they knew would give him a good upbringing. Others do not even want to know who the couple is.

Many people find it hard to understand how a woman can have a baby then give it away, but surrogates say it is not difficult when the baby is regarded as 'a gift of life' and when they know it will give an infertile couple the joy they would not otherwise have. The baby is not conceived through a loving act between the surrogate and her husband then given away because they do not want it. The baby is deliberately conceived for another couple so the surrogate knows before conception that it will not be hers. Surrogates develop a variety of different ways to cope with the parting. Most try to divorce themselves from the baby during pregnancy, constantly referring to it as someone else's baby. They avoid picking out names and looking at baby clothes.

Kansas midwife Carol Pavek believed meeting the couple made parting with the baby much easier: 'I would never give away my baby to strangers.' Elizabeth Kane said she was glad her agency prohibits surrogates and couples meeting: 'I have no desire to meet the couple. It's their baby.' Later she admitted it was hard not to think of her son.

> Sure, I miss the baby once in a while, I'd be lying if I said I didn't. His mother was nice enough to send me a picture. I felt a little sad I couldn't hold him just once, feel his warmth. But if I had the opportunity, I would have to turn it down because I couldn't trust myself.[18]

Kim Cotton said she did not feel a maternal tug when her baby was born. 'It was totally different. When I held the child it was an absolute relief, it was like I was completing a circle. I'd set out on a long road to deliver a healthy baby. I felt absolute joy and relief.' She felt it was as simple as a job well done.[9]

One concern often expressed is the effect of surrogacy on children. Several groups, mainly agencies, are studying this but it is too early for large-scale, substantial findings yet. What if the child wants to meet his biological mother? Blankfeld's agency allows the child access to the centre's files that include a photo of the surrogate and on reaching the legal age he can be given her name and address.

Some people wonder how surrogates will cope in the long term. Three months after the birth Kim Cotton said,

> I rarely wonder about her these days. Even on a Friday, sometimes, I forget it's the day she was born. But I'm sure I'll always remember her birth date. I don't find myself hankering after the baby. Not wondering what she looks like or when she will cut her first tooth . . . I don't know if I'll wonder about her as she grows to be a teenager . . . I can't imagine that it will hit me differently later . . . Surely it would have happened by now, when the experience was fresh and I was most vulnerable. I truly do not feel bereft in any way. I know it isn't because I am heartless. I cared very much what happened to the baby. But she was never meant to be mine.[21]

Six months after Kirsty Stevens handed over her baby she wrote,

> I would like to see Alan, though still out of curiosity only . . . It's been so many months now that I hardly remember what he looks like. I think that only instinct would tell me that he was a baby I had given birth to. On the few occasions when I do think about him, a strange feeling comes over me. I wonder whose baby he really was: was he mine or not? I can't answer that question now, and I don't think I will ever be able to.[22]

## WHEN IT GOES WRONG—LEGALLY AND EMOTIONALLY

On 13 April 1987, *US News & World Report* magazine carried a headline: 'Finally, a ruling—M is for Melissa', and under it two photos of the same baby being held by two different women. It summed up the most controversial and public surrogacy issue to come before the courts and the community. Simply put, one woman agreed under contract to bear a child for an infertile couple who provided the sperm and agreed to pay her $US10,000, but after the birth she found she could not hand over the baby. Could she legally—and should she morally—be forced to surrender the baby to the contracting couple? Surrogacy has raised many legal and moral dilemmas, but this questioned the most basic principles of parenthood, contract law and what is in the best interest of the child.

In the US and many other countries, surrogacy could be covered under conflicting jurisdictions including artificial insemination, adoption, custody laws and laws covering contracts. No laws in the US said surrogacy was illegal, but nor did they say it was legal. However, buying and selling children has been outlawed in most countries, and many people see surrogacy as a form of baby selling.

Surrogacy poses numerous questions that have to be considered by surrogates, commissioning couples, the law and society as a whole:

- ★ What if the surrogate changed her mind and wanted to keep the baby?
- ★ Could the father be forced to pay maintenance for the child if the surrogate decided to keep him?
- ★ If the baby is born with a defect could the couple refuse to accept him and force the surrogate to take him, and could she in turn pass the unwanted child to the state?
- ★ Can the surrogate be forced to undergo amniocentesis or *chorion villus sampling* to see whether the foetus has a genetic abnormality?
- ★ If an abnormality is discovered during the pregnancy can she be forced to have an abortion, or can the contracting couple walk away from the responsibility?
- ★ Can anyone stop her having an abortion if she decides not to go ahead with the pregnancy?
- ★ What happens if she takes drugs or alcohol during pregnancy and it results in medical problems for the baby?
- ★ Could the couple be responsible if the mother dies during the pregnancy or childbirth?
- ★ What if one or both of the adopting parents dies before the child is born?
- ★ Should the surrogate be given a 'cooling-off' period in which she can decide whether or not to surrender her maternal rights?

* What if the surrogate harassed the couple, revealed herself to the child or tried to regain control of the baby?
* What if the child wanted to know the name of his biological mother or to meet her?
* Should the surrogate's existing children have any part in the agreement?
* Should unmarried men or homosexuals be allowed to engage surrogates?

In most countries the law has not had to face these issues. However, the question of abortion in most jurisdictions is clear-cut. In the US, for example, the Supreme Court ruled in the 1973 *Roe versus Wade* case that a woman has a constitutional right to decide whether or not to have an abortion and the biological father, even if he is married to her, cannot stop her.

The lack of specific laws or guidelines has led to several disputes, not all in the US. A Taiwanese man reportedly paid a woman $US30,000 to have a son for him, then sued her for giving birth to a girl. The man claimed he signed a five-year contract with a 21-year-old woman to bear him a son. She alleged that after the daughter was born, in December 1984, she said she did not want to try again and he beat her. The court dismissed the suit and nullified the contract.

The first publicised dispute in the US was between a Californian woman, Denise Thrane (also known as Nisa Bhimani), and a New York couple, Bjorna and James Noyes, for whom she had agreed to be a surrogate. Under a contract arranged by Noel Keane, the 29-year-old divorced mother of three agreed to give the baby to the couple after the birth. She was inseminated with Noyes's sperm which had been frozen and flown to California, but during the pregnancy she changed her mind and decided she wanted to keep the child.

A few days before the baby boy was born, in March 1981, the case went before Pasadena Superior Court Judge Robert Olsen who, two months later, awarded her custody. It was to have been an important test case, but in a last-minute twist it was revealed that Noyes's wife was a transsexual and Noyes withdrew his paternity claim minutes before it was to be heard by the judge. He was listed as the father on the birth certificate but was given no visitation rights. Judge Olsen later said he probably would have ruled in favour of the mother in any case because Californian law states that if the sperm is used by a licensed physician to inseminate a woman other than the donor's wife, he 'is treated in law as if he were not the natural father'.

In a second dispute in Michigan, Wayne County's Judge Roman Gribbs refused in November 1981 to declare that the man who provided the sperm was the legal father because the law presumes that a woman's husband is the father of a child born to her.

Four surrogate cases caused international interest and are worth considering because each raised different ethical and legal questions and each had a different outcome: the Stiver-Malahoff baby born with an abnormality, Baby Cotton in Britain where local authorities intervened, Baby M in the US where the surrogate wanted to keep her baby, and the South African grandmother Pat Anthony who carried her daughter's test-tube triplets.

*Judy Stiver,* a 26-year-old surrogate from Michigan, gave birth to a baby in January 1983 and one of the main 'what if. . .' fears of surrogacy became a reality. The boy was born with microcephaly, an abnormally small head which usually indicates mental retardation. New York accountant Alexander Malahoff had provided the sperm and paid Stiver $10,000 then rejected the baby, also named Alexander, saying it was not his child. Stiver refused to take the infant too, so the little boy was left at the hospital while his mother and Malahoff took their battle to court where Malahoff filed a $50 million suit against Stiver charging that she had broken the contract. Ironically, Malahoff and his wife had separated after Stiver was inseminated and he had hoped a baby would bring them back together.

When Malahoff was told the baby had microcephaly he had ordered the hospital not to treat him, while Stiver declined to sign for his medical care. However, a judge intervened and gave the hospital permission to do so. It was revealed that Stiver's husband Ray had, in his previous marriage, fathered a daughter with an impairment similar to baby Alexander's. When Malahoff and the Stivers appeared together on the national *Phil Donahue Show* the results of blood tests were announced and showed that Ray Stiver was the natural father of Alexander. The contract prohibited Stiver having sex after the insemination, but allegedly did not mention abstinence before. The Stivers returned Malahoff's money and took the baby home, saying they would love him as if they had intended to have him. The Stivers and Malahoff then set out to sue the gynaecologists who allegedly told Stiver that she was not pregnant at the time she was inseminated.

Although there was no doubt the baby was the Stivers', the case highlighted the need for laws or guidelines stating whose child it is when a child is conceived, under contract, with the sperm of a man other than the husband. If it had been Malahoff's, could he have been forced to take the baby because he agreed to in the contract? If the contract was found to be invalid, could Judy Stiver have been forced to keep the boy because she was the natural mother, or would they take joint custody as if the child had been conceived in an extra-marital affair? Would it have been any different if the baby had been conceived after intercourse, rather than artificial insemination? Many people feared a baby born with a handicap and not wanted by either party would become the state's responsibility and they criticised the physicians and lawyers for assisting in this possibility. The case also highlighted the need for thorough counselling of both the surrogate and her husband.

*Kim Cotton* agreed to have a baby for an anonymous American couple under the first contract arranged by an American agency set up in the UK by Harriet Blankfeld. The infertile couple were to pay the agency £13,000, half of which was to be given to Cotton after the birth. As Britain's first commercial surrogate, Kim Cotton sold her story to the British *Star* tabloid, reportedly for £20,000, and 'Britain's most amazing baby' was front-page news three months before the birth.

Baby Cotton was born at the Victoria Maternity Hospital, Barnet, North London, on 4 January 1985, with representatives of the world's press outside. However, before Cotton could hand her baby to the couple, who had flown from the US, Barnet Council authorities intervened. A social worker visited Kim while she was in labour and a few hours later, before the baby was born, a court issued a 'place of safety' order which prohibited anyone taking Baby Cotton from the hospital for eight days. Barnet's Social Services director, Alan Gorst, said the council had a responsibility to safeguard the welfare of all babies and in this case it had to be sure the commissioning couple would be suitable parents.

Kim Cotton pleaded with the authorities to let the couple take her baby. 'Let us complete the circle we so carefully planned. What has been done is terrible,' she told the *Star*. 'We should be laughing and celebrating today and on top of the world. As it is, we are all crushed. But I do think the case will go in favour of the parents. Surely the judges are human.' The social workers said they had the baby's best interests at heart. Cotton replied:

> I have too, and the baby's got to go to the parents. She asked how did I know those parents were going to look after the baby. I said, after what they've gone through, what do you think? They'd love the baby more than anything ... I wouldn't have had this baby for anybody. I know this couple will love and cherish her.[23]

Two years later she said: 'When I left hospital I had a very hard time because I was not giving Baby Cotton to her mother. She was left in hospital on her own, that was the heartbreak ... I was leaving her with no mother.'[9]

A few days after the birth High Court Judge Mr Justice Latey made her a Ward of Court which had been requested by the genetic father in the hope that he would be given custody. At the end of the first week Justice Latey gave the genetic father care and control of Baby Cotton and she was taken from the hospital and flown to the US before anyone, even Kim Cotton, knew. Latey said of the new parents, 'They are most warm, caring and sensible people, as well as being highly intelligent. Looking at the child's well-being, physical and emotional, who better to have her under their care? No one.' He said they were devoted to each other, highly qualified professional people who owned two homes and were able to meet the baby's emotional needs and to handle the complex questions of her birth. He said permission to publish their names would never be given. 'For this baby girl to grow into childhood and adolescence with the finger pointed at her as "the girl who ..."—it's unthinkable.'[24] However, the anonymous 'Mr and Mrs A' ended up paying an additional £11,000 in legal fees, so Baby Cotton cost them £24,000 in total.

Baby Cotton caused controversy in Britain because it was the first case of commercial surrogacy and it happened within months of the release of the report of the Government's Warnock Committee. After a two-year enquiry the committee, headed by Dame Mary Warnock, had recommended commercial surrogacy be banned and Kim Cotton became the unofficial test case at the centre of the debate. As a result, calls to ban surrogacy intensified and within days of the birth the Secretary of State for Social Services, Norman Fowler, announced that Parliament would legislate against commercial surrogacy, which it did six months later, making it a criminal offence to advertise surrogate services, recruit surrogates or operate agencies.

There was considerable criticism of the way the Baby Cotton case was handled. As Kim Cotton had made her intentions public three months earlier, the social workers and courts could have assessed the couple before the birth rather than leaving the baby in hospital without a mother for her first eight days. Mary Warnock denounced the council for interfering and accused them of treating the little girl as if she had been 'an abandoned baby left in a cardboard box'. She said advertising of surrogacy should be banned, but not private arrangements.

*Baby M* was at the centre of what was to have been the biggest test of the surrogate contract in the US. For many years, doctors and lawyers had been asking what would happen if a contracted surrogate refused to give up the baby after it was born. Who is the mother in such a case? Would such a contract stand up in court? Would contractual law override family law? Would a court rule that the interests of the surrogate and the couple override the public interest?

In February 1985, Mary Beth Whitehead, a 29-year-old mother of two from New Jersey, signed a contract—drawn up by Noel Keane's Infertility Center of New York—agreeing to be inseminated with William Stern's sperm and to hand the baby to Stern and his wife in return for $10,000. But

Whitehead had second thoughts about giving up the baby the day it was born on 27 March 1986. She handed over Baby M but later asked the Sterns if she could have her back for a short time because she missed her. They agreed, and Whitehead then fled with the baby she called Sara to Florida where she was found three months later by police and a private detective hired by the Sterns. New Jersey Superior Court Judge Harvey Sorkow then gave the Sterns temporary custody and restricted Whitehead to twice-weekly visits.

The genetic father sued for custody and Sorkow had to decide first whether surrogate contracts were legal in that state, then deal with the custody question. Stern, a 40-year-old biochemist, was married to a 41-year-old paediatrician who turned to surrogacy because she was concerned that a mild form of multiple sclerosis might endanger her health if she became pregnant. Their combined income was said to be $90,000. In contrast, Whitehead, one-time go-go dancer turned housewife, was married to a 37-year-old $28,000-a-year sanitation worker who had lost his driving licence twice, been unemployed and alcohol dependent. Whitehead was portrayed as impulsive, narcissistic and immature by the Sterns' attorney, who said his own clients were stable, loving and had the resources to give the girl a happy, comfortable upbringing. Lawyers for the Whiteheads said they were experienced parents with an extended family, that the Sterns were 'cold', that Elizabeth Stern used a surrogate because she did not want pregnancy to interfere with her career, and that the contract should not have been allowed.

When she decided to be a surrogate in 1984, Whitehead wrote in her application, 'Having an infertile sister I understand the feelings of a childless couple. I feel giving the gift of a child would be more rewarding than working at a conventional job.' Asked if she anticipated any emotional problems, she wrote, 'I have been blessed with two happy, healthy children and a loving husband. I am content with my life and would not have any emotional problems.'[25] However, a psychologist who assessed her reported that she had serious doubts about carrying out her plan to be a surrogate for another couple. The Sterns were not shown the report. In a phone conversation taped by Stern and later played in court,

Whitehead threatened to kill the baby and herself while in Florida and said, 'I gave her life, I can take her life away'. He replied, 'I'll be her father. I'll be a father to her. I am her father.' Three mental health experts hired by Stern told the judge that Whitehead's emotional problems would prevent her from bringing up the child adequately and they recommended that the Sterns have custody. Feminists picketed the courthouse to support Whitehead, saying that surrogacy exploits women and no mother should be forced to give up her baby.

The trial lasted almost three months, attracted more than 100 reporters from around the world (including Moscow) and resulted in 7,000 pages of transcript. It ended just after Baby M turned one—without a legal name—and just after the Vatican document condemning surrogacy was released. On 31 March 1987, it took Sorkow three hours to read aloud his 127-page decision in which he said a child's interests outweighed the legality of any contract. He gave custody to Stern and denied Whitehead visitation rights. The judge described her as 'manipulative, impulsive and exploitive' and 'untruthful'. The Sterns were 'credible, sincere and truthful people' who 'have a private, quiet and unremarkable life which augurs well for a stable household environment'. In a seven-minute ceremony a few minutes after the ruling, Elizabeth Stern adopted Baby M who legally became Melissa Stern. As *US News* said, 'Finally, a ruling—M is for Melissa'. The Sterns made a statement regretting the nastier aspects of the case and expressing sympathy for Whitehead. The new mother said, 'I know it's very painful for her. Despite all the bad feelings that have gone on between both sides, she gave us a beautiful daughter.'[26]

Several polls during the trial showed the public overwhelmingly supported the Sterns, and after the ruling, 75 per cent of people questioned in one poll agreed with the judge's decision while only 8 per cent said Whitehead should have been given custody.[27]

Although the Baby M case was the first legal challenge to surrogate contracts in the US and was hailed as a landmark decision, Sorkow's ruling did not set a precedent and did little to resolve the legal arguments, because each state has its own jurisdiction and because he treated it as a classic custody dispute which considers what is in the best interest of the child.

Some American courts would rule that the legal mother is the one who gives birth and her husband automatically becomes the father, while the sperm donor has no rights or responsibilities towards the child—therefore Mary Beth and Richard Whitehead would have kept Baby M. As the *New York Times* said, 'The ruling settled the specific question of who is granted custody of the child, but other courts and state legislatures will continue to face the larger question of whether surrogate motherhood agreements are legal . . . in finding that the father would be the better parent Sorkow broke no new ground.'[28]

Before Sorkow's ruling, both Whitehead and the Sterns declared they would take the case to a higher court if they lost. And in early February 1988, the New Jersey Supreme Court overturned Sorkow's decision, saying surrogate contracts were illegal because buying or selling babies was illegal. The court ruled that Whitehead had visitation rights and revoked Elizabeth Stern's right to adopt Baby M, although the Sterns could have custody of the infant. It was the end of a 22-month long controversial, and often bitter, legal battle that left Baby M with two mothers and a publicity-prone future.

*Pat Anthony's* surrogacy ended in joy and did not go before the courts, but it raised several ethical questions. She became known worldwide as the surrogate grandmother, after giving birth to triplets in a Johannesburg clinic on 1 October 1987. The 48-year-old South African woman decided to have a test-tube baby for her daughter and in doing so made world history four times—as the oldest surrogate, the first surrogate to have triplets, the first woman to give birth to her own grandchildren and the first woman to have triplets from another woman's eggs. It was also South Africa's first surrogate birth. Her daughter, Karen Ferreira-Jorge, a 27-year-old aerobic instructor, had a hysterectomy when she nearly died during the birth of her first and only child, a son, three years earlier. She and husband Alcino were devastated at not being able to have any more children but Pat Anthony offered to carry a baby conceived through IVF with her daughter's eggs and son-in-law's sperm. Four of Ferreira-Jorge's eggs were fertilised in the laboratory with her husband's sperm then transferred to her mother's womb where three developed in a normal triplet pregnancy. The daughter then received hormone treatment so she was able to breastfeed the babies as soon as they were born.

Anthony travelled 450 kilometres (280 miles) from her home in Tzaneen to consult a doctor in Johannesburg before telling them she would act as their surrogate. 'I think children are part of married life, a vitally important part. Karen was going to be denied that,' she said.[29] Her commitment included giving up smoking 60 cigarettes a day. Despite her age (then 47) and size (150 centimetres or 4 feet 11 inches) doctors transferred four IVF eggs and on her 48th birthday confirmed she was pregnant. But not everyone agreed with her act of love. As a Catholic she was constantly reminded that the Vatican forbade both surrogacy and IVF, and because of this the family's parish priest said he might not be able to baptise the babies, the Medical Association of South Africa repeated its ruling that 'Surrogate motherhood is undesirable' because of social, legal and ethical implications, the head of the country's leading IVF programme said he opposed surrogacy and the Dutch Reform and Methodist churches in South Africa said they did not approve of surrogacy.

In Africa and the Middle East the birthing mother is generally regarded as the legal mother, even if another woman provided the eggs, but South African law did not have a definition of 'mother'. However, immediately after the birth Justice Minister Kobie Coetzee announced that Anthony would be the legal guardian of the two boys and girl until the daughter and son-in-law, who were the genetic parents, adopted them. Until then, the triplets were Karen's brothers and sister—after the adoption they became her sons and daughter. However, much newspaper space was devoted to working out the family tree and it was suggested that as the sperm came from Alcino and the eggs from Karen the boys would be Karen's brother's half brothers because they had the same birthing mother, and also his nephews. Their surrogate mother would also be their grandmother and her husband could be their legal father, grandfather or stepfather. Their father's wife (Karen) would be their stepmother and half sister.

## THE DEBATE

Giving infertile couples a child is generally seen as a charitable, noble cause, a gift of love, but turning it into a business is regarded as less attractive. For some people the commercialism of surrogacy raises fears of black market baby selling, breeding farms, turning impoverished women into baby producers and the possibility of selective breeding at a price. It could be said that surrogacy degrades pregnancy to a service, and a baby to a product. On the other hand, the service could be seen as life-giving, and the baby as the gift of love.

### IS SURROGACY IMMORAL?

Many religious institutions clearly think it is. The Catholic Church, for example, regards surrogacy as 'morally illicit', as stated in the *Instruction*:

> It is contrary to the unity of marriage and to the dignity of the procreation of the human person. [It] represents an objective failure to meet the obligations of maternal love, of conjugal fidelity and of responsible motherhood; it offends the dignity and the right of the child to be conceived, carried in the womb, brought into the world and brought up by his own parents; it sets up, to the detriment of families, a division between the psychical, psychological and moral elements which constitute those families.[30]

The Swedish Insemination Committee regarded surrogacy as 'an undesirable phenomenon' and said in its 1985 report: 'It presumes that children become objects of financial bargaining, which is ethically indefensible.'[31]

The Warnock Committee received many submissions supporting and opposing surrogacy and summed up four of the main arguments against the practice: the introduction of a third party is an attack on the value of marriage; it is the wrong way to approach pregnancy; it is degrading to the child, since, for all practical purposes, the child will have been bought for money; and 'it is inconsistent with human dignity that a woman should use her uterus for financial profit and treat it as an incubator for someone else's child'. On the other hand, the committee points out that surrogacy can be seen as a deliberate and thoughtful act of generosity on the part of one woman to another and if there are risks, then the generosity is all the greater.[32]

After a lengthy review of reproductive alternatives, the American Fertility Society issued a report in September 1986 which became the AFS guideline on the subject. It said there is concern that surrogacy will weaken marriage and 'the family'. 'Some commentators have voiced the further concern that if surrogates are paid for their services, human reproduction will become commercialised, and children might come to be perceived as a "consumer item".' However, the AFS points out that sperm donation is largely acceptable by society as a way around male infertility, and surrogacy could be acceptable as the equivalent for female infertility, 'unless it can be demonstrated to be significantly more risky to the participants or to society than [DI] or other activities that our society condones'.[33]

Although there are potential problems with surrogacy, the AFS said these can be assessed and accepted by those involved.

> Society allows competent adults to take risks (for example, trying an experimental medical procedure, donating a kidney, engaging in a risky sports activity or occupation, or joining the armed forces). In the medical realm, people are allowed to make risky choices as long as they have given voluntary, informed consent.

Harriet Blankfeld, who runs a large surrogacy agency in the US and set up a branch in the UK, said after the birth of Baby Cotton, 'I don't think people who participate in surrogate parenting are immoral people. They are caught between wanting to have a child and the inability to have a child. Does that make them immoral?'[34]

To some people surrogacy is far from immoral. Australian commentator Sonia Humphrey says if surrogacy were promoted as an honoured, respected and well-paid profession there would be fewer sad women in the world.

> For years women have been offering their services as nannies and housekeepers, to keep families functioning.

> There's nothing dishonourable about these roles so why should the act of bearing, rather than caring for a child, for money, be treated with such hostility by other women? Why should it be regarded as disgraceful to rent a uterus and OK for a dancer to take money for exhibiting a trained pair of legs . . . because she bears the child willingly, deliberately, is she less deserving of support than the woman who conceives a child as a result of rape or carelessness, bears it because she doesn't want an abortion, and then puts it up for adoption? The ultimate obscenity is that so many babies aren't growing up in homes where they're loved and wanted. An adopted child need never doubt that he or she was much desired. The child of a surrogacy contract would have the same security . . . Not every woman loves being pregnant. But some adore it and, like being a construction worker or a brain surgeon, being a childbearer is not something all women do equally well.[35]

It is worth asking: if it is not immoral for a businesswoman to use her brain, a typist her fingers, a javelin thrower her arms and so on, why is it considered immoral for a woman to use her womb? Unlike the businesswoman, typist and javelin thrower, the surrogate is giving another person something that person could not otherwise have—a child.

Carl Wood, Professor of Obstetrics and Gynaecology at Monash University, Melbourne in Victoria, says surrogacy is 'one of the most generous, loving and humane acts that one woman can carry out for another'. He believes it may have positive benefits for society:

> It will teach us how to see childbearing from a wider perspective than that of two parents . . . Most important, surrogacy automatically excludes many of those factors which are accepted by the community in natural conception, but may be disastrous for the child—unwanted pregnancy, poor parental health (emotional and physical) and the use of harmful drugs . . . [it] will be optimizing conditions for a successful pregnancy and birth so this may be an advantage for the child when compared to risks so often associated with unplanned natural conception . . . I am optimistic that skilled surrogacy could become one of the

most successful infertility therapies. It has suffered from inadequate support and study, overexposure of the complications in the media and unfair prejudice.[36]

It could be argued that women have a right to decide whether or not to use or act as surrogates, and that people who disagree need not become involved but at the same time they should not stop others using them.

## WHAT THE PUBLIC THINKS

One of the earliest surveys was by *Glamour* magazine in the US in 1981. Most of its readers were aged 18–35, almost half of them under 23. Half said childless couples should consider using a surrogate and one out of five said they would be willing to bear a child for an infertile couple, but two-thirds said they would not consider using a surrogate themselves. Thirty-four per cent said they did not think women should sell babies, 25 per cent said there are too many unanswered ethical questions and 20 per cent said there are too many unresolved legal questions.[37]

Identical polls conducted in the UK and Australia in 1982 found Australians (32 per cent) were more approving of surrogacy than Britons (20 per cent).[38] By 1986 just over half the Australian population questioned did not oppose surrogacy—16 per cent approved and more than two-thirds said they did not object.[39] A national poll in France in 1984 found just over half the population disapproved of surrogacy—only 35 per cent approved and 14 per cent had no opinion.[40] Two polls in the US show approval increased between 1983 and 1987, from 39 to 48 per cent. In 1983, more people had disapproved than approved, but three and a half years later the tables had turned and the reverse was true.[41] However, in a *National Enquirer* phone-in poll in May 1987, just after the Baby M case, 70 per cent of people said surrogacy should be outlawed in the US,[42] and a survey by the Child Welfare League of America found 64 per cent of people questioned supported regulation, 24 per cent wanted prohibition and 10 per cent said there should be no regulation.[43]

## THE RISKS INVOLVED WITH SURROGACY

There are medical, psychological, financial and legal risks that can affect the parents-to-be, the surrogate and the surrogate's family. The greatest perceived risk for the couple is that the surrogate will change her mind and want to keep the child, which would cause emotional trauma, financial loss, legal action to gain custody of the child and possible prosecution in countries or states that prohibit payment for children. In addition, the couple may be harassed in later years by the surrogate wanting to see the child. And if the surrogate is known to the couple—as a friend or relative—it may later cause tension between the surrogate, the couple and the child. However, all of these are rare.

On the other hand, the surrogate must endure physical risks involved in the pregnancy and childbirth, as well as the psychological effects of parting with the baby she has carried for nine months. Until surrogacy is more accepted by the community both parties are vulnerable to social criticism and possibly friction between other family members. And the effect on the surrogate's existing children is unknown.

It is possible that a surrogate may not take as much care of herself during the pregnancy as she would if she were to bring up the child herself, which could result in physical harm to the foetus, and she may fail to admit that she has a genetic defect, which could be harmful to the child. In addition, the child may be emotionally disturbed when he is told of his unusual beginning and may suffer an identity crisis—although experts say this is unlikely, based on experience with adoption.

Carl Wood believes the surrogate is most at risk physically.

> There are the risks of pregnancy, complications which may harm or rarely kill, the discomfort—on average a pregnant woman suffers six to nine symptoms—the reduced physical and social activity and the emotional stress . . . the pain of birth . . . possible changes in the body—weight change, varicosities, and breast distortion. Society undervalues pregnancy and parturition, ignoring the heroic, destructive and financial aspects.[36]

## CAN ANYONE BE A SURROGATE?

As we have seen, potential surrogates usually go through a screening procedure which may include several hours with counsellors and psychologists. On a broader scale, it is often argued that surrogacy should be restricted to women who already have children, as they are familiar with the risks of pregnancy—physical and emotional—and they are less likely to change their mind about surrendering the baby. On the other hand, the surrogate's existing children may be affected psychologically by their mother giving the baby away. If they are too young to understand the situation fully they may fear they too will be given away, although this can be overcome by offering an honest explanation and emotional security. Some people argue that a married surrogate would be better than a single woman and she can call on her husband's support during the pregnancy. Others say the husband's views and emotions may add conflict to the situation.

Alexander Capron, Professor of Law at the University of Southern California, is concerned about the effect on the surrogate's existing children and suggests it may be better if surrogates are women with no children.

> The children will be aware that their mother was pregnant, went to the hospital and came home empty handed—so she has sold the child. If we were primarily interested in the children, to protect the children, we ought to use women who have not reproduced so you don't involve innocent third parties—the other children whose half siblings are about to be spirited away.

However, generally surrogates are women who have children, mainly because it is too expensive and intrusive to test whether a woman is fertile and because, as Capron says, 'The people most likely to employ them want a picture so they say, oh, what a cute child she had last time, maybe she will have another cute one for us.'

The Ontario Law Reform Commission believed there should be no restriction on the eligibility of surrogates—married or unmarried, children or no children, provided they are fully assessed, with one exception—it recommended minors be prohibited from acting as surrogates. The Commission, which spent more than two years investigating surrogacy and other reproductive methods, said in its 1985 report: 'While this view may appear harsh in circumstances where, for example, a mature 17-year-old wishes to assist a close relative, we believe strongly that minors should not be exposed to the risks [of] surrogate motherhood.'[44]

The Commission also sought to protect the surrogate's existing children:

> If there are indications that they might be psychologically harmed, a court should not approve her involvement. It would be unconscionable to sacrifice knowingly the emotional stability of an otherwise secure child in the interests of creating another child.

## WHO SHOULD BE ALLOWED TO ENGAGE SURROGATES?

Most people agree a prerequisite should be that the intended parents will be suitable parents and give the child a good upbringing. This could be determined by a physician or psychologist. However, the process leading up to surrogacy may automatically select suitable parents—couples who have been through other forms of assisted reproduction and have accepted the risks involved in surrogacy are more likely to dote on the child and give him the best possible upbringing, because he is very much wanted. As the American Fertility Society said, 'A child conceived through surrogate motherhood may be born into a much healthier climate than a child whose birth was unplanned.'[2]

Generally, surrogates act for infertile couples, either married or co-habiting. But there is nothing to stop a surrogate acting for an infertile single woman or a homosexual couple, and several single men and transsexuals in the US have engaged surrogates. In addition, a surrogate could carry a child for a couple who are not infertile, for example, if the woman does not want pregnancy to interrupt her career or does not want the inconvenience of pregnancy, or because she considers the surrogate more attractive or more intelligent than herself.

The Ontario LRC recommended surrogacy be limited to

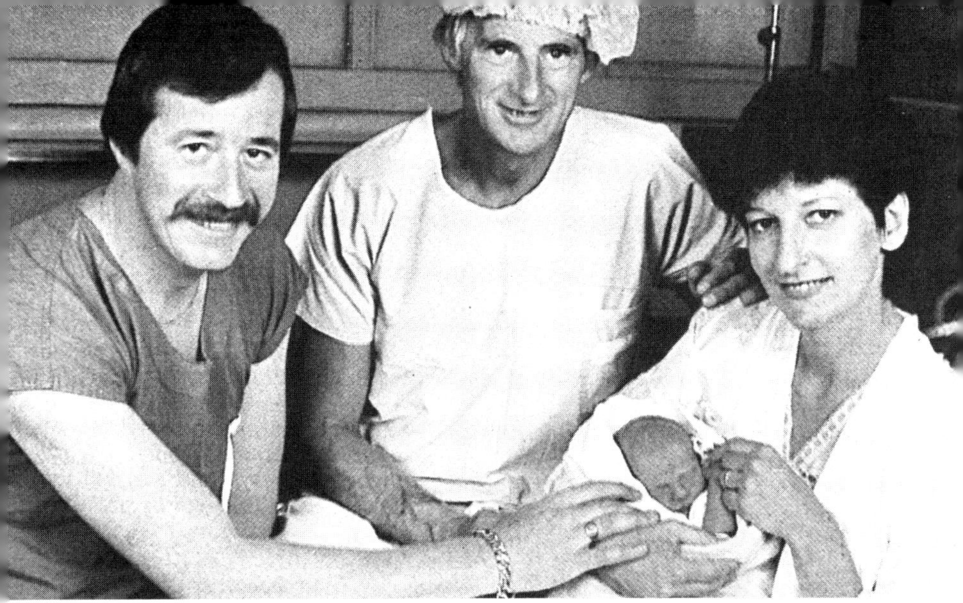

Australian IVF pioneer Carl Wood (centre) with the world's first frozen-embryo baby, Zoe Leyland, and her parents, David and Loretta. As an eight-cell embryo, Zoe was stored in a cylinder of liquid nitrogen at $-197°C$ for two months, then thawed and transferred to her mother's womb. Embryo freezing produces babies but is it morally wrong?

Christopher Chen with the world's first frozen-egg babies—twins David and Cheryl Castleton—born in South Australia in 1986. Freezing and thawing human eggs before fertilisation overcomes the ethical problems of freezing embryos but raises other ethical questions.

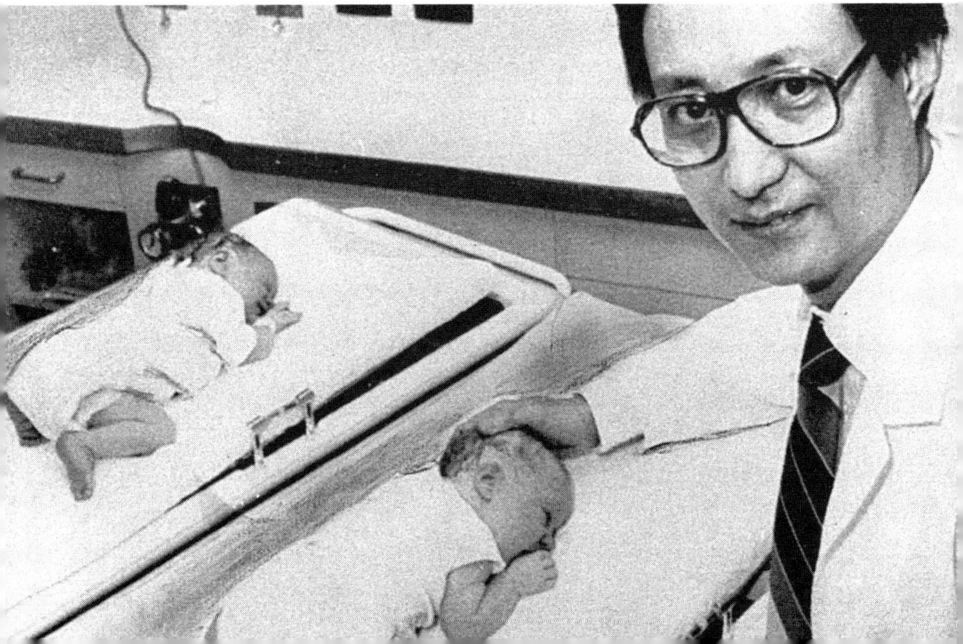

Chelsea and Rebecca Nicholds were conceived in a laboratory dish at the same time, but were born 16 months apart because the embryo that became Chelsea was frozen for 16 months before the pregnancy began. Are they twins?

women who are infertile and cannot have a child by any other means: 'Surrogate motherhood should be a solution of last resort . . . Our sole purpose in allowing individuals to pursue surrogate motherhood arrangements under strict control is to respond to infertility, not to afford individuals the opportunity to satisfy their lifestyle preferences.'[45]

It is often suggested that the same criteria should apply as for stranger adoption (when the child is not known to the adopting parent) but the Ontario LRC does not agree with the 'rigorous standards' used by adoption agencies to assess potential parents. It believes the most important point is whether the child will be given an adequate upbringing, and that would depend on the stability of the people involved. It should be limited to stable men and women in a stable marital or non-marital relationship and to stable single women.

A 1986 Australian surrogacy survey, by the New South Wales LRC, found the least suitable parents were considered to be male homosexual couples living in a stable domestic relationship (72 per cent of Australians would prohibit this), people under 18 (17 per cent), female homosexual couples living in a stable domestic relationship (70), people who could not financially support a child (66) and an elderly couple (51 per cent). Less than half the populaton would also oppose single men (49), single women (45), unmarried couples living in a stable domestic relationship (37) and people who already have children (34). In all these categories women expressed stronger opposition than men.[46]

## WHO SHOULD MAKE SURROGACY ARRANGEMENTS?

Some authorities believe surrogacy arrangements should be private and altruistic, and on this basis the British and Victorian Governments have banned all other forms of surrogacy arrangements. This limits surrogacy mainly to friends and relatives and eliminates any third party. However, other experts argue that unless there is a third party—a commercial or government agency—to match surrogates with prospective parents, and to administer the adoption procedure, surrogacy could lead to serious problems. Without a standard for screening and counselling surrogates and couples, there is a danger that those involved may run into unforeseen emotional, legal and financial problems.

Since the ban on commercial surrogacy in Britain, Kim Cotton has been the focal point for people wanting surrogacy arrangements. 'I'm not running an agency but I do put people in touch and let them get on with it. It's only commercial surrogacy that is illegal.' She said there needs to be some co-ordination and suggests something run along the same lines as adoption. 'I don't want lots of Americans making money out of people's misery, but these surrogates are wandering about in the wilderness on their own.'[9]

Given that some communities object to commercialism in surrogacy, it is logical that surrogacy arrangements be made by a non-profit-making government-appointed body, staffed by physicians, counsellors and lawyers, who could administer a government-approved screening and counselling programme and a standardised legal contract. A set fee from prospective parents could cover wages and administrative costs.

Another option, recommended by the Ontario Law Reform Commission, is for a court to approve a surrogacy agreement before conception, after assessing the suitability of the surrogate and the prospective parents. This would protect the unborn child, the parents-to-be, the surrogate and any existing children under her care. The LRC suggested that the court examine the stability, marital status and suitability of the parents-to-be and the surrogate's physical and mental state before and during pregnancy, for example, based on reports by doctors, psychologists and other professionals. The court should seek the opinion of her husband if she is married or co-habiting, and consider her existing children, or any factors that might be harmful to the foetus.[44]

New York State legislatures have also taken up the idea of pre-conception court-approved arrangements. Under proposed legislation, a surrogacy contract would be void unless approved by a judge.

More than half the people questioned in the Australian surrogacy survey said the surrogate and couple should be allowed to make an agreement themselves and another 41 per cent said they should be allowed to with the approval of a government agency. Only 17 per cent said government agencies alone should make the arrangements. More than half approved of non-profit-making agencies, such as welfare organisations or a branch of a hospital, being involved in arrangements but only 3 per cent said individuals and agencies that make a profit should be involved.[47]

## WHEN THE SURROGATE WANTS TO KEEP THE BABY

Under what circumstances can a surrogate be forced to give up a child she bore under contract? Some people say it is her child because she delivered it, others argue that the couple paid for a contracted service and the child is theirs, and others say it is half hers and half the husband's if they provided the egg and sperm. Would it be different if the man had intercourse with the woman? Or if his wife's egg had been used? And would it have made any difference if the surrogate had been a sister and done it for love, not money?

All couples who engage a surrogate take on the risk—however small—that the surrogate might change her mind and want to keep the baby. The issue becomes more complicated when the child is conceived with the egg of another woman. It calls into question one of our most basic assumptions: who is the mother—the one who gives birth, or the one who provides the genes (the egg) or the one who adopts? And who is the father—the mother's husband or the man who provides the sperm or the one who brings the child up?

The survey by *Glamour* magazine found 64 per cent of readers (mostly women under 35) believed a surrogate mother should not have the right to keep the baby and 36 per cent said she should.[37] In contrast, in another survey only 8 per cent thought Whitehead should be able to keep Baby M in 1987.[27] In the 1986 Australian survey, one-third said the married couple should have first claim to the baby, a quarter sided with the surrogate and another quarter said a court should decide.[39]

There are four options in solving a surrogacy dispute: the surrogate could automatically keep the child because she bore him; the couple could be awarded custody under the terms of the agreement; a court could decide after the birth—as in a standard custody dispute—or before conception.

Many people feel strongly that the legal mother is the

woman who gives birth, and this is the case in several religious doctrines including Jewish law. George Annas, Professor of Health Law at Boston University, says that in the US the current legal presumption that the birth mother is the legal mother should remain. 'This gives the child and society a certainty of identification at the time of birth and recognises that the gestational mother has contributed more of herself to the child than the genetic mother,' in cases where the egg has come from another woman. He believes the legal father should be *presumed* to be the husband of the child's mother (i.e., the surrogate's husband) unless he presents 'proof of nonpaternity beyond a reasonable doubt' (so long as he proves he did not consent to the procedure that resulted in the birth).[48]

Alexander Capron believes that for the protection of the child the birthing mother should always be the legal mother, at the time of birth.

> If the woman is bearing another woman's egg, the woman who donated the egg would have nothing more to do with it and we would say the mother who bears the child is the mother. And if the woman carries a child for a woman who is intended to be the mother, the woman who bears the child is still the mother. The man who is the genetic father ought to have responsibilities and some rights and the woman who bore the child should also have some responsibilities—no more, no less than the father.

However, he believes that in a dispute such as the Baby M case, where the child had spent a substantial part of her life with another couple, the paramount consideration is what is in the best interests of the child, regardless of who provided the egg or sperm.

> Suppose in the Baby M case, someone else's sperm had been used (other than William Stern's) but the child had been raised for the last eight months by the Sterns, it is probably best for the child to go with the people who have been raising it, even if they are not the genetic parents. If it turned out that Stern was genetically unrelated it would be no different than any other adoption situation. The Baby M case was complicated because Mary Beth Whitehead had

> her for the first few months—in Florida—then for eight months the Sterns raised her. So it is a closer balance, but I suppose the Sterns were the predominant figures in her life.

What if you have a baby, take it home for a year then discover there was some mix-up—do you exchange the baby? 'My answer would be no, I had raised this child as my own. I would think it wrong to the child to cast it over to someone else and say, I don't love you, when I have spent a year saying, I love you.'

Joseph Goldstein, Yale University Professor of Law, says that the upbringing is more important than the genetic contribution and made a prominent stand in the debate over the return of Jewish children after the Second World War. Some children had been put in the care of families during the war and in several instances the parents survived the concentration camps and came to collect their children, but Goldstein argued that given the theory of psychological continuity, the people who had custody during the war had become the psychological parents, and should therefore keep the children.

Lori Andrews of the American Bar Association believes a dispute should be decided by whatever the *intention* was, which means the surrogate would always be forced to surrender the child, because that is always the intention in a surrogacy arrangement. She says a surrogate and the couple's intentions are clear:

> A surrogate makes the decision to give up the child in advance of conception at a time in which she can make an informed unemotional reflection, unlike the biological mother in a traditional adoption who may unintentionally become pregnant and may encounter emotional dilemmas and stigmatization during the pregnancy, and may not be able to make an adequate assessment at that time.[43]

The baby would not even exist were it not for the couple's decision to create a child. Andrews believes that if pre-conception intent governs who the legal parents are it may discourage women who are not entirely sure that they want to be surrogates.

The Ontario Law Reform Commission believes the surrogacy agreement should be upheld, even it if means physically removing the child from the surrogate. The Commission recommended that courts approve surrogacy arrangements before conception and that the surrogate be made to fulfil her pledge to give up the child. 'Legislation should provide for immediate surrender of the child. Hence, where a surrogate mother refuses to transfer custody, she could be compelled to do so by court order. It may seem harsh and unfeeling to countenance a situation where officers may be ordered to deliver the infant to the social parents. Yet physical seizure [is allowed] under the present law in a dispute over custody.'[49]

The American Fertility Society believes the contracting couple should be the legal parents and that the surrogate should have no parental rights or responsibilities. The AFS recommended this become law so the legality of surrogacy is clear.[2]

The proposed law in New York State would forcibly remove the surrogate's rights at birth. Susan Wolf of the Hastings Center, a research institution specialising in medical ethics, told legislatures at one of the hearings: 'It should be against public policy to tear a child away from its birth mother because a deal is a deal—even with judicial approval'. She believes a surrogate should have a chance to change her mind within a specified period after the birth, which is the adoption system in several states.[50]

George Annas agrees and says she should only transfer her parental rights after she has had reasonable time to consider all the options. Carl Wood suggests she be given a 'cooling-off period' of one to two months in which to decide whether or not to surrender her rights as a parent. The baby would be in the care of the prospective parents but would legally be under the responsibility of the mother until she signs the custody papers. Some people suggest this opens the possibility—however remote—that the surrogate could refuse to sign the papers unless the couple paid her more money. However, this would not be possible if surrogacy arrangements were government-controlled.

## SHOULD THE SURROGATE BE KNOWN TO THE CHILD?

Many people who oppose commercial surrogacy say it should be limited to arrangements between close friends and relatives, but there are two potential risks: a woman may feel obliged or even pressured into being a surrogate, and the long-term effect on families involved is unknown. There is a danger of family friction at some later stage. If for instance the child's aunt is also his biological mother, she may become more possessive or protective of him than other nieces and nephews. She may find it emotionally traumatic to see what was her child on a regular basis, for example at her friend's home or at family gatherings.

At some stage the child would have to be told that he had an unconventional beginning and that the woman he calls 'auntie' is in fact his biological mother. This should be done lovingly, tactfully and with as much information as a child can comprehend at that age. If he is not told he may later find out and resent the fact that he had been deceived.

There is anecdotal evidence that the child—at least in early years—may be less affected than the adults in a known surrogacy arrangement. Some families relate how attitudes changed after the birth and in some cases developed into antagonisms. One surrogate says that after about two years she and the friend she delivered the baby for stopped seeing each other and she suspects it was because the father could not cope with the situation. Another says it split her family.

There is a very real danger that a sister or sister-in-law may unintentionally become swept along with the suggestion that she act as a surrogate. She may feel she ought to, against her better judgement. And if she declines, she may carry with her, for the rest of her life, the guilt that she denied her sister the one thing she herself loved most—motherhood. These may be extremes but they must be considered.

The American Fertility Society said one of its three concerns was that a woman who is a friend or relative may be coerced into being a surrogate. 'It is of the utmost importance to ensure that the potential surrogate mother is appropriately informed and has not been coerced into serving as a surrogate.' The AFS suggested the surrogate be interviewed separately by a physician to make sure she has not been adversely influenced. 'This may be especially important when the surrogate is a friend or relative of the couple and may have been subjected to personal pressures.'[2]

It has been suggested that a paid surrogate is less likely to be honest about her personal habits and medical questions. Would she, for example, reveal that there was mental illness in her family? This problem could be avoided if surrogacy was between friends and relatives.

## COMMERCIALISM—HOW IMPORTANT IS THE MONEY?

Kim Cotton says the £6,500 she was paid was not the main reason she became a surrogate. The 28-year-old mother of two desperately wanted to finish renovating the family's two-storey house in North London and saw surrogacy as a way of paying for that.

> I didn't go ahead just for the money, although the money was extremely important at the time and I certainly wouldn't have considered doing it without any . . . For me, it wasn't a case of having a baby for money, it was more a case of wanting a way to bring in some money that would also make me feel worthwhile. And I thought having a baby for a childless couple was terrifically worthwhile.'[10]

She said the pay for nine months' work amounted to one pound an hour. 'That's less than cleaners get paid.'

Joanne Stuart from Ohio who was paid $12,000 in 1985 commented, 'Everyone says we're making a lot of money, but my paperboy makes more.' Her friend Alicia Long added, 'When you first hear about this programme, the money is really appetising. But then you get involved and the money becomes the last thing on your mind. I'm giving them nine months of my life, so I don't feel guilty about what I'm doing.'[12] Another American surrogate said, 'No amount of money is going to motivate you really honestly to want to do this.'

Elizabeth Kane said she had not met a potential surrogate who was concerned about the money. However, in a 1981 study Michigan psychiatrist Philip Parker, who interviews potential surrogates for Noel Keane, said money was at least one factor to about 80 per cent of the women who applied to be surrogates.[18]

Some people believe surrogates should be paid an agreed fee, while others call for a total ban on commercial surrogacy. Only 17 per cent of Australians believe the surrogate should receive no payment, according to the 1986 surrogacy survey which also found 40 per cent agreed that the surrogate should be paid a fee plus her medical expenses and 34 per cent said the surrogate should be paid medical expenses only. More men than women were in favour of commercial surrogacy. The majority of people said non-profit agencies, such as welfare organisations or a branch of a hospital, should be allowed to make surrogacy arrangements. About 40 per cent said surrogates and the couples should be allowed to make their own arrangements.[39]

While many people find it immoral that a surrogate should be paid for her services, there are strong arguments in favour of payment. It seems only fair that a surrogate be compensated, at least in part, for the physical and emotional inconvenience, discomfort and risks of the pregnancy. It is generally accepted that sperm donors be given some remuneration, and surrogacy involves substantially more time, energy and commitment than sperm donation. Infertile couples are aware that they will have to pay for the services that provide them with a baby—whether it is an adoption agency, an IVF scientist or an AI physician—and it is logical that they also pay for the services of a surrogate.

One of the main criticisms is that surrogacy amounts to 'baby selling.' However, there is a major difference between this and surrogacy payment: the arrangements are made before conception, so the couple is paying for a service, not a child because that child does not exist. As the AFS said in its 1986 guidelines: 'The payment to a surrogate is made in exchange for her help in creating a child, not in exchange for possession of the child.' The Society also pointed out that the surrogate is less likely than an already pregnant woman to be coerced into giving up a child whom she wishes to keep.[2] However, it must be remembered that generally surrogacy contracts, especially in the US, only allow the surrogate full payment if she delivers a live baby, less if it is stillborn, and less again if she has a miscarriage—which could be interpreted as the couple paying for a product, not just a service.

People who oppose paid surrogacy argue that payment for people, such as slaves, is prohibited. However, as Carl Wood of Melbourne points out, payment for slaves has been associated with maltreatment, both emotional and physical, but a surrogate baby is going into a secure, loving environment. Wood believes surrogates should be paid and says, 'The event involves one year of the surrogate's life and a fee of at least $50,000 would be commensurate with the task.'[36]

While not condemning payments to surrogates, the AFS expressed reservations about brokers, especially when they serve both the couple and the surrogate or receive a finder's fee for surrogates, which the Society said, 'may have a conflict of interest or may exploit the parties'.[2]

The Victorian Government in Australia was one of the first in the world to ban commercial surrogacy. Under legislation passed in November 1984 and proclaimed in August 1986 it is illegal to pay surrogates or advertise for surrogates, and all surrogacy contracts are deemed void. Anyone engaging in commercial surrogacy in Victoria faces two years' imprisonment. The British Government took a similar stand and in July 1985 prohibited anyone receiving payment from surrogacy, negotiating surrogacy arrangements and advertising. The penalty is a £2,000 fine.

Noel Keane is the most up-front surrogate organiser in the US and is referred to as 'Mr Big of the baby trade' but he says, 'It's not totally business. If I didn't feel good about what I was doing I would get the hell out.' To him surrogacy is not baby selling and a surrogate contract is payment for services, not the baby. Asked whether he was selling babies, Keane replied, 'To whom are we selling the child? To its father? Then the answer is yes [but] he has a constitutional legal right to have his child with or without a fee.'[6]

This was a ruling of the Kentucky Supreme Court which in 1986 held that payment by a biological father to a surrogate who had been inseminated with his sperm did not violate baby-selling laws. The court said that because the biological father already had a legal relationship with the child, agreements between him and the surrogate could not be regarded as adoption. The court also suggested that surrogacy 'is not biologically different from the reverse situation where the husband is infertile and the wife conceives by artificial insemination'.[51] No one regards AI as baby selling.

Lori Andrews says baby selling is prohibited partly because children need a secure family life and should not have to worry that they will be sold and wrenched from their existing family, and payment to a pregnant woman for adoption of her unborn child is also prohibited in several states because it could put undue coercion on a woman in an emotionally vulnerable state. However, in paid surrogacy, 'the resulting child is never in a state of insecurity. From the moment of birth he or she is under the care of the individual or couple who contracted for him or her. There is no psychological stress to that child or any other existing child that he or she may some day be sold.'[43]

## SHOULD SURROGACY BE ALLOWED FOR SINGLE WOMEN, MEN AND TRANSSEXUALS?

When Joseph Orbi of Los Angeles decided that he wanted a baby but not a wife, he engaged a surrogate mother and opened a new controversy in surrogacy. Should single men be allowed to have a child by a surrogate? Orbi said he did not think there was anything morally wrong with single men using surrogacy. 'I don't think it's fair to get married only for the purpose of having children.' His surrogate was a 30-year-old divorced mother of two from Michigan who was artificially inseminated in October 1980. Orbi had stipulated that he wanted a boy and asked a genetics laboratory to separate the male and female sperm, a technique that in theory increases the chances of producing male babies.

By February 1981, several single women, bachelors and transsexuals in the US had arranged for surrogate mothers to bear a child for them. According to one newspaper report they included single professional women who did not want to take time off from their careers to have a child, single men who had no interest in marriage but wanted a child that was biologically theirs, and married transsexuals whose sex change did not give them ovaries or a womb.

Noel Keane found a loophole in the law that allowed surrogates to be paid by single men without infringing adoption laws that prohibited payment for a baby in Michigan and began promoting it in 1980. A man does not have to adopt his own child if he does not have a wife, no adoption is necessary so payment to a surrogate would not be seen as payment for adoption. In an advertisement in 1980 one of Keane's single men offered to pay a surrogate $10,000. 'It's a giant, giant thing,' Keane said at the time, 'I see it not only as a service to infertile couples, but as a way for a man to have a child. A woman can go out and have a child any time she wants. Now a man can too.'[52]

## THE LAST WORD

Deliberately creating a child for an infertile couple can hardly be considered immoral when it brings such joy to the couple, puts a child in a loving family and the surrogate (and possibly her family) benefit emotionally.

As long as 'mother' and 'father' are legally defined there should be no room for dispute—and once everyone knows what the rules are, they can accept them or choose not to become involved. The legalities of surrogacy—and any disputes involving sperm, egg and embryo donation—could be solved with three simple rules:

- Egg, sperm and embryo donors have no rights or responsibility to a child born after they surrender their gametes.
- The woman who gives birth should be the legal mother until she signs the adoption papers, surrendering her parental rights.
- The legal father should be the mother's husband, or *de facto* husband, provided he agreed with the arrangement—and no arrangement should go ahead without his consent. If the mother is single, and the sperm provider is known he should be the father, but if the sperm provider is anonymous the father is 'unknown'.

This does not mean gamete donation or surrogacy should be discouraged—to the contrary, I think they are commendable acts—but there need to be rules so that everyone can act within those boundaries.

With these three rules, the child is not left without parents if neither party wants him (for example, if he is born handicapped), and if both parties want him there is a legal definition of who his parents are. If surrogates and prospective parents are thoroughly screened both would be judged as suitable parents and both would have the interests of the child at heart, so that in the rare cases where there is a dispute, either party would be capable of offering the child a good upbringing. A surrogacy dispute should not be regarded as being the same as a standard custody dispute because the child is usually conceived without any physical contact with the sperm provider, who is often unknown to the mother and has nothing to do with the pregnancy or birth. She is cared for by her husband for nine months which should give him more rights and responsibilities than the sperm donor.

In the rare cases where a surrogate refuses to surrender her parental rights and the couple are not given custody of the child they helped create, they must write the experience off as a bad debt and find another surrogate. This may sound harsh but the success rate with surrogacy is extraordinarily high compared with all other forms of assisted reproduction—even donor insemination is only 60 per cent successful after six attempts. Several attempts at IVF cost about the same as most surrogacy arrangements, yet the success rate is only 17 per cent per attempt. The emotional let-down after a failed AI or IVF attempt may not be as great as the loss of expecting to receive a surrogate baby, but the prospective couple must go into the arrangement fully aware that (on current data) there is about a one in 200 chance that the surrogate may change her mind.

The surrender of rights to gametes may sound unfair for a couple who want to have a child that is genetically at least half theirs. However, that is the accepted practice when sperm, eggs and embryos are donated to another infertile couple, so logically it should also apply in surrogacy. Again, this would only come into effect in the unusual event that the surrogate does not surrender parental rights, in which case the couple could find another surrogate. It would be a heartbreaking prospect, but not impossible. And it is not as if they have no more genetic material available for a second surrogate—a woman can be made to produce half a dozen eggs every month and a man can produce 400 million sperm several times a day if he wants to.

Surrogacy has received a disproportionate amount of publicity compared with other social/family issues. One in three marriages in the US ends in divorce, yet only three out of the first 600 surrogacy cases came before the courts when a surrogate wanted to keep her child. If the amount of time, energy and resources spent on debating surrogacy were directed to preventing existing families splitting up, there would be a lot more happier children in the world.

# 8

# IVF: THE TEST-TUBE BABY TECHNIQUE

'Teams involved in the test-tube baby programmes do not make life; they assist in creation by using God's materials—the sperm cells of the husband, the egg of the wife, and the brains and skills of scientists, doctors and many others.' *Carl Wood and Ann Westmore in* Test-tube Conception.

Of all the new reproductive technologies, *in vitro fertilisation*, or IVF, is the most controversial. It is an expensive treatment, it only benefits a small proportion of infertile people and the success rate is low. Yet IVF and its associated practices have caused more ethical, legal and political debate than probably any other medical treatment in modern history.

*In vitro* fertilisation is Latin for 'in glass' fertilisation and despite jokes and cartoons, does not mean growing babies in test-tubes. The process involves placing an egg and a drop of sperm in a special culture solution in a test-tube or laboratory dish. In 70–75 per cent of cases one sperm successfully fertilises the egg to produce an embryo, which is then transferred one to two days later to the woman's womb where it should grow as in a normal pregnancy. However, less than 10 per cent of these embryos lead to an established pregnancy and only 7 per cent to a live baby. The difference between fertilisation rate and babies born is one of the main barriers to successful IVF. The problem may be that the culture is not yet quite right, the embryos are transferred at the wrong time, they may be damaged in transfer, the woman's uterus may not be ready to receive them—these are all areas for future research, but they may require controversial embryo experiments.

The IVF procedure is basically the same worldwide,

although some centres vary the types and amounts of drugs, the instruments and the timing of certain steps. An estimated 7,000–10,000 IVF babies have been born since the first 10 years ago, and about 550 IVF clinics have been set up worldwide, including more than 300 in Western Europe, 200 in the US and Canada, 14 in Australia, 17 in Asia, 10 in the Middle East and at least 13 in South America and Africa.

IVF used to be known as the 'end of the line' treatment, to be used only when all others had failed, but some centres are now considering IVF before more conventional treatments, such as tubal surgery, especially if the woman is in her late thirties and time is running out.

Despite the popular belief that IVF will bring the much-wanted baby when all other treatments have failed, it is only suitable for certain couples and on average only one in five couples who start on a programme end up with a baby. IVF is not possible if the woman does not have a healthy uterus and a cervix that can be traversed by a catheter. Unless she uses a donated egg, IVF is also excluded for any woman who does not have accessible ovaries that respond to stimulation from drugs. If her partner has no sperm or a low sperm count, donor sperm can be used. Although the partner is included as much as possible, the medical procedure centres almost exclusively around the woman.

Despite predictions of supermarket-style test-tube babies and initial fear that IVF would result in monsters, the technique is now well accepted, at least in Western countries, although some of the more recent variations, such as embryo freezing, have raised new ethical issues. However, a large proportion of the community will not approve IVF on religious grounds. They believe it is tampering with nature and that infertile couples should accept their childlessness.

## WHAT IVF TREATMENT INVOLVES

After infertility has been diagnosed and other treatments tried unsuccessfully, the would-be parents are generally referred to an IVF centre. Their doctor and/or a nurse co-ordinator explains the procedure, the side effects and the risks. Generally, a couple is not accepted to the programme unless it is a stable relationship and both partners understand the procedure, accept the risks and are emotionally strong enough to go through with it. Before they are accepted several tests are carried out including sperm, cervical mucus and hormone analysis. The woman undergoes a laparoscopy to assess the state of her reproductive organs (as explained in Chapter 4). The cervix and uterus are also measured. If donor sperm is to be used, it is important that both partners accept the social and psychological implications.

Some large IVF centres have long waiting lists, sometimes with as many as 2,000 couples, which could mean a wait of up to 18 months; others have no waiting lists. Because of the high proportion of subfertility and unexplained infertility, it is not uncommon for women to become pregnant while they are waiting for IVF.

The woman starts the treatment with a course of drugs to stimulate her ovaries to produce more than the usual one egg, known as *superovulation*. The drugs are usually the same fertility drugs used for women with ovulation failure (see Chapter 4), taken daily as tablets or injection. From then on she may have to give daily blood or urine samples at the IVF clinic to determine hormone levels, followed by an ultrasound, to see whether or not the ovaries are responding correctly. From these measurements the doctors can estimate when she will ovulate, and just before ovulation, about eight to 12 days after she started on the drugs, the eggs, or *oocytes*, are aspirated, or sucked, from the ovaries, in what is known as '*egg collection*'. Timing is crucial. If the eggs are removed too early they may be too immature and will not develop or fertilise. And if collection is left too late, the eggs will have already left the fluid sacs, the follicles, on the surface of the ovaries, in which case they cannot be collected.

The egg collection is done in an operating room by a gynaecologist with a nurse, a laboratory technician and an anaesthetist, using either a laparoscope or ultrasound. As with diagnosis (see p. 49), the laparoscope is inserted through the belly-button and a smaller hole is made for a pair of thin forceps, used to move the ovaries into position and hold them steady. A third incision is made for a hollow teflon-coated needle, through which the eggs are sucked. A more recent and now widely used alternative method of removing eggs is transvaginal ultrasound oocyte aspiration, which means 'through the vagina ultrasound-guided egg collection'. The needle can be inserted through the vagina then punctured through the vaginal wall to the ovaries. An ultrasound machine focused on the abdomen gives a picture on a TV-like screen that the doctor watches while he manoeuvres the instrument into place. This has the advantage that it can be done under local anaesthetic, whereas laparoscopy requires a general anaesthetic.

With its razor-sharp tip, the hollow needle punctures the follicle and by operating a small foot pump, the doctor can gently suck the follicular fluid into test-tubes which are immediately taken to the laboratory and examined under a microscope to see if there is an egg in the fluid. If there is, the technician usually calls out 'Egg', and the doctor moves on to the next follicle, punctures it and sucks again.

If an egg is not found in the fluid, some culture is gently pumped into the follicle and sucked out again. This flushing usually collects any immature eggs which may be still attached to the wall of the follicle and also gathers up any that may have become lodged in the needle or its rubber hose. Depending on how well the ovaries respond to superovulation the number of eggs collected varies from none up to 22 in exceptional cases, but is usually from four to six. Egg collection can take anywhere from 20 to 60 minutes, depending on the number of eggs, the skill of the collector and the techniques used.

Each egg, which is surrounded by *cumulus* cells, is then washed in culture to remove follicular fluid and red blood cells. (An egg cannot be seen with the naked eye, but the egg and its cumulus cells are just visible.) Each egg is placed in a test-tube or a flat glass or plastic culture dish, with the culture. This precise combination of nutrients is necessary for the egg, and later the embryo, to culture, or grow. The eggs are then placed in a laboratory incubator that is kept at body temperature (37 degrees Celsius) for between six and 18 hours. They are then ready to be mixed with sperm in a process known as *insemination* (not to be confused with artificial insemination).

About two hours before insemination, semen is collected from the man. The sperm is separated in the centrifuge 'spin-dryer' then checked for count and motility, just as it is for a semen analysis and artificial insemination (see p. 29). Most IVF laboratories also do a swim-up procedure to collect the highest concentration of good sperm which are then put, with culture, in the incubator for one to two hours. Then 10,000–100,000 of the best sperm are added to each egg in the test-tubes, which are then returned to the incubator. In the culture the sperm undergo a process known as *capacitation*. This is when the sperm sheds the coat that surrounds its head, which is necessary before it can penetrate the egg to fertilise it.

Only one sperm will fertilise an egg. By thrashing its tail and emitting special substances that dissolve the outer shell of the egg, the *zona pellucida*, it penetrates the egg and fertilisation begins to take place. After about 18 hours the *nucleus*, or core, of the sperm can be seen alongside the nucleus of the egg, inside a single cell, and this is known as a *pronuclei* egg. About 22 hours after insemination the two nuclei fuse into one and this new cell is technically known as a *zygote*, *conceptus*, or *pre-embryo*, but is commonly called an *embryo*.

About six hours later, the embryo divides in half, forming two identical cells each with a nucleus, just as it does in normal conception, and the result is known as a two-cell embryo. After about another 12 hours each of the two cells divides in half, creating four identical cells or a four-cell embryo, 48 hours after insemination. Between 14 and 20 hours later an eight-cell embryo appears. If the embryo were allowed to go on in the culture, it would continue to divide, into 16, 32 then 64 cells then into a mass of cells known as a *blastocyst*. The cells do not always divide simultaneously, so at any one time there may be any number of cells.

Not all the eggs are healthy but if the quality of the culture is good and laboratory staff are experienced, about seven to eight out of every 10 eggs are fertilised and usually five to six of them develop into embryos healthy enough to be transferred to the womb of the mother-to-be. However, generally a maximum of three or four are transferred and the rest frozen (as discussed in Chapter 10). Most laboratories prefer to transfer two-cell or four-cell embryos, others wait until the eight-cell stage.

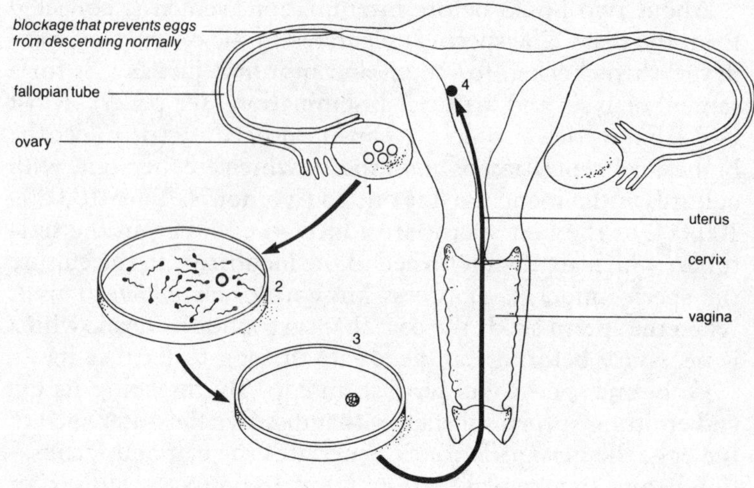


4 IVF AND EMBRYO TRANSFER
1, several eggs are surgically removed from the ovaries before ovulation; 2, each egg is placed in a laboratory dish and about 50,000 sperm are added; 3, fertilisation takes place in the dish and the embryo begins dividing; 4, about two days later embryos are transferred from the dish to the uterus

When they are ready to be transferred, the embryos are removed from the culture, washed in fresh culture and, with a tiny drop of culture, one, two, three or perhaps four embryos are gently sucked into an ultra-thin plastic *catheter* which is then passed through the woman's vagina into the uterus. She may have stayed in hospital after the egg collection or gone home and come back for the transfer one to two days later. The transfer only takes about 10 minutes and can be done in an outpatient room near the laboratory. Whether the husband is present depends on the couple and the IVF team. The woman is usually asked to remain lying down for 10–15 minutes after the transfer. Sometimes she may be given the natural hormone progesterone which is believed by some physicians to increase the chances of the embryos implanting.

The woman will be told to 'take it easy' for a few days and avoid sex and overseas travel for about two weeks, although some experts say this is unnecessary. Doctors do not know a great deal about how a patient should behave after a transfer, but they do know that the plug of cervical mucus which usually closes the uterus after natural fertilisation is removed when the catheter containing the embryo is passed through the cervix, and there is a risk that the embryo may pass out through the cervix and be lost immediately after transfer.

The woman goes home the day of the transfer, or the next, and returns a week later for a blood test to see if she is pregnant. She has a 10 per cent chance if one embryo is transferred, 20 per cent if there are two embryos and 30 per cent with three or more. As the majority of women do not become pregnant after their first attempt at IVF, the couple have to decide if and when they will try again. Most clinics allow four attempts before questioning whether they should continue, taking into account the emotional strain on the couple and the fact that other couples may be waiting for treatment; others have no limit. Some also limit the age of the woman, and 40 is the most common cut-off point.

In most cases the wife's eggs and husband's sperm are used and until recently all embryos were transferred within two to three days. This is known as 'the simple case'. The use of donor eggs and donor sperm, how many embryos should be transferred and what happens to 'extra' embryos will be discussed later.

There are certain risks involved with IVF. One of the stimulation drugs, clomiphene, can cause headaches, blurred vision, a rash or abdominal pain in some women. And too much follicle stimulating hormone (FSH) can overstimulate the ovaries, resulting in cysts forming on them, which can be painful and cause bleeding. There have been suggestions that superovulation may encourage breast cancer, but this is questionable.

There are small risks associated with laparoscopy and hysterosalpingogram (HSG), as discussed in Chapter 4. Unless the woman is tested for vaginal or cervical infections, any bacteria present may be carried into the uterus with the catheter. And unless care is taken in the laboratory, the catheter itself may transmit an infection into the uterus. A uterine infection would jeopardise the embryo's survival.

The success rate of IVF varies enormously between centres

and depends on the definition of 'success rate'. Each egg collected has a 70–75 per cent chance of being fertilised and each embryo that is transferred has a 10 per cent chance of producing a pregnancy. About 17 per cent of women become pregnant with each attempt but only 15 per cent have a live birth and it usually takes several attempts before they have a baby. Some couples have gone through as many as nine attempts. Generally only 25 per cent of couples on a programme have an IVF baby. 10 to 25 per cent become pregnant spontaneously without treatment, and after repeated failures others try different treatments, give up trying, adopt or accept their infertility. However, if couples are prepared to undergo several attempts they will be rewarded with a birth, according to Dr Wilfried Feichtinger of the Institute of Reproductive Endocrinology and IVF, Vienna, who reported to the Fertility Society of Australia in 1987 that 99 per cent of couples who stay on the programme have a baby after eight attempts.[1]

## HOW IT ALL STARTED

According to records, fertilisation of mammalian eggs outside the body was first attempted in 1878 by the Viennese embryologist S. L. Schenk using rabbits and guinea pigs. Exactly 100 years later the first laboratory-conceived human was born—Louise Brown in England on 25 July 1978. Although Patrick Steptoe and Robert Edwards were responsible for the first IVF baby, there had been many attempts before them and much of the groundwork had been laid by other biologists and gynaecologists from the Soviet Union, Denmark, China, Japan, Italy, Britain, America and Australia.

Many people prematurely claimed to have succeeded with IVF, and there were several hoaxes. In the 1960s a major US news magazine ran a front-page photo of what it said was the first human egg fertilised in the laboratory. It was in fact an air bubble. When Patrick Steptoe announced his success at a London conference, another British gynaecologist jumped to his feet and told the distinguished gathering that three babies had already been born, which was later found to be untrue. And in October 1978, a few months after the birth of Louise Brown, doctors in Calcutta announced they had delivered the world's second IVF baby that had spent 53 days in 'deep freeze' as an embryo—all of which was a figment of someone's imagination.

*Gregory Pincus,* the American later credited with developing the contraceptive Pill, was one of the first to make a major contribution to IVF. Laboratory fertilisation of rat and mouse eggs was attempted in 1912 but the first reports of success with rabbits came from Pincus and colleagues in 1930. Although records are sparse, he was probably the first to attempt IVF with human eggs.

*John Rock,* who was later responsible for the first trials of the Pill, reported in 1944 that he had fertilised human eggs in his Boston laboratory. Four years later, he gave details of two eggs that developed to the two-cell stage and one to three cells. His basic technique for preparing the egg and sperm is remarkably similar to the methods used in IVF today. Rock reported triumphantly, 'The youngest human embryo was conceived, not naturally in the fallopian tube of its mother, but in a watch glass in the laboratory, the last of almost 800 eggs, all recovered from ovarian tissue, of which 138 were exposed to human spermatozoa. After a pencil drawing was made of this two-cell individual, it was regrettably lost. A few days later another egg similarly treated began its personal existence by changing from a single cell into a two-cell autonomous structure.' It is interesting that Rock described his two-cell structure as an 'individual' with a 'personal existence'.[2] Whether an early embryo is an individual is a controversial point today and will be discussed in Chapter 12.

Rock made a major contribution with his studies of the early embryo in the womb and his understanding of implantation. But today, his pioneering work is not considered true IVF. It is more likely his two- and three-cell eggs had been stimulated to divide without being fertilised by a sperm, a process known as *parthenogenesis.*

*M.C. Chang,* the Chinese-born American who was responsible for early scientific work on the Pill, has contributed enormously to the understanding of sperm, ova, implantation, embryo development and IVF. Chang is now 80 and still principal scientist at the Worcester Foundation for Experimental Biology in Massachusetts where he started in 1945 in a laboratory converted from an old kitchen. His first task was to produce 'fatherless rabbits', but his attempts at parthenogenesis failed.

However, he was more successful at fertilising rabbit eggs *in vitro*. He became the first in the world to produce IVF animals and the scientific world celebrated the birth of the baby rabbits in 1959, which laid the foundation for human IVF. Chang also discovered that sperm have to undergo capacitation before they can fertilise an egg and he established that embryos have to be transferred to the uterus at a certain time—both essential aspects of IVF today.

*Daniele Petrucci* was probably the most controversial figure to claim he had achieved human IVF. As an anaesthetist he was interested in burns and as a surgeon he had access to ovaries, and in 1957 he set out to grow embryonic tissue as a new treatment for burns patients. He removed eggs when women had a hysterectomy that was scheduled to coincide with ovulation, as Robert Edwards did less than 10 years later, then he attempted to fertilise them in his laboratory in Bologna. He claimed to have succeeded in 1958. Petrucci made films of what he said were IVF embryos, and in 1959 showed one to a medical conference in Rome where he won an award for his cinemaphotography, but not for an important achievement in medicine! Today, sceptics say that as a master of photography he could have rigged what he filmed.

Petrucci switched from tissue for burns patients to babies for infertile women and in 1961 he was ready to transfer his first 'embryo' to a patient at a Catholic hospital when the nuns called the head of the Catholic Church in Bologna. The disappointed woman was discharged and Petrucci was stopped from further work. He received a lot of criticism from the media, the medical profession and the Church, and after a heart attack in 1963 abandoned his project. He died in 1973. Petrucci's work has never been accepted by the medical profession, partly because he published his work in a popular Italian news magazine rather than a medical journal, and because he associated with Russian rather than British or American scientists.

*Landrum B. Shettles's* early work, at New York's Columbia University in the 1950s had focused on the human egg and its interaction with sperm. Later, he announced he had fertilised a human egg *in vitro* and in 1973 he was ready to attempt his first pregnancy. But Shettles's laboratory cultures were destroyed by the head of obstetrics at the university hospital who deliberately exposed and contaminated the culture when he heard of Shettles's plan. He ordered the experiment be terminated and forbade any further IVF research. Shettles is now retired but continues an active interest in medicine.

*Patrick Steptoe and Robert Edwards* go down in the history books as the pioneers of IVF and the first to produce a test-tube baby. When their now world-famous partnership began in 1968 Edwards was a young, ambitious scientist, and Steptoe was considerably older, a well-established gynaecologist at a local hospital in the north of England.

Steptoe became one of the most respected gynaecologists in Britain, and indeed the world. Three of the main advances for diagnosing and treating infertility are the laparoscope, fertility drugs and IVF, and Steptoe, who died in 1988, helped pioneer two of them. After working as a gynaecologist in London for several years, he moved in 1951 to Oldham in Lancashire where he established a practice, a reputation and a comfortable lifestyle. Seventeen years later he met Edwards.

Edwards is an expert in genetics, embryology and immunology who cut his academic teeth studying the sex lives of mice in the 'Mouse House' at the Institute for Animal Genetics in Edinburgh in 1953.

For his early attempts at human IVF, he persuaded a gynaecologist to allow him to have pieces of ovarian tissue that were being removed from women undergoing surgery at London's Edgware Hospital. Edwards removed eggs from the ovaries and in 1965 made his first attempt at fertilising them in the laboratory. He added his own semen to three eggs maturing in culture and the next morning found one sperm had passed through the zona of one egg, although it was not complete fertilisation because the nuclei of the sperm and egg had not fused.

At Johns Hopkins University in Baltimore, Edwards and gynaecologists Howard and Georgeanna Jones made cultures that were similar to the female genital tract by adding small pieces of uterine tissue and fallopian tubes; they tried collecting living sperm from the cervix after women had intercourse; they placed eggs in the tubes of rabbits then injected human sperm; and they tried the same with rhesus monkeys—but they could not achieve IVF.

Later Edwards developed a chamber containing sperm which was inserted into the wombs of volunteers. The aim was to expose the sperm to the mucus of the uterus before attempting IVF. 'It was inserted at night and removed the next morning and I must confess I had many a sleepless night fearing the chamber would burst in the uterus, releasing the sperm with disastrous results,' he later wrote.[3]

The breakthrough came back in Cambridge where Ph.D. student Barry Bavister developed a new culture for fertilising hamster eggs. From the last piece of ovarian tissue from Edgware, Edwards and Bavister retrieved 12 eggs, placed nine in the new culture and added their own sperm. They waited in the laboratory all night, checking the culture every few hours. After 12 hours in what Edwards called 'Barry's magic culture fluid' they noticed sperm had penetrated the zona and were inside two eggs. It was March 1968 and they had just witnessed the first true human IVF.

The year before, Edwards had read an article about laparoscopy by Steptoe who was the first in the UK to use the technique. To gain experience in using the new equipment Steptoe had practised on corpses in the morgue during his lunch hour. 'How macabre, inside the mortuary when others were all eating their lunch!' he said later.[4] After four months and 30 corpses, he moved to live bodies and revolutionised diagnosis of the female pelvis.

Edwards saw that the laparoscope could be used to retrieve eggs or pieces of ovary, rather than relying on his sporadic supply from Edgware. On April Fools' Day 1968, just after his success with Bavister, he moved his equipment to Oldham and spent the next 10 years regularly travelling the 560 km

(350 mile) round trip from Cambridge. As he said, it took more than a quarter of a million miles before they reached their goal. Steptoe retrieved eggs which Edwards and his assistant Jean Purdy attempted to fertilise in their cramped laboratory. At one point they tried taking the eggs back to the Cambridge laboratory—strapped to Edwards's body to keep them warm.

In his book *A Matter of Life* Edwards described his feeling the first time he saw multi-celled embryos through a microscope.

> It was an unbelievable sight; four beautiful human blastocysts, round spheres of cells filled with fluid, with their two types of cells, one thin and delicate, on the surface of each sphere, destined to turn into the placenta, the other a beautiful disc of foetal cells, the beginning of a foetus as it started its journey towards life. I knew that instant that we had reached our goal. This was the moment when everything became possible, when my hopes and endeavours over a long time began to take on their final realisation. We had a feeling of being greatly privileged to see these human blastocysts. We had been able to witness some of the wonderful events of embryology, events occurring every day many times over within many women. We had merely observed them, nothing more; someone else designed them.[5]

After they began fertilising eggs successfully they attempted to transfer the early embryos to the oviducts of rabbits, a technique used in the livestock industry to carry prized sheep and cow embryos from country to country—in the 1960s an entire flock of prize sheep had been flown from Europe to the US as embryos in the oviduct of one rabbit, and later transferred to surrogate ewes. Steptoe was reportedly seen driving through town in his Mercedes with a rabbit in the seat next to him! But the attempt at Oldham failed.

As Edwards and Purdy developed a steady stream of fertilised eggs, they methodically squashed them on laboratory slides to study the nuclei and chromosomes for any sign of abnormalities—they had to be sure their laboratory-created embryos would not lead to deformed children. They analysed more than 100 before they decided it was safe to transfer an embryo to a patient.

But it was another four years before Steptoe, Edwards and Purdy achieved their first pregnancy. Unfortunately it was an ectopic, and the second pregnancy ended in a spontaneous abortion. It was 25 July 1978 before the world's first IVF baby Louise Brown was born, at Oldham and District Hospital, to parents John and Lesley, who were reportedly paid £300,000 for the story by the *Daily Mirror* group of newspapers.

Steptoe and Edwards's second baby, the world's first IVF boy, Alistair Montgomery, was born in Glasgow on 13 January 1979. The IVF pioneers achieved two other pregnancies, but one ended in a miscarriage at 20 weeks and the embryo in the other was found to have a chromosome abnormality. After more than 10 years' work and six pregnancies, IVF had produced two babies, but there were no more from the Steptoe-Edwards team for another three years.

Steptoe was 65 the year Louise Brown was born and had to retire from Oldham, a government hospital. Although he continued private consulting and operating, the IVF programme came to a halt while the pioneers searched for a new site. In 1980 their IVF programme was re-established at a magnificent old manor house at Bourn, a small village near Cambridge, where Edwards had been appointed Professor of Human Reproduction.

The Bourn Hall Clinic is now one of the leading infertility clinics in the world and attracts hundreds of infertile couples from Europe and the Middle East and countries where IVF is not yet established, including many from Turkey and India. In January 1988, Bourn Hall celebrated its 1,000th IVF birth.

Jean Purdy died of malignant melanoma, at the age of 39, soon after they moved to Bourn, and Steptoe died, also of cancer, in March 1988, aged 74, the day before he was to receive a CBE from the Queen for his services to the medical profession and almost 20 years to the day since he teamed up with Edwards.

*Carl Wood* was troubled by the large number of women in Australia with tubal infertility, and in the late 1960s tried several techniques to overcome the problem. He transplanted the healthy tube of one woman to a woman with diseased tubes, then developed an artificial tube, a silastic bag which he sewed into one woman. Both procedures were technically successful but dangerous to repeat so he turned his attention to IVF. His interest in IVF had been sparked by Neil Moore, a reproductive biologist who had been flushing a large number of embryos from sheep, culturing them in the laboratory then transferring them to surrogate sheep, sometimes transported in rabbit oviducts. Moore suggested IVF and embryo transfer could be done in humans.

In 1970, Wood, who was founding Professor of Obstetrics and Gynaecology at Monash University, Melbourne, set up an IVF team at the affiliated Queen Victoria Medical Centre with gynaecologist John Leeton and reproductive biologist Alex Lopata. Soon after Ian Johnston, head of the Reproductive Biology Unit at the nearby Royal Women's Hospital, began a collaborative study.

Lopata started transferring embryos in 1973 and one of the first patients developed a pregnancy in the same year, but hormone measurements indicated it disappeared after a few days. Nevertheless, Wood, Lopata and Leeton had achieved the world's first IVF pregnancy several years before Steptoe and Edwards.

As with the British pair, a pregnancy at the Royal Women's also ended in tears when the baby was lost at 19 weeks. The mother contracted an infection after amniocentesis—a one in 4,000 chance!—and aborted a perfectly normal boy. The Australian pioneers also lost their third pregnancy. They then attempted to place eggs and embryos in the tubes and eggs in the uterus, but without success. Finally, in 1979, one of Johnston and Lopata's patients, Linda Reed, developed an ongoing pregnancy and the world's third IVF baby Candice Reed was born at Royal Women's on 23 June 1980, almost two years after Louise Brown.

Animal embryologist Alan Trounson joined the team in 1977 after working with Neil Moore transferring sheep embryos and later with embryologist Bob Moore at Cambridge University freezing cattle embryos. The first sperm bank in Melbourne owes its existence to Trounson's experience with embryo freezing, which later led him to produce the world's first baby from a frozen-thawed embryo.

The two Melbourne teams had an open-house policy and helped train many of the world's top IVF workers including Jacques Testart and René Frydman from France, Siegfried Trotnow and Tatiana Kniewald from West Germany, Richard Marrs from the US and members of the Jones team in Virginia.

IVF took on a new dimension when the Monash team exported its IVF technology to the US and in 1985–6 set up what has become one of the most successful programmes in that country. The commercial company, IVF Australia, is now operating at two hospitals, at Port Chester in New York State and Birmingham, Alabama, run on Monash know-how and staffed partly by ex-Monash workers. The idea was instigated by Vicki Baldwin, an American businesswoman who was working in Melbourne when she became an IVF patient at Monash and saw the potential for a business venture.

Although Steptoe and Edwards pioneered IVF and continued to contribute to the field, the Melbourne teams have been responsible for many of the innovations and improvements in the technique and, despite restrictive legislation by the Victorian Government, Monash and Royal Women's are still regarded as world leaders in IVF. Much of the credit goes to Carl Wood's leadership and innovative approach and Trounson's scientific ability.

In the early days Australia's main contribution was to establish the success of the technique, prove that superovulation is needed, establish quality control for the culture, develop a new culture, train others, show that it was safe to transfer up to four embryos, and more recently to develop the technique of freezing embryos, establish a donor egg programme and invent micro-injection, as discussed in the next chapters.

*Howard and Georgeanna Jones* are undoubtedly the founders and leaders of IVF in the US. Now aged 77 and 75 respectively, they are two of the most eminent gynaecologists in the US, Dr Howard as an expert in genetics and gynaecological surgery, especially tubal repair, and Dr Georgeanna in female reproductive endocrinology. After retiring from Johns Hopkins University in Baltimore, where Dr Howard was professor and deputy chairman of obstetrics and gynaecology and his wife a professor in the department, they turned their energies to setting up the Jones Institute for Reproductive Medicine in Norfolk, Virginia. Theirs has been one of the most successful marriage partnerships in medicine.

Together with Mason Andrews, Gary Hodgen and Zev Rosenwaks they have built one of the largest and most respected reproductive centres in the world with a staff of more than 120. A tapestry made by two patients hangs in a waiting room and says: 'The Jones Institute produces nothing but good eggs'.

The IVF centre was the brainchild of Andrews, Head of Obstetrics and Gynaecology at the Eastern Virginia Medical School in Norfolk. There were no IVF centres in the US and the only formal attempt to start one had been made by Pierre Soupart of Tennessee, whose application to the National Institutes of Health for a grant in 1973 was rejected. Two years later the Department of Health, Education and Welfare placed a blanket ban on the use of federal funds for any IVF work, which is still in force.

Setting up an IVF centre in the US in the late 1970s presented very different problems than confronted Steptoe and Edwards and the Melbourne teams. The British and Australians were starting from scratch, and hardly anyone knew they were doing the work until they had results. The Andrews group were starting a decade later and using an existing technique.

The Joneses arrived in Virginia the day Louise Brown was born and when a local reporter asked whether it could be done in Virginia Dr Howard thought it a rather trivial question, but replied that it would be possible, with financial help. The next day's headline was, 'Doctor says all it takes is money', and the Joneses found themselves on the road to a new career in IVF.

The announcement in 1978 that an IVF centre was to be set up in Norfolk, Virginia created controversy across the country. Some people warned it would lead to genetic manipulation, cloning and surrogacy. Others objected to discarding excess eggs which was said to be equal to abortion. Religious leaders said on one hand that it was an opportunity 'to participate in God's continuing creation'; and on the other that the project was a 'misuse of priorities and could lead to things like cloning, sperm banks and experiments on foetuses'. A Right to Life spokesman described IVF as a 'drive to manufacture human beings to specification'. Others warned that rules must be set and the rights of the foetus, the rights of the parents, allocation of resources and the legal problems must be considered before the project began.

After much controversy and a public hearing, the State Health Commissioner finally gave permission for the centre to operate and the Joneses started their IVF programme in March 1980, by which time more than 2,500 couples had applied for treatment. America's first IVF baby, Elizabeth Carr, was born on 28 December 1981. 'The smallest Carr made in the USA,' as Dr Georgeanna says.

Israel and Sweden were also leaders in setting up IVF centres, followed by France, Germany and Austria. Recently, teams in Singapore and Japan have also made valuable contributions. Of the hundreds of IVF centres now in operation, some of the most prominent include those run by Richard Marrs, Ricardo Asch, Alan Berkley and Alan DeCherney in the US; Joseph Schenker and Shlomo Mashiach in Israel; Lars Hamberger in Sweden; Jean Cohen, René Frydman and Jacques Testart in France; Siegfried Trotnow, Lieselotte Mettler (one of the few women) and Klaus Diedrich in Germany; Wilfred Feichtinger and Peter Kemeter in Austria; André van Steirteghem and Paul Devroey in Belgium; Pier Crosignani in Italy; Pedro Barri in Spain and Shan Ratnam in Singapore.

## ABNORMALITIES AND OTHER WORRIES

Initially, one of the biggest fears—in the minds of the public and the medical profession alike—was that IVF might produce children with abnormalities, or 'monsters'. Although Robert Edwards and Jean Purdy examined more than 100 embryos to see if there were any chromosome abnormalities before they transferred the first embryo to a patient, they could not be completely sure their efforts were foolproof until the first IVF baby was born. Even then it only proved that that child looked normal. It would take several thousand births before anyone could say with certainty that IVF children have no increased risk of abnormalities. Early, small studies had suggested there was no increased risk, but the turning point came at the 5th World Congress on IVF in Norfolk, Virginia, in April 1987, when two comprehensive reports were presented by Professor Jean Cohen from France and Professor Doug Saunders of Australia. They also revealed findings on several other points that people involved in IVF had been concerned about: ectopic pregnancies, miscarriages and multiple pregnancies.

Cohen, director of the Centre for Infertility at Hôpital de Sèvres and Clinique Marignan in Paris, collected figures for 1,235 pregnancies at 55 IVF centres in Europe, North America, Australia, Asia and Israel and found no increased incidence of abnormalities. However, his survey showed that IVF produced higher rates of spontaneous abortion, ectopic pregnancy and multiple pregnancies. He found 5.2 per cent of IVF pregnancies were ectopic, which means IVF women are five times more likely to have an ectopic than those in the general population, but he said this was probably because a high proportion of IVF women have damaged or blocked tubes. He found most ectopics occurred in women who had one tube open, and the other either blocked or removed. Some people in IVF had speculated that the increase might be linked to the drugs used in superovulation but Cohen's study found no evidence of that.[6]

However, he said the chances of spontaneous abortion in IVF were more than double the normal rate—25 per cent compared with 8–12 per cent in the general population. Cohen believes the increase in ectopics and abortions is related to the age and condition of the women, many of whom are in their late thirties and have been infertile with damaged tubes or uteri for many years. However, the incidence of spontaneous abortion increases with age in all women and is 50 per cent in those over the age of 40.

Multiple pregnancies (twins, triplets, quads etc.), have an increased risk of spontaneous abortion and a higher premature birth rate, with babies being born smaller than the average.

Cohen found multiple pregnancies are more likely in IVF because of the practice of transferring more than one embryo to the womb. However, single IVF babies are no smaller than their naturally conceived brothers and sisters.

Cohen's study also found IVF women were 10 per cent more likely to have a premature delivery, and the chances were double if the woman had had an elective abortion before the IVF pregnancy. He believes the 10 per cent increase is possible because IVF women are older than the average at the time of pregnancy.

Both the French and Australian studies disproved the popular belief that IVF produces more boys than girls. One of the curiosities of IVF in the early days was a disproportion of the sexes—there were considerably more boys born than girls.

Australia was the first (and, at the time of writing, is the only) country to have a register of all IVF pregnancies and births, known as the Australian Register. It is run by the National Perinatal Statistics Unit at Sydney University and was set up in 1983 because of concern that IVF may result in increased abnormalities. Doug Saunders, director of the Human Reproduction Unit at Royal North Shore Hospital, Sydney, presented figures on the first 1,445 pregnancies in Australia and came to almost exactly the same conclusion as Cohen: IVF has a 5.3 per cent ectopic pregnancy rate (compared with 1.1 in the average population), and a 25 per cent spontaneous abortion rate which increases with age and is 44 per cent for women over 40.[7]

Figures presented by Dr Paul Lancaster, director of the Statistics Unit, in November 1987 show an increase in spina bifida and transposition (a heart defect) in IVF babies. It is the first time these two defects have been linked to IVF and he says there is no explanation. A study of more than 2,500 IVF pregnancies and 1,700 births found the rate of spina bifida among IVF babies was five times higher than the Australian average (six cases per 1,000 live births, compared with 1.2 per 1,000) and the incidence of transposition was 6.5 times higher (4 per 1,000, compared with 0.6 per 1,000).[8]

Another study by Saunders, also presented at the Norfolk conference, proved the chances of an IVF baby being stillborn or dying in the first 28 days after birth (the perinatal mortality rate) is exactly the same as for non-IVF babies in a matched control group. It was an important study as it was the first controlled study on IVF outcomes. Saunders was concerned about the large number of multiple pregnancies in IVF and wanted to compare IVF pregnancies to those in similar women—those with unexplained infertility who became pregnant while waiting for IVF treatment. At the time North Shore had about 2,500 couples on its IVF waiting list and 100 who became pregnant spontaneously while waiting for treatment made up the control group. They were the same age, had been infertile for several years and had similar fertility problems to the women who became pregnant on the IVF programme. He then compared these to figures for pregnancies in the general population.

He found IVF women were more likely to have a premature delivery than those on the waiting list and three times more likely than the average woman. About 18 per cent of single IVF babies were born under 37 weeks and 12 per cent of those on the waiting list, compared with the national average of 6 per cent. There was no difference in the proportion of boy and girl babies, and the ratio of natural deliveries and Caesarean section deliveries were the same.[9] Both Saunders and Lancaster emphasised how important it is that IVF patients be counselled, especially about the higher risks of multiple pregnancies.

## THE NEED FOR COUNSELLING

IVF patients not only have to endure a low success rate that often results in emotional turmoil, but the procedure itself produces stress. On top of that many patients suffer confusion and shame because they are seeking a treatment that has caused political, religious and legal controversy, and in some cases is not accepted in their own country. As one Greek physician, Haris Massouras, said, 'There is a great deal of superstition against IVF in Greece.' There are very few medical procedures that require a patient to have repeat treatments and at some point all IVF couples ask themselves, is it worth it?

Vanessa, who went to a private IVF clinic in West Germany and gave up after three attempts, echoes the feelings of many patients: 'You are sitting about in the waiting room with a full bladder and it comes to nothing. You have to get up straight away and try again. If you want a baby very much you do anything but you have to have a very stable marriage because it takes a fair amount of strain.'

Californian psychologist Linda Applegarth, herself an IVF patient, specialises in counselling infertile couples considering IVF:

> Before entering the IVF programme most of us have had to face the many physical and emotional problems associated with chronic infertility. The decision to attempt IVF is usually a very difficult one. The IVF process requires a significant commitment of time, money and physical and emotional energy [and] the chances of a viable pregnancy are low. Yet, not to pursue IVF means that we must face the painful possibility of never having a biological child. As long as IVF is held out as a medical possibility, it is quite difficult not to consider it as the answer to our many years of waiting, hoping and praying. It is not surprising that many couples find themselves in an emotional bind.[10]

She says these stresses can sometimes lead to marital distress, feelings of alienation from friends and family, overwhelming anxiety and heartbreaking disillusion, as well as feelings of personal failure, guilt and inadequacy. Added to this is the considerable cost of IVF.

In a study of 'The influence of IVF on the sex life of couples', Massouras, who runs an IVF clinic in Athens, reported to the 1987 World Congress for Sexology that several of the women on the IVF programme complained of a frigidity problem that they had never faced before.[11]

Texas psychologist Patricia Mahlstedt says the cumulative effect of diagnosis and treatment can lead to physical illness. 'A physically and emotionally healthy person enters the treatment process and, in no time, finds her/himself taking medication, having surgery and becoming depressed.' She quotes one man as saying, 'With all the medications and surgeries, I began to think of myself as a "sick" person.'[12]

The impersonal, clinical aspect is particularly hard for some IVF patients to accept, especially when babymaking should be an intimate, emotional act. But as one IVF woman in Philadelphia said: 'After nine years, if we could not laugh, we would be in trouble.' And this is how she, rather nervously, laughed her way through a five-minute embryo transfer. First she (and her husband) looked at their embryos under a microscope: 'No wonder our parents never told us how they make babies.' Getting on to the bed: 'I was never any good at hurdles . . . I knew I should have shaved my legs.' The doctor laughed: 'We were never in the romance business. It's not like in the movies.' After the transfer was complete he turned to me and said: 'This is a team effort,' to which she replied: 'Gang banging!'

In a joint presentation to the 1987 Conference for IVF Nurse Co-ordinators, Applegarth and Mahlstedt described how IVF patients feel out of control, suffer damaged egos, have feelings of extreme helplessness and many feel they are ill-equipped to cope.

> They have asked for help so often that they have begun to feel uncomfortably dependent on the time, patience, expertise and guidance of medical personnel. The couples are often lost in a maze of failed attempts to conceive, multiple diagnoses, raised and dashed hopes, painful surgeries, marital stress and the numerous losses. IVF couples have been in a state of chronic crisis. They are asked to talk about intimate, highly personal aspects of their lives in clinical settings with total strangers. They have taken their temperatures religiously; consented to uncomfortable, embarrassing and painful examinations and procedures; and agreed to try again when these things failed. They have listened to various and sometimes conflicting opinions concerning diagnosis and treatment.[13]

Even when the procedure is successful, the new parents may experience additional strain after the birth because of the great interest of friends and relatives. In *Test-tube Conception* Carl Wood and Ann Westmore quote one father as saying: 'It seemed that many people came just to see whether the baby had a glass bottom.'[14]

Relaxation at certain times during treatment is essential. Some women do yoga or meditation. Wood suggests relaxation classes. Robert Winston in London suggests couples get out of their domestic environment more often, have weekends away, short holidays or even walks together in a park.

Much of the stress and disruption to private and professional life can be reduced with careful and considerate counselling. It is one of the most important parts of an IVF programme, yet it is often overlooked, or taken lightly.

Psychiatrist Lorraine Dunnerstein of the University of Melbourne told the 12th World Congress on Fertility and Sterility in Singapore in 1986 that IVF teams must give more consideration to the patient's emotional wellbeing. IVF, she said, is often the end of 'a very long road littered with failure and disappointment' that can be magnified by the long waiting times, and unless counselling is available 'failure could trigger a crisis in their lives'. She believes psychiatrists, psychologists and social workers should become part of IVF teams and help draw up a management plan for each couple. They should see any patients if there is concern about their motivation for pregnancy, stability of the marriage or their ability to be parents.[15]

Linda Applegarth says it is important that both partners agree with the procedure and have thought it through. They must consider how the financial sacrifice will affect their lifestyle and how they will cope with a failure, particularly how they will cope with telling friends and relatives. She suggests designating a friend or family member as a 'reporter'.

Mahlstedt and Applegarth told the nurses' conference that the main reasons for pre-treatment stress are lack of information about the medical aspects of IVF and concern about logistics, success rates, insurance coverage and medical risks—all of which can be alleviated if the clinic provides information on the medical, emotional, financial and logistical aspects of IVF.

Concerns have been expressed that some clinics are not providing sufficient counselling, if any, to cover these practical and emotional problems. Mahlstedt and Applegarth talk of 'inconsistent communication, poor patient education and inadequate co-ordination'. They quote a 1986 study of patients at an IVF centre in the US in which a quarter of the patients did not answer when asked how they would cope with the stresses of the procedure. Some said they would cope by 'keeping the faith', 'living one day at a time' or 'hoping for the best'. The psychologists said, 'Their understanding of the stresses involved must be broadened beyond the fear of failure, and they must be given concrete suggestions for handling these stresses.'[13]

Patients most often comment that the stress of the treatment is more than they expected, that they were not given enough information, even though they may have spent more than two hours with a counsellor or nurse co-ordinator. And there have been complaints that some physicians do not explain to the couple what they are doing. However, because of their anxiety patients often do not absorb the information given. 'You can tell patients, give them printed material, hold "information nights", show slides, etc, etc, and they still say they had not been told anything,' said Ian Johnston, who has been treating IVF patients for more than 20 years.

Some experts believe the counselling procedure should also be a screening process. This example from the Pennsylvania University study shows how easily a couple can pass through medical screening without a problem being identified:

> Mr and Mrs Z completed all medical screening and presented themselves to the medical team as well-educated, successful, and positive about proceeding with treatment. However, as the counsellor explored their feelings about pregnancy, Mrs Z suddenly blurted out that she had agreed with her husband to 'sit, smile, look pretty and go along with what he says'. Further probing revealed she had deep-seated fears about pregnancy and motherhood and was sterilized many years earlier, before marriage because of her strong desire to remain childless.[16]

If this couple—accepted by the medical team as medically fit and positive about treatment—had not been referred to a counsellor they might have proceeded with IVF and brought into the world a child not wanted by its mother. It would have been at great cost to the couple emotionally (certainly the mother) and financially, when other patients, infertile or otherwise, could have benefited from medical expertise. This is not to say the couple should have been refused IVF, but once the problem was identified they could be counselled to either overcome their differences or accept their childlessness.

The British Government's Warnock Committee recommended counselling should be available to all infertile couples and donors, and involve a skilled, fully trained counsellor.[17] Some people believe counselling should not only be available but compulsory and that IVF clinics should not be issued a licence unless they have a fully qualified counsellor or psychologist on the medical team. However, as Alan Trounson points out, patients object to this attitude because they are infertile but otherwise normal people and legalising counselling would mark them as different.

IVF staff endure frustrations and failures just as often as patients do. They usually work long hours, are often on call day and night and have little routine in their social life. One nurse co-ordinator says there are three reasons she is not married and her job is one of them. Anna Ferraretti of the IVF team in Bologna, Italy, commented, 'You can't plan your social life more than three hours ahead.' Suheil Muasher of the Jones Institute told the nurse co-ordinators' conference: 'IVF constitutes a tremendous physical and emotional experience, not only for patients, but for physicians as well. IVF is a seven-day-a-week job. There is no daily "routine" for physicians: every day is different, every patient is different.'[18]

The medical staff also has to cope with a sense of loss with each failed attempt. And Volker Wetzel, who with his wife, Eva, and Franz Detter runs a private IVF programme in Karlsruhe, West Germany, says they continuously question what they are doing and why. 'There is a lot of stress because most of the patients will not get pregnant and you have to cope with that as well as them. And if you have no pregnancies you always ask yourself what are you doing wrong, you question *all* your work, and it is very stressing.'

Many of the younger IVF nurses and doctors also question whether they will be able to have children themselves one day. Mary English, from Pennsylvania Hospital, Philadelphia, is one of them: 'You begin to believe that no one can conceive normally. You do worry because you see what these people go through and you see how many have unexplained infertility.'

IVF is stressful to all concerned, but at least part of the stress can be alleviated with proper counselling.

# 9
# BEYOND IVF

'We do not have to be "donors" and "hosts" and "surrogates" – we can be mothers and fathers and aunts and uncles.' *Barbara Katz Rothman, Professor of Sociology, New York.*

IVF is no longer just a case of mixing husband's sperm with wife's egg in a test-tube and transferring the resultant embryo to the wife's uterus. New practices of combining gametes, donors, surrogates and recipients are becoming more common, and the emotional and legal consequences are staggering. An infertile couple could ask a surrogate to receive an embryo derived from the sperm of another man and egg of another woman and carry the child for them. In theory, such a child would have six 'parents'. And these new combinations are no longer limited to married couples: some clinics now offer babymaking to unmarried couples, single women and lesbian women. Strictly speaking, IVF means *in glass* fertilisation but in a broader sense it has also come to include other forms of assisted reproduction such as *GIFT* and embryo flushing.

## GIFT—GAMETE INTRAFALLOPIAN TRANSFER

In August 1984, Ricardo Asch at the University of Texas, San Antonio, tried a new technique for a Scottish woman who was desperate to have a child after several IVF attempts had failed. He placed sperm and unfertilised eggs directly into her fallopian tubes where they would be fertilised and move down to the womb, as in nature. It had been attempted before but this time Asch was successful and the woman gave birth to twins in May 1985. Since then, GIFT has proved to be the most successful babymaking technique since IVF. In the two years since the first birth, GIFT had been adopted by more than 100 units and more than 1,000 babies had been born. It is now responsible for two to three pregnancies a day worldwide.

GIFT or *gamete intrafallopian transfer*, literally means gametes (sperm and eggs) are transferred into the fallopian tubes. But this can only be done if the woman has at least one healthy tube. If the husband's sperm count is poor, donor sperm can be used. Because of the high proportion of women with blocked or damaged tubes, up to 60 per cent of women and 25 per cent of men on an IVF programme are not suitable for GIFT.

Sperm are collected and prepared as in IVF and the eggs collected by laparoscopy. The laboratory technician then carefully loads the sperm and eggs, with culture, into an ultra-thin catheter which is passed back down the laparoscope to one of the fallopian tubes. It is gently passed about 1 centimetre into the open end of the tube, near the ovaries. When it is in position the doctor presses the plunge at the end of the catheter and the gametes are deposited in that tube. If the other tube is healthy, he then moves the laparoscope to that and deposits the second half of the culture. If for religious reasons the couple want the gametes separated until they are inside the body, the technician can place a tiny air bubble in the catheter between the culture with the eggs and the culture with the sperm.

GIFT is more convenient for women in that the collection and transfer of eggs is done at the same time, whereas in IVF she must return to the hospital one or two days later for the embryo transfer. However, with GIFT she must undergo general anaesthesia for the laparoscopy, and GIFT has the disadvantage that the eggs are replaced while the woman is still feeling the effects of the stimulation drugs and the anaesthetic. Both GIFT and IVF can now be done on an outpatient basis. Depending on the methods used, there is not much difference in the cost — although GIFT cuts down on laboratory fertilisation and incubation, this saving is outweighed by the need for an anaesthetist and an operating theatre.

In good hands, 30–33 per cent of GIFT patients have a detectable pregnancy after one attempt, compared with 15–18 per cent of IVF patients, although it must be remembered these are different techniques for women with different problems.[1] Professor Ian Johnston of the Royal Women's Hospital, Melbourne, was one of the first to use GIFT after Asch and believes it has a much higher ongoing pregnancy rate than IVF for women with endometriosis and couples with unexplained infertility.[2] Professor Ian Craft of Humana Wellington Hospital, London, was one of the early pioneers of GIFT in Britain and up to October 1987 his team had performed the operation more than 1,600 times, with a pregnancy rate of 38 per cent per operation, and 45 per cent when donor sperm was used.[3]

The multiple pregnancy, ectopic and miscarriage rates are all about the same as with IVF worldwide. Initially, one of the main fears was that GIFT would result in more ectopic pregnancies—that the fertilised eggs would not move down to the uterus, but stay in the tubes and implant there. Asch, who now runs a large reproductive programme at the University of California, Irvine, collected figures from more than 60 centres and found no increase in ectopics compared with IVF.

Some IVF experts, including Asch, have suggested GIFT will become more popular than IVF; others, such as Patrick Steptoe, have said it will soon be surpassed by similar techniques including one where the eggs are placed in the back of the uterus, or into the tubes from below. Steptoe believed GIFT has scientific limitations. 'The process of fertilisation passes out of the control of the scientist and it doesn't contribute any knowledge to the factors which cause failure of fertilisation, because people do not have the opportunity to study the embryos.' And figures compiled by Paul Lancaster for the Australian IVF register show the perinatal mortality rate (stillbirths and deaths in the first 28 days) for GIFT is five times higher than the Australian average—the IVF rate is three times higher.[4]

To some people GIFT is more attractive than IVF ethically, because fertilisation takes place in the body, not the laboratory. While the Catholic Church opposes IVF, the Vatican hospital in Rome, the Gemelli, is using GIFT for its infertile patients who cannot have a child in any other way. Asch was approached by representatives from the Vatican in 1985 and asked to visit them in Rome to discuss GIFT. They suggested it was a good way of overcoming the ethical problems of IVF and left Asch with the impression they had been waiting for something like this.

However, the Vatican's argument against IVF, as stated in the *Instruction* released in March 1987, has nothing to do with fertilisation taking place outside the body, it is because lovemaking and babymaking are separated in the process.[5] If the Vatican allows GIFT, which also separates sex and procreation, it should logically allow IVF on the same argument.

There are several variations on IVF and GIFT and they give an indication of how fast new reproductive technologies are being developed.

*PROST* stands for pronucleus stage transfer and is also known as ZIFT or zygote intrafallopian transfer, because it is similar to GIFT. A *zygote* is a fertilised egg before it starts to divide. The technique involves transferring an egg to the tubes before its nucleus has fused with the nucleus of the sperm, so it is not yet a proper embryo, although scientists can see that the sperm has penetrated the zona. The technique was developed by Dr John Yovich of the University of Western Australia and Dr Paul Devroey of Vrije University, Brussels, and the first PROST baby was born in Perth, WA, in March 1987. By November Yovich had delivered 20 babies and had 40 ongoing pregnancies.

This technique is only suitable for women with at least one open tube. Yovich reported recently that the pregnancy rate per attempt was 31 per cent with PROST, compared with 15–18 per cent with IVF and 30–33 per cent with GIFT. The PROST pregnancy rate goes up to 45 per cent when three eggs are transferred, with a 6 per cent chance of all three developing into a triplet pregnancy. The proportion of spontaneous abortions and ectopic pregnancies was lower than with IVF.[6] Yovich believes there are two main reasons for the higher pregnancy rate and the better quality of the pregnancies: there may be a benefit from the natural environment provided by the tubes, and exposure to laboratory conditions is much less than with IVF. He suggests GIFT should be the first choice for women with at least one healthy tube, followed by PROST, and IVF should only be used where both tubes are irreversibly blocked.

*TEST* or tubal embryo stage transfer, was also developed by Yovich. Embryos are transferred to the fallopian tubes, rather than the uterus as in standard IVF. The technique had been tried in the early days of IVF without success. However, Yovich succeeded in 1986 and the first TEST baby was born in Perth in September 1987. Like GIFT and PROST, this method can only be used for women with at least one healthy tube. The difference between PROST and TEST is minimal—with the former, pronuclei stage embryos are transferred to the tubes the day after eggs are added to sperm in the laboratory, and with TEST fully formed embryos are transferred two or three days after.

*DIP* is another alternative provided at least one tube is open. Eggs and sperm are placed in the Pouch of Douglas, an area between the uterus and rectum, in a procedure known as direct intra-peritoneal insemination. Originally gynaecologists thought eggs occasionally fell into the pouch naturally and were picked up by the fimbria, the open end of the tube, but some now think this happens in almost all cases. The fimbria can even reach down and collect eggs from the opposite side of the cavity, and women have been known to become pregnant after having the left tube and right ovary removed, or vice versa. Placing eggs in the Pouch of Douglas is therefore perhaps even closer to nature than GIFT.

Eggs and sperm are collected as in GIFT and deposited in the pouch via a needle that is passed through the rear of the vagina. The gametes are then picked up by the fimbria and pass along the fallopian tubes. Fertilisation takes place in the tube, as it does naturally, and in GIFT, and the embryo then moves down to the uterus for implantation and presumably a normal pregnancy.

*POST* or peritoneal ovum and sperm transfer, is similar to DIP. The peritoneum is the interior of the abdominal cavity and the eggs and sperm are inserted into this cavity through an incision in the abdomen, under ultrasound. As with DIP they are collected by the fimbria and ideally fertilisation and pregnancy follow.

Many gynaecologists believe both DIP and POST will be successful alternatives to GIFT and will be cheaper as there is no need for laparoscopy, although POST requires ultrasound.

## EMBRYO FLUSHING OR LAVAGE

The technique of flushing an embryo from a uterus has revolutionised the livestock industry, especially for cattle breeders. A prized cow can be inseminated with sperm from a top-line bull, then the embryos flushed out and transferred to more ordinary cows who act as surrogates for the highly bred calves. The surrogate can be in the same herd or in another country 10,000 km away—the embryos can be frozen and flown there. When reproduction is left to nature, a cow can produce only one calf a year but with embryo transfer she can have 10 or more, and an estimated 100,000 cows a year in the US and Canada receive an embryo flushed from another cow. This method is known as embryo flushing, surrogate embryo transfer or *lavage* (which literally means washing out an organ, in this case the uterus).

The principle of human embryo transfer is the same, and this advertisement appeared in several community and college newspapers in Los Angeles' South Bay area in 1982:

> Help an infertile woman have a baby. Fertile women aged 20–35 willing to donate an egg. Similar to artificial insemination. No surgery required. Reasonable compensation.

It had been placed by John Buster, Professor of Obstetrics and Gynaecology and head of reproductive endocrinology at the University of California Los Angeles (UCLA), Harbour, who wanted to find women willing to undergo embryo flushing. The ad attracted almost 400 phone calls and after careful medical, genetic and psychological screening, he accepted 15 women as his first donors and the world's first lavage babies, a boy then a girl, were born in Los Angeles in January 1984.

The technique is reasonably simple, although it does have risks. A woman is artificially inseminated and five days later if one of her eggs has been fertilised, the 60–100-cell embryo is flushed from her uterus before it implants. This is done by gently pumping into the uterus fluid to gather up the embryo which is then carefully loaded into a catheter and transferred, as it is in IVF, to the uterus of the recipient, who is waiting in an adjacent room. The embryo imbeds in the second woman's hormonally prepared uterus and ideally proceeds in a normal pregnancy. This means the first woman effectively acts as a surrogate mother for five days.

Buster chose his embryo donors as healthy women in their twenties and early thirties who were psychologically stable, women who already had at least one child and did not have the genes for any genetic diseases. Generally, recipients should be women with damaged or removed fallopian tubes and those whose ovaries have been removed, ceased ovulating prematurely or never fully developed. They must have a healthy uterus and be capable of carrying a pregnancy to full term. Embryo flushing is also suitable for couples for whom AI and IVF have failed. Ideally the two women should be of the same ethnic background and have similar physical characteristics so the child looks as close as possible to the woman who gives birth. He does not have her genetic material, which comes from the woman who provided the egg, but if the sperm is provided by the infertile couple's husband, the child is genetically half his.

Instead of adopting a baby, the mother is adopting an embryo, and so is the father-to-be if donor sperm is used. It is part way between egg donation (which will be discussed on p. 213) and surrogacy, and the child has both a genetic and a gestational mother. The advantage is that the infertile woman carries the baby for nine months and gives birth, whereas in surrogacy she and her partner accept the baby after the birth and miss the experience of pregnancy. In addition, the infertile woman does not need a general anaesthetic to remove eggs, an advantage over IVF, and the embryo is only outside the body for about an hour, compared with two to three days in IVF, which is an important ethical consideration for those opposed to scientific 'tampering' or externalising embryos. It is also an important medical consideration because the longer an embryo is exposed to laboratory conditions, the less chance it has of producing a viable pregnancy.

However, there are four medical risks and because of this the procedure is banned by the National Health and Medical Research Council in Australia, and Britain's Warnock Committee recommended lavage not be allowed 'at the present time'. First, the embryo may not be flushed out and so the donor becomes pregnant. Second, the embryo may be forced into one of the fallopian tubes where it could develop into an ectopic pregnancy. There is a danger that more than one egg may be fertilised but only one embryo flushed out and the other may remain and start an unwanted pregnancy—the American Fertility Society has expressed concern about this. A fourth risk is that the recipient may have an infection passed into her uterus—from her own cervix, the instruments or the donor—and it could lead to the loss of the embryo.

There are other ethical considerations with embryo transfer. A donor could became accidentally pregnant and decide not to have an abortion. If she refused to part with a baby intended for another couple, the arguments would be the same as in the Baby M case: she has broken an agreement; the baby is genetically half hers and half the male partner's but she is the birthing mother.

Buster and his then assistant Maria Bustillo reported in 1985 that they had inseminated 10 donor women a total of 53 times and 25 embryos were flushed out, a success rate of 47 per cent. One of the donors became accidentally pregnant when the embryo was not flushed out and later spontaneously aborted. Four of the women who received embryos became pregnant. Of them, one was an ectopic, one ended in a spontaneous abortion at 13 weeks and two babies were born.

## SOME ETHICAL CONSIDERATIONS

Human embryo transfer was the brainchild of Richard Seed, a Chicago biomedical engineer who joined with Buster to develop the technique. The pair wanted to set up a network of surrogates and recipients across the US through a chain of franchises in a huge commercial venture that they estimated could benefit up to 50,000 infertile couples. They patented a catheter that Buster designed for lavage and attempted to patent the technique, but it brought an outcry from the medical profession. It is not uncommon for medical equipment and instruments to be patented but almost unheard of for a corporate company to patent a method.

The question of commercialisation of medical treatments is controversial. On the one hand, researchers who have spent many years working on a technique are entitled to some financial return, as they would be if they were in industry. Steptoe and Edwards were not paid for the extra hours, disappointments and disruption to personal life they endured in more than a decade of research developing human IVF. It is difficult to imagine the consequences if they had patented the test-tube baby technique, or if there had been a patent on laparoscopy or amniocentesis.

A patent stops anyone else using a technique without a licence, which limits its use and prevents others altering the technique, so that improvements or advance are suppressed or very slow to come into effect. IVF has undergone numerous variations and improvements in the last 10 years, which would not have been possible had it been patented. The more a technique is used and experimented with, the safer it becomes. Researchers and clinicians report their findings in medical journals and they are reviewed, questioned and criticised by their peers, a process that leads to a safer, more effective technique.

Some doctors have suggested that lavage could be used routinely for all pregnancies where there is a risk of an abnormality or genetic disease being passed to the child. The embryo could be flushed from the uterus, examined and, if all is well, returned to continue a normal pregnancy. Such a system would reduce the proportion of children born with a genetic disease. While not referring specifically to embryo flushing, but to embryo analysis in general, Mary Warnock said in *Moral Dilemmas in Modern Medicine* that such possibilities 'would certainly, by means of medical intervention, greatly reduce the number of severely handicapped families. And my personal view is that such an outcome is greatly to be desired.'[7]

Women who want to have a baby without a pregnancy could also use surrogate embryo transfer. Woman A may ask woman B to carry an embryo that has been conceived naturally with her own egg and her partner's sperm. The embryo would be transferred from A to B and after the birth she would give to the As a baby that was genetically wholly theirs, whereas in conventional surrogacy the surrogate would be inseminated with A's partner's sperm and the child would have only half their genes. However, the As need not be infertile and A could be a single woman.

This idea has already been adopted on a small scale to keep champion horses in the show ring while still breeding from them, particularly in dressage and showjumping, where a horse usually reaches its professional peak in its best reproductive years. Generally, a horse has not more than four or five foals in a lifetime and the owners of champions have to decide whether to retire them from competition and breed more champions or sacrifice offspring for more trophies.

The analogy with humans is not unrealistic. The most likely women to use such a system are athletes who do not want to give up their careers when the peak of their performance may last only a few years, or dancers and models who are worried that their body shape may not be the same after a pregnancy. A top sportswoman, for example, may not reach her peak until her early to mid-thirties and she has to decide whether to abandon her career and have children before time runs out or continue and perhaps regret her childlessness in later life.

The ability to transfer embryos from person to person and animal to animal has forced some people to consider the extreme possibility of whether human embryos may one day be transferred to other animals.

## IVF FOR SINGLES, LESBIANS AND TRANSSEXUALS

In most cases, single women and lesbian couples who want to have a baby can do so with donor sperm, either from a friend or a fertility clinic. But just as a proportion of women in the general population are infertile, so too are a proportion of single and lesbian women, and in the end they have to rely on the same fertility treatments as all other women, including IVF. If a single woman was infertile and wanted hormonal treatment or surgery for blocked tubes, generally she would not be denied treatment. But if this was unsuccessful and she needed IVF, in almost all cases she would be turned down.

Very few countries allow IVF for single and lesbian women. Many clinics around the world are bound by guidelines, laid down by medical associations or ethics committees, to treat only married or *de facto* couples. Some, such as those in Victoria, face a criminal penalty if they offer the service to anyone other than married couples. Belgium is an exception. Single and lesbian women can have both donor insemination and IVF, but not before strict psychological screening and counselling.

Why do single women and lesbian couples want IVF? Basically, for the same reason as any woman who wants a child. They may not always be the 'right' reasons by a psychologist's definition, but they are the *same* reasons. The difference is that married women do not have to prove they have the 'right' reasons. And this is where the medical and legal professions become the self-appointed protectors of 'the family', which they believe must include mother, father and child. In some cases the protector is the community, represented by committees made up of ethicists, religious leaders, politicians, social workers, physicians and lawyers. Opinion polls—the few that have been conducted—show the public believes it is right that IVF only be allowed to married or *de facto* couples.

However, Mieke Felix says single women have just as much urge for a child and provide just as much, if not more, love and care. She is 35, has never married, nor has any plans to, but she has just had an IVF baby, after six attempts. She lives in Ghent, Belgium, with her son who was born in May 1987, eight years after Mieke first tried to get pregnant to a man she had a relationship with. Five years ago a laparoscopy confirmed blocked tubes and she was preparing to apply for adoption when someone mentioned that the Vrije (Free) University in Brussels would accept single women for IVF.

After seeing the infertility counsellor, Hilda Olbrechts, she left the clinic with a new destiny.

> Suddenly in the middle of the street I started crying because I was so happy. For the first time someone said, of course you want a baby, it's normal. People cannot say you don't have a right to have a child. People had said it won't work. This was the first time someone said, you are normal.

One criticism often expressed is that IVF for single women is deliberately creating a one-parent family. 'I think I can make a combination of the two and be a father and mother,' said Felix. 'He won't have any problems growing up alone because there are other children living here and I have many close male friends.' How will she explain to her son who his father is? 'I will tell him the man who gave the sperm was a very nice man, kind and generous.'

About 20 lesbian couples on the Vrije University programme attended a reunion in mid-1987, including several who already have IVF babies. Since the first IVF baby was born to a lesbian woman in 1983, the Vrije programme has brought great hope to women who could otherwise not have a child of their own. One of them is Angele who at 40 has turned to IVF as her last chance. After five unsuccessful AI treatments, she was found to have blocked tubes. She attempted to adopt but was disallowed. At first she was very reluctant to use IVF and only reached the decision to after deep soul-searching. 'I have agonised over whether it is right to bring a child into the world in unusual circumstances. Most people don't decide to have a child, it just happens, so I have thought about it a hell of a lot more than most women.'

One of her main concerns is that the child will not have a father to identify with.

> When a father dies or parents divorce you can say, this was your father. Is it fair to bring a human being into the world when you cannot do that? There are a lot of children who have been disappointed by their fathers and I'm sure in 50 years, a lot of IVF and AI children will not know their fathers.

Her partner, Michele, has a teenage daughter who she says does not have problems with the fact that her 'parents' are two women. 'She thinks she's lucky because she's the only one with two mothers!' Angele says they both know it will be important to give her child a balanced exposure to the world. 'Michele has a terrific brother and friends who will provide a good male model. I think it's important to have a male figure around. A lot of children grow up without a man in the house but I don't see that as a problem.'

One may or may not have sympathy for single and lesbian women who want a child of their own, but what about transsexuals, men who have become women? By 1984, when IVF was still in its infancy, the Monash programme had received six requests from transsexuals wanting to have a baby by IVF. All were rejected. One of them was Estelle Croot.

Estelle was a man who knew something was different from his first school days. After working as a dancer, one of the few jobs available for transsexuals, and four years of hormone treatment, he became a woman in an operation that surgically removed the male genitalia and replaced them with the female equivalent. She is now a stunning blonde with the figure of a model. 'I suddenly realised what it was like to be a real woman. You feel it through your whole body. I looked feminine before the operation but afterwards my whole body changed.'[8]

Now she wants to have a baby of her own. 'I am a woman and like any woman I want to feel complete, I want to be fulfilled and for me that means having a baby.' She is 30 and for the last four years has been living with the man she wants to father her child. Estelle has the genitals of a woman but not a womb. She says she could have a donor egg fertilised and transferred to her abdomen where it would implant and grow. The child could be born by Caesarean section. Medically this is not impossible, but it is extremely dangerous, to the mother and the baby.

Physicians involved in IVF have discussed the medical and ethical implications of such pregnancies. At the time of Croot's request, Professor William Walters, then Chairman of the Department of Obstetrics and Gynaecology at Monash and co-ordinator of the Gender Identity Clinic at Queen Victoria Medical Centre, said, 'Ethically, it would be quite wrong to conduct such experiments in human beings when there is a 50 per cent chance of having an abnormal child.' He told Croot that the procedure would be experimental as it had never been done before, there were no animal studies, therefore it would be risky, and that personally he did not think society was ready ethically to accept it yet, so such requests could not be considered without substantial change in the views of most people in society. However, he said he could understand why transsexuals want to have a baby: 'These people have a conviction that dates from childhood that they are members of the opposite sex. It is therefore a natural corollary that they should want to have children.'[8]

## IMPROVING THE SUCCESS RATE

Doctors and scientists as well as patients have been disappointed with IVF's low success rate. Medical teams are constantly striving to find ways, however small, to improve it. Gynaecologists have fine-tuned some of the patient procedures and scientists have adjusted laboratory techniques and developed new ones. Together they have added a few per cent to the success rate. But there are so many different stages in IVF that failures could be due to any one, or all of them.

The majority of couples go through the IVF procedure without a pregnancy. 10—20 per cent of women don't even have eggs collected because their ovaries fail to respond to the stimulation drugs and in another 4–5 per cent of cases ovulation has already occurred and egg collection is too late.

Even when eggs are collected, each one only has a 5 per cent chance of producing a baby. Taking the best results, for every 100 eggs collected from the ovaries, 80 are fertilised *in vitro* but only about 70 are good enough to be transferred and of them, only 6–7 result in a pregnancy. Of these, two abort or become an ectopic pregnancy, which means only four to five end in a baby being born.

The biggest problem is not getting the eggs to fertilise in the laboratory but to implant in the uterus. It may be that the culture is not quite right, the embryos are transferred at the wrong time, they may be damaged in transfer, the uterus may not be ready to receive them or the culture surrounding the embryo is rejected by the uterus.

Research into IVF and other infertility treatments is proceeding at an extraordinary rate, far faster than the public can hope to keep abreast of—in many cases even those involved in infertility treatment cannot keep up with the latest advances going on around the world. For example, the 5th World Congress on IVF, held in Norfolk, Virginia, in April 1987, was attended by more than 1,100 physicians, scientists and researchers who between them presented almost 400 papers. Many included new techniques or instruments aimed at improving egg collection, fertilisation and implantation.

Nevertheless, in the last five years since IVF became established worldwide little, apart from GIFT, has been done to increase the chances of an infertile couple having a baby. However, sperm injection may prove to be the exception. This involves manually fertilising an egg with one, or only a few, sperm under a laboratory microscope. It requires sophisticated and expensive equipment and can only be done as part of IVF. It has been hailed as the biggest breakthrough in treating male infertility for a long time, particularly for the 20 per cent of infertile men who have sperm that are not capable of penetrating the egg's outer shell, the zona pellucida. The procedure is known as micro-manipulation and there are three different approaches: to inject a single sperm through the zona, to drill a hole through the zona and allow sperm to find their own way into the egg, or to remove the zona completely.

The first, known as micro-injection, was developed by Alan Trounson at Monash University, Melbourne, and has been taken up by several IVF centres around the world. In 1984, Trounson discovered he could take a single sperm on the end of an incredibly thin needle and, with a steady hand and powerful microscope, pass it through the zona. With his first group of six men, 75 per cent of the eggs were fertilised—with sperm that would otherwise have had no chance of producing a pregnancy. His plan to develop micro-injection for clinical use was halted when the Victorian Government passed legislation on embryo research. Trounson wanted to examine a number of embryos to see if the technique caused any changes in the chromosomes, which could result in abnormalities in babies. This would involve fertilising about 40 embryos with conventional IVF and 40 with micro-injection then examining the two groups, but the legislation prohibited creating embryos for research. However, it was amended in December 1987 to allow the micro-injection and other work to go ahead.[9]

Dr Jon Gordon at New York's Mt Sinai Medical Center developed a similar method, known as 'zona-drilling', by making an opening in the zona with acid then allowing any of ten sperm to fertilise the egg. The acid 'drills' a hole in the zona just as boiling water cuts a path through ice, leaving a hole for the sperm to make their own way into the egg. He says the technique is safe and practical and 'has great potential for treatment of infertility'.[10]

In Cambridge, Robert Edwards's team chose to remove the zona completely by chemically dissolving it, in what is known as 'zona-stripping'. The aim is to increase the chance of fertilisation, though it also increases the chances of more than one sperm fertilising the egg, known as polyspermia, in which case the resultant embryo is not viable.

Gordon's experiments showed that in animals with low sperm counts, fertilisation went from zero to 15 per cent, and in animals with normal sperm counts the fertilisation rate rose from 22 per cent to 75 per cent with micro-manipulation.[11] Micro-manipulation is also suitable for women whose eggs have an unusually tough zona.

The main fear with micro-manipulation is that it could result in abnormalities in embryos, and therefore in children, because the procedure may damage chromosomes or because the sperm already have some abnormality. When sperm are weak or have damaged heads or twisted tails it may be because they have some genetic or chromosome abnormality, which could be passed on to the child. If that is the case, rather than improving the genetic line, men with poor sperm will be producing boys, and hence men, with poor sperm—a case of negative eugenics. So far animal experiments and some using human sperm have shown micro-manipulation results in only healthy embryos, but it is too early to say what the long-term result may be.

One new tool of trade for infertility treatment is an

ultra-thin flexible cannula developed by Drs Robert Jansen and John Anderson at Royal Prince Alfred Hospital, Sydney. It is designed for placing eggs and sperm in the fallopian tubes for GIFT. It can also be used in TEST to place embryos in the tubes, which is where fertilisation takes place naturally, rather than the uterus where they are placed in conventional IVF. The cannula is guided through the vagina and uterus to the tubes under ultrasound. If eggs are collected by ultrasound and placed in the tubes with the cannula, GIFT could be done without laparoscopy, thus avoiding the adverse effects of a general anaesthetic, which would be a major comfort for patients and may improve the chances of a pregnancy.[12]

An unmistakable swing back to nature is taking IVF out of the laboratory and putting it back in the body. The first instance of this was GIFT where fertilisation takes place inside the body. Two other new 'back to nature' techniques have now been introduced, although they are not yet widely used: a vaginal tube and a new culture for growing embryos.

The French-designed vaginal tube is one of the most innovative ways of fertilising human eggs. Sperm and one to four eggs are placed, with culture, in a tube which is less than 3 centimetres long and half a centimetre across and is held in the vagina with a commercially available diaphragm. After about 48 hours the tube is removed and the eggs that have been fertilised are taken out of the tube and placed in the uterus. Rather than the eggs being fertilised in a laboratory incubator, the woman's body becomes a human incubator. Because fertilisation takes place inside the body (albeit inside a tube) it may be more ethically acceptable than conventional fertilisation in the laboratory. One reason some institutions, including the Catholic Church, object to IVF is that the embryo is at risk of damage because it is 'externalised' in the laboratory process.

The technique was invented by Dr Claude Ranoux and colleagues at the Clinique Universitaire de Port-Royal, Paris. Of the first 100 women at the IVF clinic who tried it, 20 per cent had an ongoing pregnancy, compared with a 15–17 per cent pregnancy rate for conventional IVF. Ranoux believes the higher pregnancy rate was probably because the woman's natural body movements help break down the cumulus cells which surround the egg, making it easier for sperm to reach the zona and penetrate it.[13]

Ranoux believes the vaginal tube incubator also has a major psychological advantage because it gives the woman a sense of belonging and because she is taking an active part in the fertilisation of her eggs. And there are practical advantages: 'The mother doesn't have power shortages and her temperature is fixed.' Ranoux has suggested that the majority of IVF patients will be able to use the vaginal tube, in most cases doing away with expensive and space-consuming laboratory incubators. But other IVF experts are less optimistic and further study is needed to see if these early results are reproducible.

Many scientists believe the failure in IVF is often due to poor culturing and poor implantation. The nutritional medium in which the eggs are fertilised and generally spend their first 48 hours influences the number that fertilise and the proportion that are good enough to be transferred. Cultures over the years have varied from salt water to one derived from the placentas of new-born babies, but they have since proved ineffective.

A new culture, developed jointly by Alan Trounson at Monash University and Luca Gianaroli at Bologna University, could lead to a substantial increase in the fertilisation rate. The culture is amniotic fluid and is based on the same principle that Italian surgeon Daniele Petrucci is said to have used in the early 1960s while trying to achieve IVF. Amniotic fluid surrounds the foetus in the womb and is probably the most natural substance for embryos to be cultured in. The Australian and Italian teams have shown the pregnancy rate from embryos cultured in the fluid is 25 per cent, compared with 15 per cent from the conventional culture.[14]

But growing the embryos is only half the problem. One of the biggest disappointments with IVF is the small number of embryos that implant and develop after they are transferred to the uterus. Scientists may in future be able to pick which ones are most likely to lead to a pregnancy, with two similar tests. They both rely on detecting substances given off by the embryos in the culture.

Professor David Clark of McMaster University in Hamilton, Ontario, found that one of these substances is a protein known as a 'suppressor factor'. Normally when cells or an organ are transferred from one person to another, the recipient's body rejects them as foreign, which is why kidney, heart and liver transplant patients need heavy doses of drugs that suppress the rejection. Half the material in an embryo has come from another cell—the man's sperm—and for a long time scientists were not sure why the embryo was not rejected by the woman's uterus. It now appears that the embryo produces its own suppression factor, equivalent to the drugs used in transplants. But according to Clark's research, which has since been repeated by researchers at London's Humana Hospital, only about 40 per cent of embryos produce it, and it is assumed those that do not are subsequently rejected by the uterus.[15]

An alternative way to pick the embryos most likely to develop in the uterus may be to look for a protein, known as 'platelet activating factor', or PAF. Dr Chris O'Neill, scientific director of reproduction at Syndey's Royal North Shore Hospital, found that PAF is a molecule given off by the embryo within the first few hours after fertilisation and indirectly prepares the uterus for the embryo to implant. O'Neill found only about 40 per cent of embryos produce PAF and therefore have the potential for pregnancy; the others do not produce the protein and are not considered viable. As with the suppressor factor, scientists could select just the PAF-producing embryos but O'Neill says that is not the aim: 'Our ultimate goal is to find an agent that will stimulate those other 60 per cent of embryos so they can be used too.' However, PAF's role in IVF is questioned by other researchers.[16]

The next step is to find out what happens after the embryos are transferred to the uterus, and scientists may be closer to understanding how an embryo implants itself in the womb after research by Dr Peter Rogers, scientific director of IVF at Monash. By transferring rat embryos to the eye chambers of other rats, he has proved that an embryo will implant in almost any tissue, and failure to implant is most probably the fault of the uterus and not the embryo. His research points the way for scientists to concentrate on preparing the uterus to receive the embryo. It may also help scientists to understand, and maybe prevent, ectopic pregnancies. Rogers has found that the embryo puts out a powerful reaction that causes damage to the blood vessels and massive bleeding, both of which are controlled by the uterus but not by the fallopian tubes, which is why ectopic pregnancies are so dangerous.[17]

As we have seen, 25 per cent of women do not have any eggs collected, despite stimulation treatment with drugs—about 20 per cent have their treatment cycle cancelled because their ovaries do not respond properly to the hormones and in 5 per cent of cases ovulation occurs early. Generally, the hormone levels can be adjusted for a second attempt, but a proportion of women are still not suitable for IVF.

Several recent advances have overcome this problem. One is a synthetic hormone, developed for men with prostate cancer, that is now sniffed by IVF women around the world in an attempt to improve the number and quality of eggs collected and to prevent early ovulation. It is an analog (variation) of the natural hormone *GnRH* (gonadotrophin hormone-releasing hormone) which indirectly controls ovulation. In 1982 Ian Coutts at the Royal Infirmary, Glasgow, discovered that a GnRH analog could be used to treat women with unexplained infertility and it has since been used for polycystic ovarian disease. Soon after, Dr Ric Porter, an Australian gynaecologist working with Professor Howard Jacobs and Ian Craft at the Cromwell Hospital, London, proved it could be used by IVF women. The world's first 'GnRH baby' was born in London in June 1985 and the analog is now being used at several centres around the world.

In IVF the hormone is usually given as a nasal spray which the woman takes every four hours for 13 days before egg collection. It halts the release of eggs until the doctor is ready to remove them, by which time they should be fully developed and of equal size, although in practice this does not always work.

Craft's team, which later moved to the Humana, has since introduced an analog-containing pellet which is placed under the skin with a special syringe. The drug is then slowly released into the bloodstream. It is a vast improvement for the woman as she does not have to remember to take the spray every four hours and no longer has to set her alarm in the middle of the night. Some women experience flushes while taking the drug but no effects have been noticed on the babies so far.

One of the most ardent supporters of the analog is Dr Hossam (Sam) Abdalla who used to run the IVF clinic at the Cromwell. More than 90 per cent of his patients now take it, as a spray, instead of the conventional drug clomiphene, and he says it has social and medical advantages. The most important is that none of the women have to have their treatment cycle cancelled.

The ability to delay ovulation also means doctors no longer have to do egg collections morning and night, seven days a week. Abdalla says:

> You have complete control so if the patient is ready on Sunday, you can wait till Monday. Sometimes the husband cannot come on a certain day, so now you can delay. Sometimes the follicle may be ready but the endometrium [the lining of the uterus] is not.

In his first trial, the analog gave a pregnancy rate of 28 per cent compared with 18 per cent among the women on conventional treatment with clomiphene, and women using the analog had only half as many early miscarriages as those on clomiphene. Although it has yet to be proved, Abdalla believes the analog results in better quality eggs, and therefore a better chance of pregnancy, than clomiphene. And, he says, there is no need for hospitalisation—all his women on the analog are treated as outpatients.[18]

Another benefit for the parents-to-be is 'programme cycles', a system developed by IVF expert Dr René Frydman and colleagues at the Hôpital Beclere, Paris, in 1985. The key to it is the oral contraceptive which women take to control their menstrual cycle in the month before egg collection. Although it does not improve—or reduce—the pregnancy rate, it is economical and practical because it reduces costs, allows for more efficient use of operating rooms and better scheduling of staff, and means the couple is not left wondering when their treatment will begin.

It means the couple know on exactly what day their IVF treatment will start, even if it is as far away as 14 March 1991, according to one of the first to use it, Shlomo Mashiach of Sheba School of Medicine, Tel-Hashomer, Israel. 'We have a waiting list of four years and we encourage women to take holidays during the treatment and we like to tell them when they will start so they can arrange time off, but you cannot do this based on the natural menstrual cycle. Now we can tell them exactly.' This is psychologically less stressful, and means doctors can book hospital beds and theatre time accordingly, and avoid working weekends.

Robert Edwards's team at Bourn Hall, Cambridge, recently developed a new test for indicating when a woman is about to ovulate. It is a quick, cheap and precise way of testing luteinising hormone (LH) levels in the urine that is collected every three hours by the woman. LH rises just before ovulation and a peak tells doctors when to do the egg collection.

Several do-it-yourself LH-testing kits are now on the market. One British infertility expert described them as 'an accurate method of forecasting ovulation', but one of his equally eminent colleagues called them 'expensive red herrings'.

The quality of the culture in which IVF embryos spend their first few days is vital, and most major IVF centres test the culture by growing mouse embryos in it first, a practice developed by Alan Trounson at Monash in 1980 and now used worldwide. A lot of mouse embryos are needed, not to mention a 'mouse house' and a mouse farmer. Rio Vista, a firm in Texas that specialises in cryopreservation for the livestock industry, has started supplying frozen mouse embryos—by the straw-full! The embryos are packed into laboratory straws, quick-frozen in liquid nitrogen and sent all over the world where they are quick-thawed when needed. If the mouse embryos grow in the culture, it is deemed fit for the more precious human embryos.

The fact remains that most of these new techniques are aimed at reducing time, cost and stress, and few of them directly improve the chances of an infertile couple having a baby, except for micro-manipulation which holds great promise for couples with male infertility. In the meantime the IVF world is still waiting for a major breakthrough that will lift its poor success rate.

10

# EGGS AND EMBRYOS IN IVF

When Steptoe and Edwards set out to fertilise human eggs *in vitro* they concentrated on 'the simple case', although they envisaged that one day eggs and embryos could be donated, and frozen, like sperm. Today's babymaking technology includes swapping eggs and embryos, freezing, flushing and dissecting embryos, and research on embryos that a decade ago was no more than science fiction.

## EMBRYO DONATION

Normally in IVF, the infertile couple receive an embryo that has been fertilised with the woman's egg and man's sperm, or occasionally donor sperm. They can also receive an embryo that is the union of another woman's egg and another man's sperm, in other words a donated embryo. Most IVF centres remove as many eggs from the ovaries as possible to ensure maximum fertilisation, but this often results in more embryos than the doctors want to transfer immediately—most only transfer three or four because of the risk of multiple pregnancies. Until recently all excess embryos were discarded or used for research, but now they can be frozen (see following section) and transferred later, or donated to another infertile couple.

The world's first donated embryo baby was born in Melbourne in January 1984, but the baby boy did not start out as a 'spare' embryo. A 38-year-old woman at the Monash IVF centre, Melbourne, had been infertile for 18 years and attempted artificial insemination with donor sperm 23 times without success. She had healthy ovaries but the eggs could not be collected because of other medical complications. She agreed to accept an egg from a 42-year-old woman in the same hospital who was undergoing IVF treatment and had had more collected than was needed. Because the 38-year-old woman's husband was infertile, the donated egg was fertilised in the laboratory with donor sperm.[1]

The embryo—which was not genetically hers, nor her husband's—was transferred and she became pregnant. But the foetus aborted at 10 weeks. Analysis showed it had an abnormal chromosome and Carl Wood's team was publicly and harshly criticised by Steptoe and Edwards for using an egg from a 42-year-old woman. Steptoe said they had been 'reckless' and used a veterinary rather than a medical approach.[2] The chance of a chromosome abnormality in an egg increases as a woman gets older, which is why amniocentesis is routine in most Western countries for pregnant women over 36. However, the Monash patient knew and accepted the risks before she agreed.

The Monash case highlighted two important points: the danger of using eggs from older women and the psychological effect on patients. In this case, the recipient became pregnant but the woman who donated the egg did not, which caused emotional problems. Monash, and most other centres, now only accept egg donors under 40 and the donor is not told whether or not the recipient became pregnant. All parties involved must undergo psychological evaluation and give written consent to either donate or receive an embryo.

There are four reasons for one couple to receive the embryo of a second couple: when the second couple, for ethical reasons, does not want their spare embryos frozen; when they freeze embryos but subsequently become pregnant and do not need the spare ones; when serious illness, accident or death means the second couple cannot use their frozen embryos; or when both receiving partners are infertile or one partner is infertile and the other has a genetic disease, or as in the case of Monash's first patient, the gametes (eggs or sperm) are inaccessible. It is mostly used when the receiving woman has no ovaries or non-functioning ovaries.

Medically embryo donation is no different to normal IVF treatment except that the uterus needs to be prepared to receive the embryo, so if the recipient is not ovulating naturally she has to undergo hormone treatment at the same time as the donor.

However, there are social and legal complications with embryo donation. Several countries have overcome the legal question of 'Who is the parent?' with laws that state the couple whose gametes created the embryo give up all rights and responsibilities to any resulting child and the recipients—the infertile husband and wife—become the legal parents. Californian lawyer Lawrence Nelson is concerned that the question of who owns embryos and decides their future has not yet been solved in the US: 'In this country there has never been any question of ownership of embryos or what should be done with them.'

And there are other unanswered legal questions. Could the 'parents' of an embryo do anything if their embryo is given to another couple when they asked the IVF programme to destroy it, or if they are accidentally given someone else's embryo in a case of mistaken identity?

Many people draw a parallel between embryo donation and adoption, and some refer to embryo donation as pre-natal adoption. In genetic terms, embryo donation is indeed adoption at an early stage, but there the similarity ends. A baby offered for adoption is usually an unintended baby, whereas a donor-embryo baby is deliberately conceived and only comes after searching ethical questioning, psychological examination and a conscious decision by the donors. The second major difference is that a donor-embryo baby is carried and delivered by the woman who will be its mother and the pregnancy can be experienced by her partner. And a third is that a couple find it far easier to give away a four-cell embryo than a woman does to part with a new-born baby.

It is difficult to gauge public support for embryo donation, but two surveys give some indication. When Britons were asked in a 1982 opinion poll whether they approved of embryo donation, 43 per cent said yes and 38 per cent no. The result was exactly the same when a second poll was taken two years later. An Australian poll in 1982 found 44 per cent of the public approved and 29 per cent disapproved of embryo donation.[3]

The majority of government, law and medical committees approve of embryo donation, according to LeRoy Walters, director of the Kennedy Institute for Ethics in Washington DC, who has studied 18 major reports on IVF and related practices from around the world. The two committees that disapproved were the 1984 South Australian working party on IVF and AID and the US Department of Health, Education and Welfare's advisory board which made the decision in 1979 before embryo donation was a reality. The French National Ethics Committee said embryo donation should not be allowed until laws have been established to regulate the practice, and the Benda Committee of West Germany decided in 1985 that embryo donation was acceptable but only if necessary to preserve the lives of 'spare' embryos.[3]

Britain's Warnock Committee recommended that donation of IVF embryos be accepted and that the woman who gives birth be regarded by law as the mother. It recommended that UK law should be changed to allow the birthing mother and her partner to be registered on the child's birth certificate as the parents. It also recommended that donors of gametes remain anonymous, but that the parents, and child at age 18, should have access to information about the donors' genetic health.[4]

As with donor insemination, it is possible for an infectious or genetic disease to be passed to the child from those who provide the gametes, and the American Fertility Society (AFS) suggested in its 1986 guidelines that where possible the donors (men and women) should be tested for any diseases with a genetic link such as diabetes, asthma, rheumatoid arthritis, epilepsy and hypertension. It also suggested that black donors be screened for sickle cell anaemia and Jewish donors for Tay-Sachs disease.[5]

Almost all donors want to remain anonymous to the recipients, but unless records are kept there is no way of tracing a donor when a child is born with an infectious disease or genetic defect. Generally, centres keep some records but it is not standardised practice and it is not compulsory.

Most of the organisations and committees that have considered the subject argue that laws are needed, for the reasons expressed by the Californian Medical Association: 'Legislation is necessary to clarify ownership of gametes and to assure donor anonymity. In all cases, the law must speak clearly as to the rights and responsibilities of those parties who produce gametes.'[6]

Some states and countries already have laws covering embryo donation under another name. The US, for example, has laws covering foetal research and, according to Lori Andrews of the American Bar Association, whether embryo donation is allowed legally depends on whether it technically runs foul of a particular state's foetal research law. She points out that organ transplant laws in Columbia, Michigan, Maryland, Texas and Virginia could be used to ban payment to egg donors, and laws in Columbia, Maryland and Texas could be used to ban payment to sperm donors.[7]

## EGG DONATION

Egg donation is the female equivalent of sperm donation, although in practice it is far more difficult and less frequently used. The main advantage over embryo donation is that a donated egg is usually fertilised by the partner of the woman who carries the baby, so it has half his genes, whether it is conceived in IVF or GIFT.

The Monash team began research on egg donation in 1981 and was responsible for the first donor-egg birth in November 1984. The egg had been removed from one woman, was then fertilised in the laboratory and transferred to another woman. It was a major breakthrough and now means that women whose ovaries do not function or have been removed, or those who carry the gene for an inherited disorder, such as haemophilia, can have a child they could not conceive themselves.

Women suffering from premature menopause can also benefit. According to Professor Ricardo Asch of the University of California, Irvine, about 1 per cent of women (150,000 women in the US) reach menopause early and stop producing eggs.[8] Other experts estimate the figure may be as high as 3 per cent. To the majority of women the end of menstruation does not matter, and indeed may be a blessing, but it comes as a rude shock to those who have delayed having children or want a second family. Many Western women are marrying later or starting a family later than has been the norm, often because they want to pursue a career, but a small proportion of them find they cannot have children because they no longer ovulate. The increase in divorces in Western countries has also added to the problem because many women who remarry want a second family but have stopped producing eggs, possibly in their thirties.

Asch is enthusiastic about egg donation in IVF and GIFT as a way of helping them. 'One year ago no one was able to talk about pregnancies in women with premature ovarian failure,' he told a Florence conference in May 1987. 'Until now, they could do nothing but now, for the first time, we can do something for these women.'[8] The Warnock Committee estimated one out of 20 infertile couples might benefit from egg donation.

However, there are problems. As in embryo donation, the donor and recipient have to be artificially stimulated simultaneously, so that the woman receiving the egg is at the same stage in her cycle as the donor. Then there are legal and psychological problems. Who are the legal parents? Some people suggest that egg donation should only be allowed within families, for example between sisters. Others argue that the child should have access to his genetic mother when he turns 18. Should egg donors be paid, as many sperm donors are? Asch summed up the present policy at most centres: both donor and recipient sign consent forms; both parties are anonymous; no money changes hands; and the results are not given to the donor for psychological reasons.

Two other major IVF centres followed Monash in setting up a donor-egg programme: the Jones Institute in Virginia and the Hadassah University Hospital in Jerusalem, and both reported their first pregnancies in 1985. The first at Hadassah was a 38-year-old woman from the Galilee town of Tiberias who was born without ovaries and the second was a 27-year-old Israeli who had her ovaries removed at the age of 22.[9] The Jones Institute's first was a woman in her forties who had unsuccessfully tried IVF several times, did not respond well to stimulation and requested a donor egg.[10] This gives some idea of the range of women who can benefit from the technique.

Professor Joseph Schenker of Hadassah reported to the 5th World Congress on IVF in April 1987 that 18 IVF centres were offering egg-donation programmes and between them they had achieved 69 pregnancies, including 30 births. He found the pregnancy rates were the same as with conventional IVF, although he said that ironically in the majority of cases the recipient woman became pregnant before the donor and half the women became pregnant after only one embryo was transferred. But he found the spontaneous abortion rate in recipients was higher than in traditional IVF—32 per cent compared with 25 per cent.[11]

The ideal donor is 18–35, healthy and preferably with previous proven fertility. Most are women having ovarian surgery or a hysterectomy, or they are IVF patients who have had more eggs removed than they need. Schenker found in most centres the donors were married, and all centres preferred anonymous donors, although some used friends and family members. He pointed out that egg donation has an advantage over donor insemination because both partners contribute to the birth. The father has no biological role in DI but in egg donation he provides the sperm and his wife provides nine months life-support, even though she has not contributed her genes to the egg.

Zev Rosenwaks, reproductive endocrinologist at the Jones Institute, is enthusiastic about egg donation. He pointed out that as one of his recipients was in her forties, age is not as important as the quality of the embryo. The first to use egg donation in Britain was Professor Ian Craft at the Humana Hospital, London, and the first donor-egg babies—twins—were born in early 1987 to a 46-year-old woman.

While a woman's eggs deteriorate with age, the uterus's ability to carry a pregnancy appears not to—although animal research suggests the endometrium may 'age'—so an older woman using a young woman's egg could have a child. For this reason, egg donation will be suitable for women regarded as too old to use their own eggs in IVF, and it may even be possible for 55- or 60-year-old women to have babies, although there would be risks involved.

However, many in the medical profession question the ethics of helping older women to conceive with the expensive and limited resources of IVF and GIFT. Ian Cooke, Professor of Obstetrics and Gynaecology at Sheffield University, asked, 'Should you be encouraging 40-year-old women who will be 60 when the youngsters are 20? Is that desirable? Doing it spontaneously is one thing, using substantial resources is another.' Mr Keith Edmonds, obstetrician/gynaecologist at Chelsea Women's Hospital, London, says there are medical, as well as ethical, dangers: 'Theoretically it is possible to have a baby at 60 but it may not be desirable. At 40 you have increased risks and at 50 and 60 they rise faster and faster. You may end up killing women because you give them medical complications that are fatal.'

Egg donation poses another ethical question that was raised at a recent lecture in Washington DC by Australian ethicist Peter Singer, Professor of Philosophy at Monash. He agrees that a woman who carries a serious genetic defect should be allowed to accept an egg from another woman, but asks where should the line be drawn:

> What if the defect is a very minor one? What if there is no defect at all, but the woman wants a donor egg from a friend whose intelligence or beauty she considers superior to her own? Women are already conceiving with sperm from Nobel prize-winning scientists. It is only a matter of time before eggs are offered in the same manner.[12]

Many people believe egg donation will become standard practice for infertility, just as sperm donation is, especially when egg freezing (discussed on p. 227) is established—this will have the advantage that donor and recipient cycles need not be synchronised. Today, the biggest drawback with egg donation is the lack of eggs, basically because it is not easy to provide them. Sperm can be collected by masturbation but eggs require hormonal treatment, egg collection (and therefore surgery, laparoscopy or ultrasound) and synchronisation, which is tedious and time-consuming. Some women who are having ovarian surgery are prepared to have the hormones for the benefit of giving an infertile couple the chance to have a child, but few other people, except for close friends or relatives, could be persuaded to undergo the daily hormone injections and blood testing. Although the chances are minimal, there are medical risks in superovulation and egg collection.

Carl Wood would like to see more egg donation between friends and relatives and his team was the first to achieve a birth from a donation between sisters, in mid-1986. Previously donors had been infertile women undergoing egg retrieval and this was the first case where the donor was both fertile and known to the recipient. He says this system would partly overcome the problem of lack of donors. Under the Victorian legislation, known donors are legal and the concept is generally well accepted. However, not everyone favours donation between relatives. The British Voluntary Licensing Authority strongly suggests that donations from close relatives should be avoided and donation should be completely anonymous.

Logically, the law covering donor insemination should be the same for egg donation. For this reason the Warnock Committee recommended that egg donation be accepted, provided the clinic is licensed, the donor is anonymous, no more than 10 children are born from the eggs of one donor, all parties give informed consent and the child has the right to know his genetic origin. The committee emphasised that all those involved in donations between sisters or close friends should have careful counselling and that thought must be given to how and at what stage the child be told. It also recommended there should be legislation stating that the woman who gives birth be regarded in law as the mother and that the egg donor has no rights or obligations to the child.[13]

On the whole the committees that approved embryo donation took the same stand on egg donation, except the one in South Australia which approved of egg donation but not embryo donation. The French committee did not make a decision on egg donation in its 1986 report and the Benda Committee of West Germany decided in 1985 that egg donation was acceptable in rare circumstances and only if the child can learn the identity of the donor when he/she turns 17.[3]

The relationship between egg donors and recipients was explored in a survey of donors in the Monash programme.

Although the numbers were small (34) it revealed some interesting attitudes, especially towards the child: 73 per cent of the women who donated eggs said they would not feel any connection with the child and 53 per cent said they would not mind if the child contacted them in 18 years' time, but 88 per cent of the donors said they would not want to meet the mother and 91 per cent said their identity should not be given to the recipient. Just over half said records should be destroyed except for non-identifying information about the donor. Asked had they been conceived by a donated egg, would they want to know about the donor, 59 per cent said no. All the donors said they did it to help another infertile couple and only one suggested donors should be paid. Just over 40 per cent said they did not want to know if a child was born from their egg. And 65 per cent of the donors said they would be happy for their eggs to be given to a single woman.[14]

The researchers John Leeton and Jayne Harman compared their results to similar attitudes expressed by men who had donated sperm, and found that egg donors were less interested in knowing whether a child had been born, were less enthusiastic about donating to single women and were less interested in payment than the men.

There have been few surveys on the public's attitude towards egg donation but one opinion poll conducted in Australia in 1983 found 74 per cent of the community approved of egg donation and 13 per cent disapproved.[3]

Keeping information on sperm, egg and embryo donors and recipients is essential in connecting a donor to a child if in the future the child develops medical problems that may be genetically linked. Good record keeping also ensures there are not too many pregnancies from the gametes of any one donor. In Britain, both the Warnock Committee and the Council for Science and Services recommend this be done through a central computerised register that controls the number of donations made by each donor throughout the country, using a numbering system that ensures anonymity. And the CSS points out that information on the donor and recipient may be valuable to sociologists studying the effects of assisted reproduction on the child.

## EMBRYO FREEZING

In a private room on the fourth floor of the Queen Victoria Medical Centre on the edge of Melbourne's central business district, I found a woman sitting up in bed, surrounded by flowers and cards, feeding a baby. He was an ordinary-looking baby but he had a most extraordinary beginning. As an eight-cell embryo he had spent two months in a cylinder of liquid nitrogen at –196 degrees Celsius before being 'de-frosted' and transferred to his mother's womb. I was looking at one of science's wonders, or as the front-page headlines said the next day, a 'miracle baby'. Margaret Brooks's new son, 'Frosty', was the world's second frozen-embryo baby.

He had been born amid champagne and flowers the night before, on 16 August 1984, and named John as a thank you to the obstetrician/gynaecologist who made it possible, John Leeton, medical director of the Monash/Queen Victoria IVF programme. Later Margaret Brooks, who used to wear an 'I'm a test-tube mum' T-shirt, became one of the most outspoken critics of the Victorian Government's restrictions on embryo research and was instrumental in persuading the Government to amend its controversial Infertility Act.

The world's first frozen-embryo baby, Zoe Leyland, had been born in an emergency Caesarean section a few months before John Brooks, on 28 March, at Queen Victoria. Her parents Loretta and David Leyland had been married for 12 years and spent the last seven having drugs and operations for infertility. Loretto had damaged fallopian tubes and the first IVF attempt ended in an ectopic pregnancy. During the second attempt, three embryos were transferred but did not develop and six others were frozen. One of them later became Zoe, a Greek name meaning 'gift of life'. In July, just before John was born, Steptoe and Edwards announced two of their patients were pregnant with frozen-thawed embryos and the first was born on 8 March 1985.

The Monash team started experimenting with freezing human embryos in 1980, building on Alan Trounson's experience in freezing sheep and cattle embryos. Although freezing was done almost routinely in the cattle industry it was unheard of in human reproduction and the idea was bound to promote opposition from religious and Right to Life leaders. However, the Queen Victoria ethics committee allowed Trounson and Ph.D. student Linda Mohr to begin embryo freezing, known as cryopreservation (literally, freeze-preservation) four years before Zoe Leyland was born.

Their work involved fertilising eggs as usual in IVF but instead of transferring them to the woman two or three days later, they were left another day to develop to the eight– or 12-cell stage. Each embryo was then placed in a cryoprotectant (freeze-protectant) solution, which prevented crystals forming inside the embryo during the freezing and thawing. They were then placed in special, tiny glass ampoules and lowered into a cylinder of liquid nitrogen, which looks something like a beer barrel with a lid on top. The temperature was very gradually lowered to –196 degrees Celsius, the boiling point of liquid nitrogen. When the embryos were needed, they were very slowly brought back to room temperature then transferred to the woman. A couple of these steps have been changed slightly since then but the Trounson-Mohr principle is the same today and embryo freezing is now offered at most major IVF centres.

There are several advantages in freezing embryos: spare embryos can be stored until needed, it cuts down on the number of times a woman has surgery and anaesthetics for egg collection and most IVF gynaecologists believe it is better to transfer in a later cycle when the effects of the stimulation drugs have worn off. Occasionally a transfer cannot take place immediately after egg collection, for example if the woman becomes ill, and her embryos can be frozen until she is ready to receive them.

The world's first frozen-embryo pregnancy was to an anonymous Victorian woman who, in July 1983, spontaneously aborted a healthy boy at 24 weeks. It is interesting that the embryo emerged from its freeze-thaw experience with two of its eight cells damaged, but it still successfully implanted in the womb and went on to develop in a normal pregnancy, to 24 weeks. When the foetus was examined, the abortion was found to have nothing to do with the damaged cells. Linda Mohr pointed out at the time that damage like this rarely caused problems in animal implantations. The embryo's ability to develop despite partial damage is an established fact in animal and human embryology and this is what allows scientists to remove some cells for genetic testing (see Chapter 12) without jeopardising the embryo's chances of developing in the womb later.

Today, even in the most experienced hands, 30–40 per cent of the embryos do not survive the freeze-thaw process. The survival rate has improved in the last few years and may continue to improve, but that does not placate the Right to Life movement which sees freezing as 'killing children'.

Not long after Zoe Leyland was born the Monash team were thrown into a murky ethical dilemma when a couple on the programme were both killed, leaving behind a vast estate and two frozen embryos. The multi-millionaire Californian couple, Elsa and Mario Rios, had gone to Australia in 1981 for IVF. In June, they had three eggs fertilised with donor sperm. One was transferred but was aborted 10 days later. The other two were frozen so the couple could make a second attempt later. However, three years later, in June 1984, the Rios couple were killed in a plane crash in Chile.

What was to become of the 'orphan embryos'? Whose were they? There were three possibilities: to discard them, to use them for research or to thaw and transfer them to another woman. If the last option was taken, and a child was born, would it be a Rios and inherit the Rios fortune, or would it be the child of the woman who gave birth? Although Carl Wood and Alan Trounson suggested that because the embryos were frozen in 1981 when the technique was in its infancy they were unlikely to result in a pregnancy, the public and parliament debated the fate of the 'orphan embryos', while they remained at –196 degrees.

Mario Rios's 25-year-old son from a previous marriage reportedly filed for guardianship, but Elsa Rios' mother, the only other known relative, told Californian courts she would not make a claim on the embryos. However, Australian law was found to take precedent over Californian law. In Australia, the Right to Life Organisation campaigned strongly that the embryos be transferred to another woman. About 90 women volunteered to 'adopt' the embryos and attempt a pregnancy, including half a dozen in the US. In its report on IVF embryos the Victorian Government's Waller Committee recommended that embryos should be removed from storage if their parents died without leaving instructions. Finally, in December 1987 the Victorian Government decided the Rios embryos could be anonymously given to a couple on the IVF programme. The chances of a pregnancy were said to be about 5 per cent. However, any resulting child would be born five years after the death of his mother.

The American equivalent of the Rios 'orphan embryos' were the 'hostage embryos'—complete with armed guards! Soon after physician Clarke Bundren and scientist Ed Wortham started an embryo-freezing programme at a private hospital in Tulsa, Oklahoma, Bundren was asked to leave. He refused, saying he had eight embryos in a freezer that he was responsible for, so the hospital called in guards to prevent him entering the building. Finally, after a court case, the embryos were transferred to an IVF centre run by Richard Marrs in California. The first four that he thawed resulted in two live births, and at the time of writing the other four were still frozen.

Most major IVF centres now have compulsory consent forms covering embryo, egg and sperm donation and freezing. As a typical example, patients on the Cornell University IVF programme in New York sign a declaration that after the woman's 45th birthday, unless both partners agree in writing that the embryos are to be donated or deposited, they become the property of the medical centre, in which case they would most likely be used in research. If one donor dies, the ownership and rights are passed to the surviving donor but if the survivor dies (or if they both die at the same time) ownership and rights are passed to the centre.

Cornell patients also have to sign a form stating they understand that some of the embryos may not resume normal growth when they are thawed; that there can be no guarantee of a normal pregnancy after transfer of a cryopreserved embryo; and that the viability of the embryos may be compromised by a malfunction in laboratory equipment. This is now standard at most other centres.

Until all centres insist on declaration statements it is up to the local law to decide what happens in the unlikely event of another orphaned embryo case, or the more likely situation of a couple divorcing while they have embryos frozen. If the couple have not signed a declaration, there are two arms of the law that could prevail. If an embryo is regarded as a *being*, or having the potential to be a human being, a judge may deal with it as a custody case. He may consider what would be in the best interest of the (unborn) child and award the embryo to one party or the other. If it is awarded to the man, he could have it gestated by a second wife, or in extreme cases by a surrogate. Presumably both parties want the embryo so that they can have a baby, in which case the judge could suggest that when the baby is born it be regarded as a child in a standard divorce case. Or the court could draw up a pre-birth custody arrangement.

On the other hand, the embryo could be regarded as joint *property*, which in the event of divorce is usually shared between the two parties. It may be possible to come to a property arrangement—she has the embryo and he has the house—or, as with most property settlements, it could be split down the middle—literally. Embryo splitting (as discussed in Chapter 12) is an established part of livestock reproduction and could soon be used in IVF for specific purposes. Whether divorce is one of them remains to be seen.

The Monash team has frozen more than 2,500 embryos since the freezing programme started, and has 400–450 frozen at any one time. By May 1987, 25 of the 153 registered IVF clinics in the US were freezing embryos. Like many involved in IVF, Dr Alan Berkley, director of the Cornell unit, believes it will soon be routine. 'It will be a standard part of IVF, there is no question of that, everyone is going to do it, it's just a matter of how quickly people get into it.'

Embryo freezing is now used mostly to store extra embryos, thus avoiding the need for additional egg collections. It is far less stressful on the patients and works out at about half the cost of a conventional IVF treatment. There is no need for an anaesthetist, a theatre or a bed in the recovery ward—the woman only comes into the hospital for the transfer, which takes no more than half an hour. But people who oppose freezing embryos, on the grounds that it is freezing a human being, point out that even within IVF, embryo freezing is not necessary to bring a child to an infertile couple—it merely makes the treatment easier for the woman.

However, it does increase the chances of a couple having a child, according to Alan Trounson. Studies at Monash show it adds another 3 per cent to the existing 19 per cent pregnancy rate per attempt. This could be because the rigours of freezing and thawing mean only the most viable embryos survive, and because the embryos are transferred after the woman has recovered from the effects of the stimulation drugs.[15]

Experiments with monkeys at the University of California, Irvine, show there are three times more pregnancies if the embryos are transferred in a natural cycle. Says Jose Balmaceda, assistant director of the Center for Reproductive Health:

> The level of hormones produced in superovulation act on the endometrium [the lining of the uterus] and can interfere with the possibility of implantation so you have better results if you postpone transfer until the woman is under less stress and the level of hormones has fallen. There is no doubt it is a stressful situation for the woman, she has ultrasound almost every day, blood is drawn every day, then the anaesthetic and laparoscopy, and it has to have some detrimental effect on her chances of a pregnancy. Most women are able to return to normal by the next cycle so if you could delay the transfer I think you would have better results.

He wonders whether in the future it should not be standard practice to delay transfer—although this could only happen if freezing could be improved sufficiently.

Like egg and embryo donation, public opinion is hard to gauge but one poll in Australia in 1982 found 43 per cent of population approved and 32 per cent disapproved of embryo freezing. Two polls in Britain, also in 1982, showed only 38 and 40 per cent approved and 45 and 47 per cent disapproved. Two years later approval had increased and an equal number of people (42 per cent) approved and disapproved.[16]

It is not uncommon for a couple to have one IVF baby and want a second. Some couples may still have embryos in the freezer after their first child has been born. When the couple is ready to try for the second they can have those embryos thawed and transferred. And that's how the Australian girls Rebecca and Chelsea Nicholds came to be. In August 1983, the embryo that became Rebecca was transferred to her mother's uterus and at the same time the embryo that is now Chelsea was frozen. The first girl was born in May 1984 and the following December doctors transferred the frozen embryo and Chelsea was born in September 1985, 16 months after her sister.

Many people regard the two as twins because they were conceived at the same time but, at the risk of disappointing them, it has to be pointed out that the definition of twins is two born at the same time. The media delight in talking about 'twins born 16 months apart', and one British mother, who had two 'twin' daughters born 18 months apart, was quoted as saying: 'They came into being at the same time, they lay in the deep freezer together. And they look very, very much alike. They have the same shaped face and the same upper lip. It would be difficult to tell them apart if they were the same age. They look like the same child.'[17] Unfortunately, this gives the impression that somehow IVF—or freezing—creates children that are similar, but her two children came from two independent eggs and two independent sperm, exactly the same as any two children naturally conceived 18 months apart. And like many children in a family they inherited similar traits, such as the face and lips, from their parents. If this woman had been given adequate information and counselling she should know better than to make such suggestions.

Some people have expressed fears that freezing will be used, or abused, in the future for less ethical practices. One is to skip a generation. If a couple had a daughter by IVF and left another embryo in the freezer the daughter, when she was ready to have a child, could gestate that embryo. She would then give birth to her genetic brother or sister. This is being done in mice to study the differences between several generations.

Because skipping a generation in humans is considered unethical, and for other reasons, most government and medical committees have suggested a limit on the time human embryos can be left in storage—generally five years. However, in theory embryos could remain in liquid nitrogen for hundreds of years, and perhaps 2,000 years, according to British scientist David Whittingham of the Medical Research Council.[18]

Dame Mary Warnock, in *Moral Dilemmas in Modern Medicine*, suggests that an embryo fertilised *in vitro* in 1985 could be transferred in 2085, resulting in a child being born 100 years after it was conceived. However, she has no objection to this: 'The result would emphatically be a non-cornflakes family. It strikes me personally as a curious, rather than a horrifying, possibility.'[19]

We could consider a more realistic example. A couple marry young and in their early twenties find they cannot conceive. They join an IVF programme and have several spare embryos stored for future attempts. Soon after the woman becomes seriously ill and cannot go ahead with the planned pregnancy. The couple hope she will recover and carry their much longed-for child, but finally, in their late forties, they realise she cannot carry the baby herself and ask another woman to be a surrogate. The child would be born almost a quarter of a century after it was conceived. Yet, this is not beyond the realms of reality. Psychologists might argue that a single child brought up by a couple in their late forties could experience emotional problems, but there are plenty of only children in the world, and women having babies in their late forties is not unheard of.

One of the ethical arguments against embryo freezing is the number of embryos that are lost: 30–50 per cent, depending on the centre. The pro-life movement regards embryos as human beings and the loss of embryos during freezing is seen as the deliberate death of a child. As Janet Carroll, national legislative director of Right to Life in the US said bluntly, 'Half the children are killed.'

Right to Life regards freezing embryos as 'freezing children'. Said Carroll, 'It is outrageous from our perspective because you have a frozen human being in someone's refrigerator and that there should be such a situation is awful. We have never frozen human beings before. It is a violation of human rights.' However, although we do not put humans in 'someone's refrigerator', we do anaesthetise them, cut them open, remove organs and in some cases replace these with organs from other people.

It could be argued that an embryo should not be frozen because it does not have a say in whether or not it is frozen, but nor do new-born babies and young children. Most babies would presumably say 'no' to circumcision if they were able to decide, but as they cannot, the parents make the decision for them. And parents continue to make decisions for children until they are old enough to do so themselves. In freezing embryos, the parents have made a decision for them.

Several recent technical developments in embryo freezing could improve pregnancy rates, cut costs and lead to better diagnosis of genetic disease.

In the near future, embryo biopsying and splitting (see Chapter 12) will probably be combined with freezing to detect certain genetic diseases. An embryo would be split in half, creating two equal, identical but self-contained group of cells. One would be frozen while the other is analysed for abnormalities. Although one embryo is lost, its identical twin is in the freezer. If no abnormality is found, the embryo in the freezer is thawed and transferred to the woman. If an abnormality is found, the woman can decide whether it is to be used for research or allowed to die.

Embryo flushing, or lavage, could be combined with freezing as a way around the problem of synchronising the cycles of the donor and recipient. The donor could be inseminated and five days later the embryo flushed out and frozen until the recipient is ready. It would also overcome the problem of not having enough donors in the same city as the recipients. The embryos could be lavaged, frozen and sent to recipients in other cities.

Embryo freezing is now being used in animal husbandry to help protect rare and precious species. Humans may not want to preserve rare humans, but they may in time want to send frozen embryos from one state to another if there is a shortage.

## EGG FREEZING

On 4 July 1986, twins were born at the Flinders University Medical Centre in South Australia straight into the history books, and into controversy. David and Cheryl Castleton were the world's first frozen-egg babies. Obstetrician/gynaecologist Christopher Chen, who froze the eggs and later delivered the babies, developed a method whereby an egg is removed as in standard IVF, then frozen and later thawed and fertilised. The difference between this and embryo freezing is that the egg is frozen and thawed *before* it is fertilised. Freezing eggs is a way of overcoming infertility and the ethical objections to embryo freezing.

Freezing eggs is more difficult than freezing embryos, and so far only two other IVF teams have been able to produce pregnancies—both in West Germany, where embryo freezing has been banned. Dr E.R. Siebzehnruebl at the University of Erlangen transferred frozen-thawed-fertilised eggs to 11 patients, and a healthy girl, Christine Blume, was born on 17 February 1987. Dr Klaus Diedrich of the University of Bonn reported two pregnancies in October 1986 but they were both lost in spontaneous abortions.

When the West German Board of Physicians banned embryo freezing in 1986 for ethical reasons, some centres started to develop egg freezing as an ethically acceptable alternative. However, the success rate was not good and Siebzehnruebl was concerned about a high number of miscarriages in frozen-egg patients, so his team is now only freezing pronuclei eggs (at the stage after fertilisation but before the egg and sperm nuclei have fused).

If egg freezing is to be a standard part of IVF in the future, it needs a lot more research and Britain's Warnock Committee recommended that it should not be used for patients until 'research has shown that no unacceptable risk is involved'.[20]

It is potentially more dangerous to freeze eggs than embryos. If one cell in an embryo is damaged it will generally still survive, but an egg is a single cell and any damage destroys it. In addition, scientists have to be certain that the egg's 46 chromosomes divide into two groups of 23 before it is fertilised because too few or too many chromosomes could lead to a baby being born with abnormalities.

Egg freezing has not yet gained the approval of the scientific community and several IVF experts, including Patrick Steptoe, have expressed concern that pregnancies are being attempted before proper scientific work has been carried out.

Alan Trounson warned colleagues at the World Congress on Fertility and Sterility (Singapore, October 1986) that irresponsibility in this area could jeopardise other infertility research.

Trounson did extensive experiments in freezing mice eggs which showed abnormalities could treble. At the 5th World Congress on IVF (Virginia, April 1987), he and Christopher Chen clashed publicly over the safety of egg freezing. After Chen announced the world's fourth frozen-egg baby had been born at Flinders the week before, Trounson announced that his mice experiments had produced chromosome abnormalities that resulted in limb defects in both foetuses and newborns at rates three times higher than when non-frozen eggs had been used. He later admitted it sounded like 'scientific bitching' but said he was concerned that there has been a tendency over the last few years for researchers to try to be first when it is more important to be right. (The same criticism was levelled at Wood and Trounson by Steptoe and Edwards at the beginning of their donor egg/embryo programme in 1983.)

Chen dismissed the mouse experiments, saying they were based on a different technique, and said he was confident freeze-thawing eggs does not damage chromosomes.

To prove scientifically whether freezing damages chromosomes it is necessary to do a controlled experiment by fertilising, say 40 frozen eggs and 40 fresh eggs under identical conditions then analysing the chromosomes, a process which would destroy 80 embryos but prove whether freezing was safe—the same process as proving whether micro-injection is safe. Ironically, Trounson could not do this because of the Victorian Government ban on creating embryos for research, although there were no rules to prevent him, or anyone else, transferring the embryos to patients without scientifically evaluating the technique first. He regarded this as much more unethical and unscientific than destroying two- or four-cell embryos to develop a technique which would guard against the birth of deformed children. After considerable public debate an amendment to the Victorian legislation in December 1987 gave Trounson and colleagues permission to do the experiment. However they can only use 'embryos' up to the pronuclei state—where the two nuclei fuse—usually about 22 hours after insemination.

There is an ironic twist to this story which is worth remembering when considering whether we should have regulation or legislation. Chen's team, working in South Australia, was not restrained by legislation in that state so went ahead and transferred the embryos to patients. After three babies had been born at Flinders and two more were due, he approached his ethics committee and was given permission to go ahead with the chromosome tests.

There was nothing to stop the Monash team doing the same and bringing children to infertile couples, except that Wood and Trounson would not use the technique until they had tested it scientifically, which they could not do without creating embryos which would be destroyed, and that was a criminal offence under the Victorian legislation. Different laws in different states and different countries encourage what Trounson calls 'over the border to Mexico' practices.

There are important medical and ethical advantages in freezing eggs. It offers all the same advantages as embryo freezing—less stress and less cost with fewer egg collections and maybe a higher pregnancy rate with the natural cycle—plus others. Without egg freezing there is no way for women undergoing surgery or chemotherapy to 'save' their eggs. If they have the foresight, married women can get around that by using their husband's sperm and freezing the embryos. A single woman could have her eggs fertilised with donor sperm but it would be preferable to keep the eggs until she finds the partner she wants to have children with, and she could do this by freezing her eggs before surgery and fertilising them sometime after, as men do with their sperm before chemotherapy or surgery. Similarly, the system could also be used for women working in hazardous environments, for example with chemicals or radiation. Their eggs could be removed and preserved before they start work.

As more Western women delay having children because they want to establish a career, egg freezing will allow them to do that and still have a family. Said Chen, 'A woman may want to carry on her working life but by the time she wants to start a family, in her thirties or perhaps forties, her eggs are old and there is a higher risk of chromosome abnormalities and a greater chance of losing the pregnancy. She could store her eggs in a bank and use them at later intervals.' He suggested that when she is, say 23, a woman could have eggs removed and frozen, then thawed and fertilised when she is 33 or even 43. He admits this is in the future, but not too far down the track.

Chen, who returned to Singapore in 1987 after delivering his fourth frozen-egg baby in Adelaide, sees egg freezing as having made a social as well as a scientific advance. Freezing and thawing an egg before conception is more acceptable because it is not tampering with 'life'. 'It presents a major breakthrough in IVF and it should find multiple applications in the future, but the most important thing about egg freezing is that it overcomes the horrendous legal, ethical and social consequences of freezing embryos,' he said, and quoted the Rios 'orphan embryos' as an example.

## EGG AND EMBRYO BANKS—THE ETHICS

Sperm banks have operated commercially in many countries for many years so it seems logical that egg and embryo banks will follow, now that the technology is available. The question is not just, should we allow this to happen, but how should we control it when it does come? Who, for example, should benefit from them, contribute to them and run them? Who should pay and who should be paid?

The 'banks' could be separate commercial enterprises or part of hospitals or clinics that have assisted reproduction programmes such as IVF and embryo flushing. Like sperm banks, they would be both a method of storing eggs and embryos for self-use—like depositing and withdrawing money from a financial bank—and an exchange house for donated eggs and embryos.

The main medical advantage of storing is that the embryos can be transferred in the natural cycle. It also overcomes the ethical problem of discarding excess embryos (although some people argue it creates another ethical one by freezing a potential human being). And it has psychological and organisational advantages, because the more gametes or embryos a bank has in storage, the better the chance of matching donor and recipient.

However, while it is generally regarded as acceptable for IVF centres to store gametes and embryos for infertile patients on their programme, commercialism in medicine is generally frowned on by the medical profession, and to a lesser extent by many governments, the US being one exception. It is easy for private sperm banks to operate independently of a hospital or infertility clinic, but storing eggs and embryos involves IVF, either before or after freezing, and therefore specific laboratories.

Commercial storage could be incorporated with an existing practice such as the embryo-flushing programme established by John Buster in Los Angeles. The menstrual cycle of the donor and recipient would not have to be synchronised and there would be more chance to match the two women's characteristics. And if the flushed embryos could be frozen and transported, it would overcome the problem of not enough donors in the same city as the recipient, and would reduce, or almost eliminate, the chances of a half brother and sister meeting in the school playground or worse still, marrying. If the possibility of inbreeding were reduced the surrogate donors could each offer their services more times and there would be more embryos available for infertile couples.

Flushed or donated embryos could be frozen, held in storage and later flown across the country, or the world for that matter, to an infertile woman, just as frozen sperm and embryos are in the livestock industry. Is this as ludicrous as it sounds? If freezing embryos is acceptable and sending frozen sperm from one city to another is acceptable, is it not logical to also allow frozen embryos to be sent between IVF centres? It would be cheaper and less disturbing for a woman to have the embryos sent to her nearest IVF centre where they could be transferred by a local doctor with her husband present. It would be a case of the embryos coming to her, rather than her going to Los Angeles, or wherever the embryos are being flushed or donated.

Apart from the Nobel bank, commercial sperm banks have operated for many years with minimal controversy and little or no regulation, although concern has been expressed recently about the standard of screening and the keeping of records. Guidelines on sperm banks vary between countries, and even states, but the same principles should apply to egg storage in that state or country. And, with some exceptions, guidelines for the storage and distribution of embryos should also be along the same lines as those for egg and sperm storage.

The Ontario Law Reform Commission believes that gamete banks are 'ethically and socially acceptable' as they provide a necessary service to the infertile. However, the Commission recommended they be licensed, operate under the supervision of licensed doctors and only provide gametes to licensed physicians, hospitals or approved health centres.[21]

The British Council for Social Science believes commercialism should not be allowed and suggests that the operation of sperm, egg (and presumably embryo) banks should be restricted to the National Health Service. 'Private practitioners, as well as those in the NHS, could draw on them as they draw now on blood in the national transfusion service.'[22]

The Warnock Committee said it would like to see all such banks in Britain licensed and accountable to a licensing authority. It recommended the storage of eggs and sperm be reviewed every five years, and where the donors could not be contacted, the right to use or dispose of them should pass to the storage authority. And it recommended embryos be stored for no more than 10 years, after which the bank should have the right to use or dispose of them.[23] Australia's National Health and Medical Research Council recommended 10 years and the Waller Committee recommended five years for Victoria. However, some people argue that as a couple has the right to decide what happens to their embryos in IVF they should also have the right to decide how long to leave them in storage.

After considering the question of who has the right to decide what happens to embryos and what happens when one partner dies, the Warnock Committee recommended legislation be enacted to ensure there is no right of ownership in an embryo. But, it said, a couple who have stored an embryo should be recognised as having rights to decide its use and disposal. The Committee recommended there should be a new law to allow one partner to take on the rights to the embryos if the other dies. And if both die—or divorce and cannot agree on the future of their embryos—the right should pass to the storage authority—the clinic or the embryo bank.[24]

While not suggesting legal changes, a report by the British Council for Science and Society says: 'Frozen embryos should be regarded as being under the continued control of the parents and particularly of the mother.'[25]

If the parents are invested with the right to decide the future of their embryos, does it follow that a man can still make that decision after the embryo's 'mother' has died? Few people would deny him the right to decide whether it should be used for research or disposed of. But should he be allowed to transfer the embryo to a surrogate woman who would then hand the baby over to him?

As the embryo is the union of his sperm and his deceased wife's egg, as far as genetic material is concerned, this is the same as a woman being inseminated with her deceased husband's sperm. Here, the law is open to interpretation. In France, when a woman asked to have her husband's sperm the court allowed her to, but made it clear this was not to be seen as a precedent.

The Council for Science and Society points to the British Law Commission which states that when a woman is impregnated with her deceased husband's sperm, the provider of the sperm is no longer her husband and in theory it could be regarded as a case of donor insemination and the child would not have a father. 'However, it is understood that in practice, if the mother declares that her former husband is the father, he will be registered as such.' The Council then says the status of sperm, egg and embryos should be regarded as the same.[26]

If the man did transfer the embryo to a surrogate who had a child for him, what should be put on the birth certificate—is the 'mother' the surrogate who gave birth or his dead wife who provided the egg, the genetic material? Or should it say 'donated' or 'deceased'? If the surrogate is deemed to be the mother, under certain laws her husband automatically becomes the father. Would the man then have to adopt the child that was genetically his in the first place? And what happens if he remarries; does his new wife become the child's mother? The child could have three mothers: genetic, gestational and social.

How does a child explain this to his friends in the playground? He may see them as 'my first mummy, my second mummy and my third mummy'. Or he may say 'my dead mummy, my old mummy and my new mummy', which would be no different to a child whose mother died and father remarried twice. To quote New York sociologist Barbara Katz Rothman again, 'We do not have to be "donors" and "hosts" and "surrogates"—we can be mothers and fathers and aunts and uncles.'

# 11
# INFERTILITY TREATMENT: THE ETHICS

Many people have voiced concern about the ethics that the new medical wizardry has unravelled. Under what circumstances and to whom should reproductive technologies such as IVF be allowed, they ask. Can the enormous cost of producing one baby be justified when neo-natal mortality is so high, even in developed countries? Many more babies are lost through miscarriage and ectopic pregnancies than are created by assisted reproduction, so shouldn't research concentrate on preventing these losses? Or would the money be better spent on preventing infertility? Some people accuse gynaecologists of concentrating on high-profile IVF rather than more common (and less glamorous) problems such as sexually transmitted diseases. There have been many criticisms that some infertility centres are so obsessed with getting good results, they are ignoring medical ethics; and because some scientists are in such a hurry to be the first with a new development, basic scientific research procedures are being by-passed.

Undoubtedly, IVF is the most controversial of all recent medical advances. As Australian law reformer Russell Scott told the 1st International Conference on Health Law and Ethics in Sydney in 1986:

> Examples of new and problematic technologies are the treatment of grossly defective new-born babies, live organ transplantation, cloning, the diagnosis of brain death, and manipulation of genes. But if there is one procedure that typifies the extreme reactions aroused by the New Biologies, it is IVF, the technique whereby human eggs are fertilised outside the human body.[1]

While many patients and doctors embrace high-tech reproduction as a wonder of modern medicine, there are many objections to IVF. British gynaecologist and member of the WHO Infertility Task Force, Timothy Hargreave, pointed out some of them: infertility is not life-threatening; IVF separates procreation from sexual union; it uses expertise and resources to produce children in an already over-populated world; it produces more embryos than can be transferred; and it is morally unacceptable to create embryos that die in experiments. Probably the biggest concern of all is that IVF is the start of the 'slippery slope' to unacceptable forms of manipulating life.

## REPRODUCTIVE RIGHTS

When infertility treatments are available who has a right to use them? Could a childless couple demand the service as a basic human right?

IVF pioneer Patrick Steptoe believed no person has the indisputable right to have a baby. He said that right must be governed by society. 'This has always been the case in the past. All societies have had their own rules about reproduction. But now we need new rules to take account of new reproductive technologies.'

Tor Sverne, the former Swedish ombudsman whose committee drafted the recent Swedish legislation on reproductive technology, agrees and says that what is in the best interest of the child should come before the desire of a couple to have a child. 'Having children is not an unconditional human right and [these] activities should only be permitted on condition that the child will be able to grow up in favourable conditions.'[2]

However, not everyone agrees. The Ontario Law Reform Commission pointed out in its 1985 report on artificial reproduction that the right to found a family has achieved wide recognition, and has received strong legal and moral support at international level.[3]

Various international declarations on human rights, including that of the United Nations and the European Convention, state that reproduction is a right. The UN Declaration of

Human Rights, for example, includes the right of every man and woman to 'marry and found a family'. But should they be allowed to by whatever means is available, including expensive and controversial methods such as IVF and surrogate mothers? If a government bans one of the options available to them, say surrogacy, is that discriminating against an infertile couple wanting a child? Some authorities argue that it is discrimination and that governments have no power to limit a person's right to reproductive choice.

The International Covenant on Economic, Social and Cultural Rights, which came into force in 1976, demands that: 'The widest possible protection and assistance should be accorded to the family . . . particularly for its establishment.' Countries that adopt the Covenant 'recognise the right of everyone . . . to enjoy the benefits of scientific progress and its application'. Does that mean governments should provide the latest scientific advances in reproduction? The Ontario report interprets this to mean that member countries are obliged to allow people access to these advances, or at least not to deny that access where it is available.

Austria's former Minister of Law, C. Broda, agrees and says governments should not interfere in reproductive choice. He told the Austrian enquiry into reproduction in 1985 that a fundamental character of society is that 'the members of our society have the legitimate desire to arrange their personal relations free from state regimentation and under their own responsibility'. He said legislators ought to respect that desire by avoiding putting obstacles in the way of people who want to use medical science in order to have children.[4]

Broda said the European Convention for the Protection of Human Rights deals with the rights of any human being to life. He told the enquiry:

> Indirectly, this right to life also seems to comprise any person's right to give life and freedom in the choice of giving life. I agree that it is part of the basic rights of the human being to determine the means he wants to use for having children. The starting point for all considerations concerning medically assisted reproduction ought to be a person's responsible self-determination, i.e., the autonomy

> of persons whether living alone or in partnership to decide about having children. We are not authorised to deny responsible persons the happiness to have children.

Several major courts around the world, including the US Supreme Court, have ruled in favour of allowing reproductive rights on issues such as contraception, abortion and sterilisation of criminals. However, none have been asked to pass judgement on whether an infertile person has the right to use assisted reproduction, and whether there should be a law restricting his or her reproductive choice.

Recommendations put to the 21 member countries of the Council of Europe include a ban on: surrogacy; payment to gamete donors; the use of sperm after the death of a man except in special circumstances; embryo research unless it is for the benefit of that particular embryo; and the mixing of husband and donor sperm for artificial insemination. Bernard Dickens, Professor of Law at the University of Toronto, Ontario, believes these recommendations may breach the European Convention for the Protection of Human Rights and Fundamental Freedoms and he warns that they could be challenged in the European Court of Justice.

The American Fertility Society, in its 90-page document 'Ethical Considerations of the New Reproductive Technologies', released in September 1986, points out that in at least four important cases the Supreme Court has upheld that reproduction is one of 'the basic rights of man'. The AFS presents a strong argument that if the law does not interfere with the right to sexual reproduction, it should not interfere with what it calls noncoital (non-sexual) reproduction, such as IVF and the use of donor gametes and surrogates. 'The couple's interest in reproducing is the same, no matter how reproduction occurs. The values and interests underlying a right of coital reproduction strongly suggest a married couple's right to noncoital reproduction as well—and, arguably, to have the assistance of donors and surrogates.' They would then have the right to create, store, transfer, donate or dispose of embryos created by their egg and sperm, and presumably to use a surrogate, the AFS said.[5]

If an infertile person has the right to reproduce by whatever means is necessary to have a child, should governments be passing laws that stop them? In one case on reproduction, a US Supreme Court judge stated: 'If the right of privacy means anything, it is the right of the individual, married or single, to be free of unwarranted government intrusion into the decision whether to bear or beget a child.' The AFS says, 'States might then regulate the circumstances under which parties would enter into reproductive contracts (with donors and surrogates), but they cannot ban such transactions.'[5]

Nancy Gertner, a Boston lawyer well known for her interest in reproductive law, believes there is a right to create, avoid or terminate a pregnancy regardless of race, colour, religious creed, age, national origin, marital status, sexual preference or disability. At a forum, 'Reproductive Laws for the 1990s', in New York in May 1987, she said the goal of the law should be to maximise reproductive choice and suggested that legal action could be taken against those who interfere with that choice.[6]

John Robertson, Professor of Law at the University of Texas, argues that a couple has a constitutional right to have children and legally the state cannot stop them using the necessary technology if it is available.

> The state has never tried to interfere with the right of married couples to reproduce by coitus. If one or both partners lack the genetic or gestational factors necessary to procreate, it should follow that they have the right to enlist the willing assistance of donors and surrogates. If married couples—and possibly unmarried people—have a right to procreate, that right should include the right to make contracts with providers of gametes and embryos and with surrogates, if that is essential to enable them [have] a child. Unless a tangible harmful impact on offspring or others is demonstrated, such contracts could not be prohibited or limited, though they could be regulated to assure that they are knowingly and freely entered into.[7]

Speaking at a seminar, 'Legal Regulation of Reproductive Medicine', in Cambridge in September 1987, Robertson said this right could be extended to the use of embryos: 'If this analysis is correct, couples would have a constitutional right—a right against state interference or prohibition—to create, store, transfer, donate and possibly even manipulate embryos in order to acquire offspring.' It could be argued that prohibiting the sale of embryos would violate the right to reproduce. 'Embryo donation should be treated like coital reproduction or artificial insemination by donor [and] banning payments might interfere with a couple's ability to obtain an embryo, and thus infringe their procreative liberty.' If the right to assisted reproduction applies to married couples, he said, it should be extended to unmarried couples and singles.

How far can this right be taken? Does a government have to provide the method or treatment necessary for producing a baby? In his opening address to the Health Law and Ethics conference, Sir Zelman Cowen, former governor-general of Australia, lawyer and now provost of Oriel College at Oxford University, argued a person does not have a right to medical treatment. And he quoted a case under English law where the right to treatment had been rejected. In 1980 four patients in Staffordshire who had been waiting for surgery for some years, argued that under the National Health Service Act the Secretary of State had not fulfilled his duty to provide a comprehensive health service, including the service they sought. The case was rejected by the judge, Lord Denning, who said, 'It cannot be supposed that the Secretary of State had to provide all the latest equipment, and it could not be supposed that he had to provide all the kidney machines which are asked for, or for all the new developments, such as heart transplants, in every case where people would benefit from them.' The same argument would undoubtedly apply to reproductive technologies including IVF.[8]

Cowen also pointed out that in the US, the 1982 President's Commission on Ethical Problems in Medicine concluded that 'society has an ethical obligation to ensure equitable access to an adequate level of health care for all without excessive burdens' but no individual right to health care was found.

## THE MORAL QUESTION—FOR WHOM?

Even if the resources are available, should doctors or health authorities be able to stipulate that some people cannot use the facilities while others can? Generally, infertility clinics restrict AI and IVF to married couples, and most stipulate married couples in a 'stable' relationship. Should doctors decide whether a particular woman is suitable to be a mother, and withhold the service if they think she is not?

A fertile woman can get pregnant if and when she chooses and no one would consider questioning whether she will make a good mother, even if she is on a low income and not married. Yet couples seeking infertility treatment are subjected to rigorous medical and psychological testing. Often this delves into very personal aspects of their sex lives, their attitudes towards pregnancy and children, and their financial and emotional stability. There is an important distinction between counselling, discussed in Chapter 8, and the screening process which eliminates people who are judged by a third party to be suitable or unsuitable for parenthood.

Nancy Gertner says sometimes disabled, poor and coloured women are excluded from reproductive technologies. She told the New York seminar: 'Health clinics and hospitals ostensibly making choices about the allocation of scarce resources have abrogated to themselves the right to decide who may have children and who may not according to their own views of social engineering.'

Lori Andrews of the American Bar Association expressed similar views at the same seminar and said screening should not be used to eliminate potentially unfit parents. 'People should be allowed to have children via alternative reproduction without advance assessments of their fitness for parenthood, particularly in light of past abuses in this country with respect to the involuntary sterilisation of people who were thought to be unworthy of being parents.'[9]

Although several governments have restricted AI to married or *de facto* couples, few have gone any further in stating who is or is not eligible for infertility treatment. The exception is the Victorian Government which decided that selection should be on medical and marital grounds. Under the 1984 legislation, a couple can only have AI or IVF if they are married, have been investigated for infertility for at least 12 months and an independent doctor is convinced they would not conceive any other way. This obviously discriminates against co-habitees,

Embryology technicians at the IVF Australia clinic in the US. Human embryos are frozen in long, thin "straws" which are lowered into liquid nitrogen and can be stored this way for hundreds of years—held in suspended animation indefinitely.

Many women have had a hysterectomy but still want to have a baby, and it might be ethically acceptable and medically possible. Estelle Croot has no womb because she is a transsexual—should she be allowed to attempt a pregnancy? The next step would be male pregnancy.

The Kentucky horse that gave birth to a zebra in 1984 after gestating the zebra embryo. The research aims to preserve endangered species. Would it be possible—and acceptable—for an ape to gestate a human embryo, or vice versa?

single women, homosexuals and transsexuals and anyone wanting to use reproductive technologies for non-medical reasons. The penalty for not complying with the Victorian law is up to four years' imprisonment for each offence.[10]

Under Sweden's new law on AI, a physician has to 'ascertain the couple's psycho-social circumstances' and ensure they are both medically fit. A doctor can refuse to perform AI but the couple can complain to the National Board of Health and Welfare if they feel the decision is unjust.

Psychiatrist Dr Cécile Ernst, who was a member of the Swiss Government's committee on artificial reproduction, believes infertility treatment is self-selecting as far as emotional stability is concerned. The low success rate, the long and tedious diagnosis and the stress of the treatment are sometimes enough to deter those who are not psychologically able to cope. If a team of 'experts' are used for screening they will venture into 'the grey zone of minor disorders' and she warns that disallowing a couple will become an arbitrary decision, causing damage to the couple screened out.

> They will have to live with the information that they are not only infertile but 'not good enough' to have a child. Selections in the grey zone will lead to a black market of artificial procreation. The donor insemination technique is simple enough to be used by almost anyone. Today a black market for adoptive children has developed, because official adoption has become so difficult. An uncontrolled black market for donor insemination would entail extremely dangerous risks for mother and child because of the spread of AIDS.[11]

Some people see screening as an example of medical power or social engineering, and many women see it as the power of men over women's reproductive rights.

## IN THE BEST INTEREST OF THE CHILD

In assisted reproduction, doctors are faced with a conflict of interest. On the one hand, they must decide what is best for the infertile couple, and weigh that against what is in the best interests of the child not yet conceived.

Hilda Olbrechts says the child's interest must always be paramount. As the infertility counsellor at the Vrije Univerity's Centre for Reproductive Medicine in Brussels, she has to assess who will be accepted to the IVF and AI programmes, and many people are not, including about half the single and lesbian women who apply.

> If they come because they don't want a man, we don't allow them because they will put this vision to their child. You must always think of the child. I tell them it is of no importance to me if you are not happy without a child. I must have a happy child.

John Robertson points out that arrangements involving donor eggs and embryos and surrogates are similar to artificial insemination, adoption and step-parent arrangements, which are both common and accepted. 'Creating further variations is not radically different and should be treated accordingly.'[7]

There is no evidence that children born through assisted reproduction suffer emotional trauma, parental discord, bewilderment or family tension, according to Cécile Ernst. Speaking at the Cambridge seminar, she said studies show that DI children have above-average development, and fears that children born from donor eggs or embryos and surrogacy will suffer emotionally are anecdotal and scientifically unfounded. 'Studies make it evident that the quality of emotional relationship within a family is more important than family structure. Nonetheless, artificial procreation should not be used to *promote* change and to create new structures.'[11]

Who should decide what is in the best interest of the child? The Benda Committee of West Germany believes it should be the parents: 'The physician is not authorised to decide on the possible happiness of the child in the place of husband and wife.'[12]

## THE SOCIAL QUESTION: AT WHAT COST?

Babies don't have price tags, but every childless couple has to decide at some point how much it means to them emotionally and financially to continue infertility treatment. Some are prepared to give up their careers, mortgage their homes or even move to another city, others go through more than a decade of heartbreak and despair before accepting their childlessness. They have a right to do as they please with their money and their emotions, but society as a whole must ask itself what the process costs the community—in money, personnel, lost opportunities and civil liberties. We have to look at what other health needs have been sacrificed, what research has been forsaken, at what price gynaecology has shifted away from more fundamental work. As one commentator said, 'One man's freedom in health is another man's shackle in taxes and insurance premiums.'

The 4.5 million infertile people in the US spend an estimated $500 million to $1 billion each year seeking treatment yet, as Congressman George Miller pointed out at the New York seminar: in the US, one in five children under 18 live in poverty; nearly 25 per cent of children are born to women who received no pre-natal health care; over 40 per cent of pre-school children are not immunized against one or more of the preventable childhood diseases, and infant mortality in the US is higher than in many developing nations. Figures from elsewhere show that of America's 230,000 babies born each year weighing less than 2,500 grams, only half live.[13]

A 1982 US survey found that 18 per cent of married or separated women aged 15 to 44 had used medical services for infertility at some time in their life and 3 per cent (one million women) had seen a doctor about infertility at least once in the 12 months before the survey. Commented one health authority: 'This represents a substantial use of health care services with correspondingly large implications for health care costs.'[14]

In another survey, 7 per cent of American women said they had sought medical help for infertility during the previous three years. It also showed the number of infertility-related visits to private physicians increased by 50 per cent from 600,000 in 1968 to 900,000 in 1980, and that a higher proportion of doctors' cases were infertility-related.[15]

There have been few studies of the costs, but one analysed more than 1,100 couples who went through an infertility clinic in Nova Scotia, Canada, in 1980. Less than half received treatment and only 171 had a pregnancy as a result. The cost to the health system of diagnosing all the patients and treating half of them meant each pregnancy averaged $US10,700. The most expensive treatment, at $31,800 per pregnancy, was surgery for tubal damage, which is the most common cause of infertility in women. This compared with between $3,000 and $10,000 for adoption and about $20,000 for surrogate mother arrangements in 1980.[16]

In the US in 1987, any couple undergoing IVF would pay $US5,000–8,000 per attempt. It must be remembered that each attempt has only a 10 per cent chance of producing a baby, and that only 25 per cent of couples who join a programme succeed. If the chance is 99 per cent after eight attempts, as reported recently by Wilfred Feichtinger, it could cost some couples $40,000–64,000 to have a baby.

With an infertility rate of 5–15 per cent, all countries in one way or another devote a slice of their health budget to infertility treatment. IVF is only a small proportion, but receives a disproportionate amount of attention and criticism. Yet IVF is more than just producing test-tube babies. It has broadened immeasurably the understanding of conception, implantation, ectopic pregnancies, miscarriages and genetic abnormalities.

The mushrooming of new technology has brought with it other advantages, social as well as medical. For example, the first IVF programme set up in Malaysia, at the Subang Jaya Medical Centre in Kuala Lumpur, is a subsidiary of an Australian company, Pivet, with an all-Australian trained team. By establishing clinics in developing countries, foreign companies such as this not only provide the community with a service that the government does not have to pay for, but it 'imports' a higher level of training in gynaecology generally.

Dr T.C. Anand Kumar, director of the Institute for Research in Reproduction in Bombay, says infertility treatment is not just a matter of helping a couple to have a child, there are several other spin-offs: 'By looking at infertility, you have a greater understanding of what fertility is all about and research on infertility will help develop contraceptives.'

In 1985 Singapore's Professor Shan Ratnam, who pioneered

IVF in Asia, commented, 'We have begun a new era in human reproductive technology. This will undoubtedly expand our knowledge on human infertility and early embryonic development both of which have been rather meagre in the past.'[17] And in a joint article infertility experts Dr Basil Tarlatzis (Greece) and Alan DeCherney (US) said, 'IVF has opened new avenues in the treatment of infertility but has also offered new opportunities of research in the area of reproductive endocrinology and biology.'[18]

Those who criticise the amount spent on infertility usually focus on IVF because it is expensive and high-tech. But many of the IVF centres in Europe and the US are private, and the public's attitude is that the patients who can afford it should be allowed to pay for it. Many people frown at the thought of developing countries and overpopulated countries investing in high-tech reproduction, but the same 'user pays' argument applies in these countries as well. Alan Trounson told a recent Asian conference that countries such as Thailand are justified in setting up private IVF centres because people who can afford it should not be denied the service.

In contrast, the *New Straits Times* of Malaysia believes the services should be offered without prejudice: 'Such facilities as IVF need to be available equally to all deserving couples, irrespective of socio-economic status. Human and social needs must remain free from considerations of monetary payment. Only in this way can medical technology contribute tangibly to national development.'[19] And Professor Shan Ratnam's IVF centre in Singapore has assured patients they will not be refused treatment if they cannot afford it. In many cases this means those who can afford it subsidise those who cannot.

IVF is not cheap—in Singapore, it costs patients about $3,000–6,000, in the US $US5,000–8,000, in Britain, £1,100–1,800 and in Germany DM3,000–5,000. Each country has different arrangements: in Britain, there is only one National Health Service centre, but patients going to the private centres often have preliminary treatment at an NHS hospital then transfer to a private programme for the rest of the treatment. In Australia, the drugs are not covered under Medicare, the national health scheme, but 85 per cent of the doctors' fee and a public hospital bed are; and private health funds will cover the cost of the drugs for those who are insured. In the US, where there is no national health, most major private health funds now accept IVF as an insurable treatment, although until recently American patients paid everything. In Germany the treatment is free—patients who go to a public programme are covered by social insurance (unless the woman had her tubes tied in voluntary sterilisation) and those who choose a private clinic pay and are later reimbursed by a private insurance company.

In many cases private and public programmes run alongside each other. Patients referred to a public centre do not pay for the treatment but those who do not want to join the long waiting list can opt for the private programme. They see the same doctors and have the same treatment but they pay and are treated sooner. Britain's only government-funded IVF centre, in Manchester, has a three to four year waiting list, but at the more than 30 other, private, clinics it is generally only a few months.

## PREVENTING INFERTILITY

In theory, a fifth of the world's infertility could be prevented by eliminating sexually transmitted diseases, according to the US Centers for Disease Control. 'If we could wave a wand and get rid of STDs as a cause of preventable infertility we could reduce the total infertility by 20 per cent in the US,' says Ward Cates, the Centers' director of STDs. And possibly 14 per cent of tubal damage in Western countries, and more in developing countries, could also be eliminated with better gynaecological care. Both these contribute to infertility, through pelvic inflammatory disease (PID), and both are preventable, though it is unlikely either will ever be completely wiped out.

In developing countries STDs are common but much harder to prevent because of the lack of physical and financial resources and understanding, manpower and education. Health authorities in many African, Asian and Middle Eastern countries also have to contend with traditions and cultures that actually encourage PID, while many patients prefer to seek help from traditional remedies rather than Western medicine.

Because of the high incidence of infection-related infertility in Africa the WHO has called for renewed emphasis on prevention, including STD control programmes to reduce the incidence and risk of complications; education programmes to inform the public about causes, dangers and ways to prevent STD; improvement in obstetric care to reduce postpartum infection; and family-planning programmes to prevent the need for illegal abortions. The WHO Infertility Task Force places high priority on the development of a simple, rapid, accurate and inexpensive test to detect evidence of past or current infection. It is currently collaborating on antigen kits that will test blood, cervical mucus or semen.

The US Government began funding syphilis control programmes in 1939 and in the early 1970s directed its attention to gonorrhoea, and now all STDs are the subject of government-funded control programmes. Nevertheless, the incidence of STDs continues to rise, and to make matters worse, in the late 1970s scientists dicovered that one strain of the gonorrhoea bacteria was resistant to penicillin. After the first few cases of penicillin resistance were reported in 1977, the figure rose to more than 8,700 in 1985.

Few governments are prepared to spend a sizeable proportion of their health budget on prevention when the benefits may not be felt for decades, or at least long after they have been removed from office, and often patients have higher priorities themselves. As Sir Zelman Cowen said, 'Open-heart surgery is both expensive and of uncertain value, but for many who suffer from angina it offers a greater prospect of relief than an expanded programme of health education or safer highways.' He pointed out that in the US only 2–2.5 per cent of the 1977 national health budget was spent on disease prevention and control, half of 1 per cent on health education and a quarter of 1 per cent on environmental health research.[8]

In Britain, very little, if any, of the £19 billion a year health budget is spent on preventing infertility. In the 1980 BBC Reith Lectures, Ian Kennedy, Professor of Medical Law and Ethics at King's College, London, argued for prevention in health care through education and quoted the then Under-Secretary of Health, Sir George Young, as saying, 'For many of today's medical problems, the answer may not be cure by incision at the operating table, but prevention by decision at the Cabinet table.'[20]

An estimated 50,000 new cases of infertility are diagnosed each year in Britain, and between 1982 and August 1987 the total number of people diagnosed with AIDS was 950. Yet the British Government missed an opportunity to make a contribution to infertility prevention with its recent controversial campaign on AIDS. The Department of Health in November 1986 allocated £21.5 million for a one-year AIDS campaign which included extensive national media advertising. Although the campaign advocated a change of sexual behaviour which will hopefully reduce the spread of all STDs, not just AIDS, no part of the campaign mentioned the other consequences of STDs, such as infertility.

Gynaecologist Peter Greenhouse, of London's Royal Northern Hospital, believes IVF cannot be justified without, at the same time, attempting to reduce infertility. 'There should not be another penny spent on infertility treatment by the NHS until they have set up a prevention campaign. By doing infertility treatment you are trying to shut the door long after the horse has bolted. Now you have to stop more horses getting out.' He says the money spent on *one* IVF clinic would be better used to run a national prevention campaign. 'It would be infinitely better spent on prevention—better for individuals and the population as a whole.' But that does not mean IVF should be abandoned. 'If you have women with infertility you cannot turn your back on them just because you are going to be concerned with only prevention. My criticism is that there is no prevention at all. You have to realise your responsibility to prevent infertility *at the same time* as offering IVF.'

The key to prevention lies in STD clinics and routine gynaecological screening, and Greenhouse is critical of the medical profession for abandoning this less than attractive arena in favour of high-tech 'after the horse has bolted' treatments such as IVF.

> Infertility treatment is a multi-million pound industry that has attracted the best resources of the profession, including the finest brains. They have gone lock, stock and barrel into

treatment with scant consideration for prevention. Mass investment in treatment is an unacceptable paradox of modern gynaecological practice in Western medicine.

## QUALITY OF SERVICE

Infertile people are not outwardly ill but are sometimes dismissed or poorly treated by health systems. Although infertility is not life-threatening it is a life crisis and the emotional effect can be devastating. A common complaint from infertile patients is that they are often misunderstood or not always taken seriously by doctors and nurses.

One of the most difficult problems faced by couples, especially women, during treatment is that they share facilities such as wards with women who are having abortions or deliveries.

There is a strong case for making infertility a separate speciality. Couples are almost always seen by a gynaecologist, yet one-third of infertility is in men. In Britain, the Royal College of Obstetricians and Gynaecologists suggested in 1982 that a division of reproductive medicine be created to offer a better service, better training and cost-cutting, but so far the offer has not been taken up.

In a 1986 study of infertility services in England and Wales, the Shadow Health Minister Frank Dobson found that even in the best regions more than 40 per cent of health authorities had little or no provision for infertility treatment. Some patients had to wait up to 30 weeks for an appointment with a consultant, and others waited four years before investigation or treatment began. The report said that because of the high cost of infertility drugs, in the majority of health authorities they were not being used or were being used 'blind'. There are also complaints, especially in Britain, of poor monitoring, mis-diagnosis and failure to carry out basic tests.

There has also been criticism from the public, patients and the profession that some doctors are too eager to prescribe expensive treatments such as IVF without properly assessing the cause of the infertility and evaluating cheaper alternatives. They are sometimes said to dismiss the role of stress too quickly.

Bernard Sandler, founder/director of the Infertility Clinic at the Manchester Jewish Hospital believes a woman may only conceive when she is emotionally ready and he suggests more stringent assessment. 'We must beware of forcing these patients into a role for which they are unprepared. It is one to which insufficient attention has been paid by many of those who have to deal with infertility.'[21]

Although the WHO regards infertility as 12 months without a pregnancy, many doctors prefer to wait 18 months to two years before recognising there is a problem, and starting treatment. Considering the number of women who become pregnant while waiting for treatment, some people say the 'trying' period should be much longer, unless the woman is in her late thirties, after which the chances of a viable pregnancy diminish. One of them is the Reverend Michael Newman, chairman of the Methodist Church's Committee on Marriage and the Family in Britain: 'Perhaps people have been too quick to accept infertility. It is being discovered that couples who were thought—by themselves and experts—to be infertile are in fact not infertile, and I would prefer more work to be done to prevent infertility rather than going down the road to alternatives such as [DI].'

The medical profession cannot agree among themselves on the quality and value of infertility treatment, especially IVF. In a public debate in the British medical journal *The Lancet*, in September 1987, Professor Robert Winston of Hammersmith Hospital, London, referred to IVF as 'the most disappointing and expensive of all treatments', while his colleague, Professor Richard Lilford of St James's University Hospital, Leeds, said it was 'one of the "best buys" possible in medicine' which produced 'brilliant results'.[22]

Although some areas of infertility treatment have been questioned or criticised, it is generally recognised that in the majority of cases the service is provided with professionalism and dedication.

## THE DANGERS AND ETHICS OF SUPEROVULATION

Some people—in the media and the medical profession—are starting to question the long-term effects of fertility drugs, whether they are used for ovulation induction and natural conception, or IVF. Some wonder whether the drugs may have similar results to DES, which was used to prevent recurrent miscarriage, and warn that the effects may not be known until the next generation, when 'fertility drug babies' attempt to have babies themselves. Several recent articles in medical journals by researchers in Britain, America, Sweden and Australia show a higher incidence of abnormalities in the eggs of women who have been given stimulation drugs, compared with those of women who have not. There is mounting evidence, and concern, that these drugs may be damaging to the eggs while they are developing in the ovaries. An article in the *New England Journal of Medicine* in January 1987 reported a higher than normal number of deformed eggs after superovulation. This followed similar reports in the *American Journal of Obstetrics and Gynaecology* and the *Medical Journal of Australia*. The MJA article discussed the risks of superovulation on the ovaries and thrombosis, and the American journal compared clomiphene with DES.[23]

Any alteration to the 23 paired chromosomes in an egg (or sperm) leads to a defective embryo if fertilisation takes place. The most obvious chromosome abnormality seen in babies born in Western countries is *Down's syndrome* but there are many others which are much more subtle. Nature ensures that very few of these embryos develop into babies and the majority of defective embryos are lost in spontaneous abortion in early pregnancy. Only 2 per cent of babies born in Western countries have an abnormality caused by an alteration of the chromosomes.

In the mid-1970s, J. and A. Boue analysed foetuses that had spontaneously aborted and found a higher proportion of chromosome abnormalities in the ones where the mother had been stimulated. And in 1983 Professor Alan Templeton's team at the University of Aberdeen reported chromosome abnormalities in eggs after stimulation for IVF, and suggested this probably contributes to the high failure rate after embryos are transferred.[24]

More recent research from Sweden also shows an increase in chromosome abnormalities in eggs that were analysed after the women had been stimulated with clomiphene. The research, by Hakan Wramsby and colleagues at the universities of Lund and Uppsala, found many of the eggs analysed had less than 23 chromosomes and some had more than 23. Almost one in six had less than six chromosomes. Wramsby's team suggested this may be one reason for the low success rate of IVF. The chances of one IVF egg leading to a birth is about 7 per cent. In nature it is about 25 per cent and the Swedish researchers suggest the difference may be partly due to chromosome abnormalities resulting from the IVF procedure which involves ovulation stimulation with the same fertility drug.[25]

London gynaecologist and infertility specialist Sam Abdalla, formerly of the Cromwell Hospital, is one of several in the medical profession who are questioning whether the fertility drugs are affecting the chances of a healthy pregnancy. 'A lot of patients have high LH (hormone) and when you give [HMG] and [Clomiphene] you raise it, and there is some thought that high LH in the immediate pre-ovulation period is detrimental to the eggs.'

If such an effect caused damage to the chromosomes in the egg it could prevent fertilisation, end in a spontaneous abortion or lead to an abnormality in the baby. It has been proved that the incidence of abnormalities after stimulation with fertility drugs is no greater than in the general population, but some people, including psychologist Robyn Rowland of Deakin University, Victoria, Australia, draw a parallel with DES. Such abnormalities, if they exist, may not be apparent, until the baby girls attempt to have children themselves, in maybe 25 years' time. 'The warnings are here. We are yet to see the long-term consequences of superovulation.'[26]

## MULTIPLE PREGNANCIES

A more immediate risk from fertility drugs is the increased chance of a multiple pregnancy. Many couples who have been infertile for several years welcome the arrival of twins as a bonus, but not five, six or seven babies all at once. With careful monitoring, this should not happen, but occasionally it does.

In 1964 and 1965 the world's press reported a frenzy of

multiple births: septuplets in Australia, quins and sextuplets in West Germany, quins in New Zealand, quins in Sweden. The reason was the introduction of the 'fertility drug', but its inventor, Professor Carl-Axel Gemzell of the University of Lund, had not yet learned to control the dose and its effects on the ovaries. By 1966 Gemzell found half of his first 100 patients had more than one baby.

A drug-induced multiple birth in 1987 is not something to celebrate. It is not a freak of nature, nor a great achievement. On the contrary, it is the result of mismanagement. The chances of a multiple pregnancy should be minimal if the effects of the drugs are properly monitored. From hormone tests and ultrasound a doctor can tell how many follicles are developing and if it is more than one or two the treatment is normally cancelled and attempted again in the next cycle, with a lower dose of the drug.

Despite this, the media is usually overjoyed with the birth of quads, quins, sextuplets and septuplets, expounding the virtues of modern medicine and gleefully fingering their cheque books for the 'exclusive' story from the parents when it would be more appropriate to condemn the doctors responsible and point out to the public the medical and psychological dangers of multiple births that could, and should, be avoided.

Attitudes started to change, in the UK at least, with the birth of Britain's first septuplets in Liverpool on 15 August 1987. Initially it was hailed as 'a record-breaking achievement', but the seven premature babies died one after the other, and the celebration turned into a mourning. It was a stark reminder that fertility drugs are still not completely under control and the public, the media and the medical profession started asking questions.

Susan Halton had been given the fertility drug FSH and was delighted when she found she was pregnant. But she went into labour 14 weeks early and the seven grossly premature babies weighed less than 4kg (9 lbs) between them. Half an hour after the delivery, at the Liverpool Maternity Hospital, the first, a boy, died. The remaining four girls and two boys were put on separate life-support systems but died progressively over the following 17 days.

As the *Sunday Times* headline said the following week: 'It should never have happened'. The paper described the event as 'a nightmare which is unlikely to leave the public consciousness for many years'. While many people felt extreme sympathy for the Halton family, they also hoped the tragedy would focus attention on the ethics of the new reproductive technologies. To quote the *Sunday Times* article again:

> Were the sad events in Liverpool a sign that modern medicine had gone too far in challenging nature's own intricate reproductive checks and balances? . . . Many believe that public as well as professional 'moral views' on the circumstances in which technology is allowed to intervene in nature's arrangements for childbirth need to be considerably sharper than they have been to date.[27]

The birth of the Halton septuplets raised several ethical questions that apply to all multiple pregnancies resulting from fertility drugs. Why wasn't the mother's treatment cancelled when it produced seven follicles? Should she have been offered a termination as the pregnancy endangered her own welfare—physically and emotionally—as well as the lives of the seven babies? And what financial, emotional and social help do the parents of multiple births have when medicine goes wrong? The impact of multiple pregnancy can be devastating to the parents, whether the premature babies live or die. After the public acclaim and media attention dies down, the couple are faced with the reality of an unplanned instant family which can overwhelm them emotionally and financially.

The septuplets in Britain resulted from fertility drugs and natural conception, but the same arguments apply to multiple pregnancies created in IVF. When the world's first IVF quads were born in Melbourne in January 1984, I flew down from Sydney to report on this 'medical miracle'. It was hailed as a great achievement by the doctors responsible and the four Muir boys were proudly shown to the world. The medical profession is now less enthusiastic about such births. And the practice of transferring as many embryos as possible has been curtailed because of the increased risk of, and dangers of, large multiple pregnancies. Most of the leading centres around the world now only transfer three embryos, and four in special cases, in IVF, and the same number of eggs in GIFT. The Voluntary Licensing Authority in Britain has made this a prerequisite for centres if they are to be licensed.

However, not everyone agrees with a limit on the number of eggs or embryos to be transferred. Professor Ian Craft, who runs the infertility unit at the Humana Hospital in London, defied the VLA ruling and the unit's licence was withdrawn in September 1987. Craft says each patient is different, has different reasons for her infertility and different responses to treatment. How many embryos he transfers depends on each woman's condition and previous medical history. For example, a woman who has never had a pregnancy has less chance of a multiple pregnancy than one who has been pregnant before. In the unit's first year 1,500 IVF procedures resulted in two sets of quads and one set of quins. Since they started adjusting the number of embryos to suit each patient, there have been no more quads or quins.

'Our duty is to give an infertile couple the best chance of achieving and maintaining a pregnancy . . . The decision on the number of embryos to be transferred should remain a matter of clinical judgement, involving the couple concerned and their medical advisors,' Craft said in a letter to *The Lancet*. 'GIFT should not be of direct concern to the VLA, any more than medical indication for ovulation is . . . In our experience of 900 GIFT procedures we find that a flexible policy is in the patient's best interests.'[27] After considerable public debate Craft's team agreed to comply with the guidelines and the VLA reinstated the licence in early 1988.

It is not just a case of limiting the number of eggs or embryos transferred, but a matter of whether a voluntary body such as the VLA should interfere with a doctor-patient decision. As *The Lancet* commented: 'The VLA seems to be taking an authoritarian stance on what should be a matter of clinical judgement.'[28]

However, Dr John Loudon, obstetrician/gynaecologist at the University of Edinburgh and one of the VLA's 13 members, believes the restriction protects the patients and other doctors. He said, 'Those who persist in replacing more than three embryos appear to forget that they may well be the clinicians who have to manage the pregnancies.

The woman cannot be fully aware of the enormity of the problems she may be facing.'

## SELECTIVE REDUCTION

In extreme cases the couple may opt for an abortion if they know they have a multiple pregnancy but a controversial alternative to terminating the pregnancy is a new technique of selectively terminating some of the foetuses while allowing the others to continue in a normal pregnancy. The procedure was developed in Sweden and modified by Professor Charles Rodeck at London's King's College Hospital in 1980. It is now being used experimentally in a handful of hospitals in other European countries.

By the time the Liverpool septuplets were born Rodeck, now at the Queen Charlotte Hospital, had used the technique on six pregnancies, and two other UK hospitals had also attempted it, but with less success, although it is being used at several clinics in France and Germany. However, one Paris clinic reported recently that in half the cases where selective reduction was used, all foetuses were lost.

A long, ultra-thin needle is passed through the mother's abdominal wall under ultrasound and a local anaesthetic, with the surgeon watching the image on a screen. Potassium chloride is then injected into the heart of the targeted foetus, killing it instantly. The procedure usually takes about half an hour, and the terminated foetus withers and is usually absorbed into the uterus, but occasionally remnants can be delivered later, along with the live brothers or sisters.

There are several occasions when the technique may be considered: if one of a twin is found to have an abnormality or the gene for a hereditary disease; if the woman is certain to miscarry with a multiple pregnancy because of a weak cervix; and in the case of a multiple pregnancy where survival of all the babies is unlikely or the mother's health is at risk.

Selective reduction was originally developed for cases where one twin had a genetic abnormality, such as *spina bifida* or Down's syndrome. Until recently genetic diseases were diagnosed by amniocentesis about 16 weeks into the pregnancy, and selective termination was done by injecting air into the circulation of the foetus. More recently, *chorion villus sampling* (CVS) has allowed diagnosis much earlier in the pregnancy, at about eight weeks after conception. As the circulation system is not developed at that stage, potassium chloride is used.

Those who use the technique argue that as long as at least one foetus remains, technically it is not an abortion because the pregnancy has not been lost. But the definition of abortion, according to *Blakiston's Medical Dictionary*, is 'spontaneously or artificially induced expulsion of an embryo or foetus before it is viable'.

The most difficult part, Rodeck says, is not the technique but deciding when to use it. 'The technique starts with making sure it is being used in the right circumstances and the indications are correct.' Instead of looking at selective termination as a way out, doctors should put more effort into avoiding multiple pregnancies from fertility drugs and IVF. And, he said, the risk of losing the whole pregnancy has to be considered in terms of the long-term psychological loss to the mother.

> There are ethical problems in killing perfectly healthy foetuses. It is done widely in single pregnancies where the woman wants a termination but they are unwanted pregnancies. Multiple pregnancies are wanted pregnancies with an unwanted number of foetuses. It comes after strenuous efforts have been made to create the pregnancy, usually after a long period of infertility. And that could lead to problems in the woman who may have wanted a child desperately for 10 years and then has to make a decision whether to kill off a life inside her. The dispassionate view is to say the foetus is no different to another foetus but it happens to have a few more with it. And it could be argued that the more we do the more we will know. But in the meantime, we don't know what harm we are doing to the woman.

One London woman (not Rodeck's patient) who had five embryos develop after IVF opted to have three terminated but the operation ended in a total abortion. She described her feelings in an interview in the *Guardian*:

> It felt like the end of everything. Being infertile was pretty awful. But this time I felt I had deliberately destroyed life I had created. I had been greedy and I was punished for my greed. It was my decision. The doctor explained the risks. I knew what I was doing. He seemed as depressed as I was when it all went wrong. But that's the end of it. I won't try again. Maybe we'll think about adoption, when the scars have healed.[30]

John Loudon is uncomfortable about terminating some of the embryos for the sake of saving the woman the burden of carrying and rearing several babies at once. If five embryos grow, three could be terminated but he believes the procedure can only be justified when the risk of total pregnancy failure is greater than if selective termination were used.

## THE RELIGIOUS ARGUMENTS

Few religious groups have made their position clear on assisted reproduction, although several are reviewing their policy and will soon issue guidelines. Three of the most prominent to have made official statements are the chief rabbis in Israel, the Moslem leaders in Indonesia, and the Vatican. All three oppose DI. The Moslem council said it approved of IVF provided the husband's sperm was used, and the Catholic Church said it condemned all forms of artificial procreation.

The Vatican statement is by far the most comprehensive, covering everything from artificial insemination with husband's sperm to cloning, in a 40-page document, *Instruction on Respect for Human Life in its Origin and on the Dignity of Procreation—Replies to Certain Questions of the Day*. It had been prepared, after three years' deliberation, by the Congregation for the Doctrine of Faith, which acts as the guardian and promoter of Roman Catholic orthodoxy, and had been approved by Pope John Paul II.

The driving force behind it was the former Bishop of Munich, Cardinal Joseph Ratzinger, head of the Congregation, who is often referred to as the second most powerful man in the Vatican. On 10 March 1987, he sat behind a row of microphones, representing radio and TV stations around the world, and declared that conception could not take place without intercourse and that childless couples could not turn to science for help. The Catholic Church opposed artificial insemination, IVF, surrogacy and embryo research, Ratzinger said, and called on the world's governments to outlaw such practices.

The *Instruction* made a strong condemnation of IVF saying it was 'illicit' because, like artificial insemination, it did not involve the conjugal act. This was surprising for three reasons: in 1978 Pope John Paul I had congratulated the parents of the world's first test-tube baby, Lesley and John Brown, saying if they had acted in good faith and with the right intentions, he had no right to condemn them; there were numerous Catholic hospitals providing IVF around the world, including several in Italy; and in the first nine years IVF had been practised, the Vatican had not made any statements opposing it.

The *Instruction* said the Church objected to artificial procreation because, 'The one conceived must be the fruit of his parents' love. He cannot be desired or conceived as the product of an intervention of medical or biological techniques; that would be equivalent to reducing him to an object of scientific technology.' The only exception is where 'the technical means is not a substitute for the conjugal act but serves to help so the act attains its natural purpose'.[31]

There were five main objections to IVF: it is not the result of conjugal union, it reduces the child to an object of scientific technology; it 'entrusts the life and identity of the embryo into the power of doctors and biologist' rather than The Creator; it involves masturbation and it exposes the embryo to risks because it is outside the body. Contrary to a widespread belief that the Vatican condemns IVF because fertilisation takes place outside the body, the *Instruction* makes no mention of that.

The use of gametes from a donor is 'morally illicit' and 'constitutes a grave lack of regard to that essential property of marriage which is its unity'. Artificial fertilisation of an unmarried or widowed woman 'cannot be morally justified'. Freezing embryos constitutes an offence against the respect due to human beings by exposing them to 'grave risk of death or harm'.

The document discussed many of the points non-Catholics,

and indeed non-religious people, had been debating—especially the use of donors, surrogate mothers, and embryo research—but it lost a lot of credibility and support because of its opposition to IVF. And, unfortunately, the opposition to IVF drew most of the public and media's attention away from the more pressing issue of how human embryos should be respected and protected.

It was soon obvious that the document had no direct relevance to the vast majority of people and that the few Catholics involved in IVF would not stop seeking and providing treatment because the Vatican condemned them. Most Catholic patients said their desire for children was stronger than their dedication to the Church. IVF clinics in Catholic countries such as France, Belgium, Holland and even Italy declared they would continue offering IVF to infertile couples and many others have since followed them in rejecting the Vatican's 'urgent appeal' to Catholic doctors, scientists, nursing staff and hospital administrators to follow the *Instruction*.

The American Catholic theologian, Father Richard McCormick of the University of Notre Dame, Indiana, was outspoken in his dissent from the Vatican's no-sex, no-child rule and said the more he listened to 'the Howard Joneses of the world', referring to America's leading IVF specialist, the more he saw the fragility of the Church's argument against such treatments. McCormick, who was also a member of the American Fertility Society's ethics committee, said he saw IVF as a way of completing the conjugal act for childless couples. 'It is not the ideal way to have children, but that does not mean it is morally wrong. There are many human actions that we judge morally acceptable even when they involve disvalues.'[32]

He agrees that 'the one conceived must be the fruit of his parents' love' but adds: 'To move from that general premise to the conclusion that the child must be conceived via sexual intercourse involves a gap in logic whose implication is that sexual intercourse is the only loving act in marriage.'

McCormick sees the document as much more about contraception than about conception and points out that if the Church separated sex and procreation for IVF, it would have to do the same for contraception which the Catholic Church has opposed since the early 1960s.

Catholic leaders see different reasons for opposing IVF. The Reverend Albert Moraczewski, of the Pope John XXIII Center in Massachusetts, objects that the embryos are destroyed in IVF and the process 'externalises' the embryo (places it outside the body), opening the way for maltreatment and experimentation. As an embryo is a human being, he said, both these practices are contrary to the rights of the individual. He said the fact that the conjugal act was not involved in procreation may not be that important: 'It is an area that needs further theological reflection, whether it is absolutely necessary.'

Father Peter Brady, of the Holy Spirit Seminary of the Catholic Diocese of Hong Kong, offered another view: 'According to civil and church law, if a couple is incapable of having sexual intercourse [because of impotence], then the pair cannot get married. But if it is permissible to have children without sex, it would seem unfair that those who are incapable of having sex are prevented from getting married.'[33]

It was the Church's stand that intercours is only for procreation and that procreation can only result from intercourse that most people found hardest to accept. The *Australian* accused the Vatican of 'lack of compassion and of understanding' and said in an editorial, 'an uncompromising application of this doctrine imposes hardship on innocent individuals'.[34] An American Catholic father of an IVF baby, Gary Bagnato, summed it up: 'The Church wants it all. They want you not to practise birth control so that you can conceive, but they want you to conceive their way. They're boxing you into a corner.'[35]

Many IVF patients publicly defied the Vatican's stand and accused the Church of being unfair. Lida Van Gent, Sydney's first IVF mother who now has two IVF babies, said, 'I don't think it will stop anyone going ahead, but it will bring added guilt feelings to strong Catholics. Undergoing the programme is stressful enough as it is. They don't need this extra stress from the Church.' When their first baby, David, was baptised the Van Gents made it clear he was conceived *in vitro* but the priest replied, 'He cannot be blamed for that.' Margaret Brooks, mother of the world's first frozen-embryo boy, says she and her husband have a clear conscience. 'It stems from our belief that procreation is fundamental to our faith. You have to find some peace of mind for yourself. We really believed the work of the IVF programme would be strongly supported by the Church, that it would be welcomed because it creates families.'[36]

The Church argues that artificial conception takes away some of the bond between husband and wife and that the child loses dignity because of medical intervention. However, experience shows an IVF child is born out of a deeper love and stronger commitment than most children, simply because of the determination of the couple to have a child. As Australian IVF parents, and devoted Catholics, Mick and Marian Bell said: 'To claim Andrew was not born out of an act of love is ridiculous—it may not have been sexual intercourse, but it was still an act of love. I think for a couple to go through an IVF programme is much more an act of love.'[37]

Mick Bell pointed to his eight-week-old son and asked, 'Is he evil . . . is he immoral?' His wife added: 'If you firmly believe in God, then this child was meant to be. If he wasn't meant to be, then he wouldn't be here. I think if you are a true Christian and believe in God, then you believe in everything, which includes scientists, embryo freezing, sperm banks and test-tube babies.'

Dr Georgeanna Jones, infertility pioneer of the Jones Institute, Virginia, warned the Church:

> In this twentieth century you must change your definition of conjugal love. It is unjust to burden Catholic couples with a medieval definition. Intercourse has not one function but three: reproduction in the early years; a bond to maintain family formation as childrearing becomes important; and in the later years, solace to the elderly. The Vatican viewpoint that intercourse is only for reproduction and that every intercourse must be open to the possibility of reproduction [implies] no sterile man or woman should have intercourse and post-menopausal women would be condemned to abstinence. The Vatican should redefine conjugal love between human beings in terms which emphasise all-compassing *love* rather than reduce it to sexual intercourse, an act which human beings share in common with animals. When we know the facts, we must sometimes change our definitions and even our minds.[38]

The Catholic Church believes that God is the creator of life and that by creating embryos outside the body, reproductive scientists are taking life into their own hands, and playing God. 'Fertilisation [by IVF] entrusts the life and identity of the embryo into the power of doctors and biologists. Life and death are subject to the decision of man, who thus sets himself up as the giver of life and death by decree,' the *Instruction* says. By destroying human embryos 'the researcher usurps the place of God; and sets himself up as the master of the destiny of others inasmuch as he arbitrarily chooses whom he will allow to live and whom he will send to death. God alone is the Lord of life from its beginning until its end.'

# 12
# THE EMBRYO AND EMBRYO RESEARCH

'I will maintain the utmost respect for human life from the time of conception; even under threat, I will not use my medical knowledge contrary to the laws of humanity.' *The Declaration of Geneva, passed by the World Medical Association, 1948.*

American gynaecologist Howard Jones declared at a medical conference in Vienna in 1984; 'An egg is an egg is an egg.' Few people could argue that an egg is nothing more or less than an egg. But what is an embryo—is it a human being or merely a cluster of cells that may later develop into a human being? When does human life begin—when an egg is fertilised or when a child is born, or at some point in between? Does an embryo have a soul? And if an embryo is harmed in the laboratory, could a scientist be charged with malicious damage?

At one end of the scale some people argue that the early embryo has the full status of a child or adult 'from the moment of conception' and to destroy it is to commit murder. At the other end, it is argued that the early embryo is nothing more than cellular material and that it is not entitled to rights until it is born as a live human being. In the middle, others see it as having the same rights of protection as a rare fish or bird but not necessarily a right to life.

The whole debate over the meaning of the word 'embryo' and when life begins is crucial when it comes to deciding whether or not we should allow scientists to carry out laboratory research involving embryos.

The most immediate work would ensure, first, the safety of

egg freezing, which would overcome the ethical objections to freezing embryos, and, secondly, micro-injection of sperm into eggs, seen as a major breakthrough for male infertility and as a way of improving the success rate of IVF.

Other research could lead to an understanding of and hopefully prevention of miscarriage, the development of new contraceptives and the treatment of certain childhood disorders. Some of the proposed work will reduce chromosome abnormalities such as Down's syndrome and hereditary disorders including cystic fibrosis, haemophilia, sickle cell anaemia and many other distressing and debilitating diseases. In theory, given time, there would be no more children born with hereditary mental or physical handicaps in a given community. If allowed to go ahead, this type of research will also help treat and maybe prevent immune deficiency diseases, cancer and heart disease.

But research involving embryos also has the potential to create 'super-humans', a system of using embryos to test new drugs and genetically engineered 'new' species. The public is becoming more concerned about the possibility of scientists going beyond the bounds of reasonable research. The horrific stories of scientific experiments carried out on humans during the Nazi regime are a vivid reminder of what can happen when there is no control over research. Added to this is the more recent realisation that scientists are already creating 'super-animals' and crossing different animals to make hybrids, while the emergence of embryo farms is now more than an idea in the minds of science-fiction writers; they are a future possibility discussed openly by lawyers, scientists and ethicists around the world.

*In vitro* fertilisation, or the creating of life outside the human body, is probably the most controversial medical advance we have known. But we have gone beyond 'the simple case' and have the ability now to swap, freeze, dissect, split and fuse embryos. And it is this 'tampering' with life outside the body that is the most contentious part of IVF. This is what provokes the cry, 'Where do we draw the line?'

In order to answer some of these questions and decide whether embryo research should be allowed, and under what controls, it is necessary to look at how an embryo is formed and how different people regard its moral and legal status. If, as some people have suggested, embryos should not be tampered with after 'life' begins, it is necessary to decide when that is. All cells are alive and the question is when does an *individual* life begin.

## WHEN IS AN EMBRYO AN EMBRYO?

Robert Edwards was one of the first to see a human egg fertilised outside the body and to witness later the early development of an embryo. In *A Matter of Life*, written shortly after the birth of the world's first test-tube baby in 1978, Edwards described how he regarded an early embryo:

> The beginnings of life have never failed to fascinate me. It is a period rich and strange in change and movement. The microscopic embryonic cells move elegantly and precisely along their appointed pathway, forming a succession of shapes before they emerge into the pattern of their human form . . . I am still thrilled as an egg divides and develops for, in addition to the beauty of its growth, the embryo is passing through a critical period of life of great exploration; it becomes magnificently organised, switching on its own biochemistry to increase in size, and preparing itself quickly for implantation in the womb. After that its organs form—the cells gradually become capable of development into heart, lungs, brain, eye. What a unique and wonderful process it is, as the increasing number of cells diverge and specialise in a delicate, integrated and coordinated manner. One day all the secrets of this early development may be known, and these same secrets may help us to repair the ravages and defects in the tissue of sick and ageing men and women.[1]

The *nucleus*, or core, of every cell in the human body contains 46 *chromosomes*, the tiny particles that carry the *genes*, or bags of information that determine how our bodies will function and what physical characteristics we will have, such as height, eye colour and foot size. The one exception is the sex cells, the sperm and eggs, which each contain 23 chromosomes, so that when they come together to form a single cell, it has the normal 46 chromosomes.

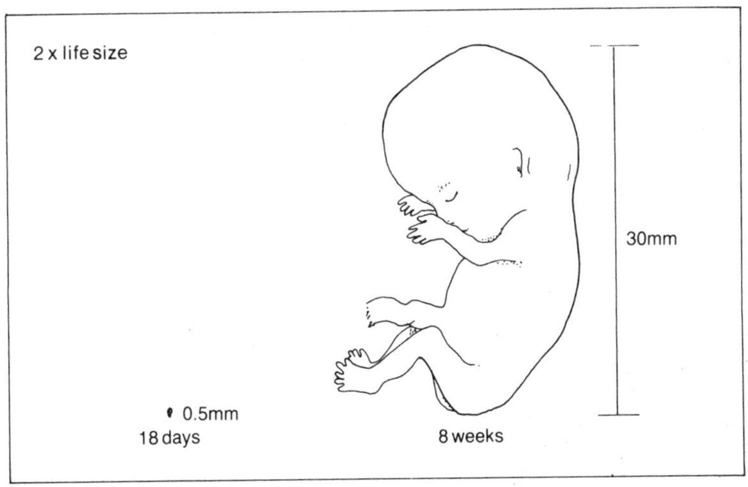


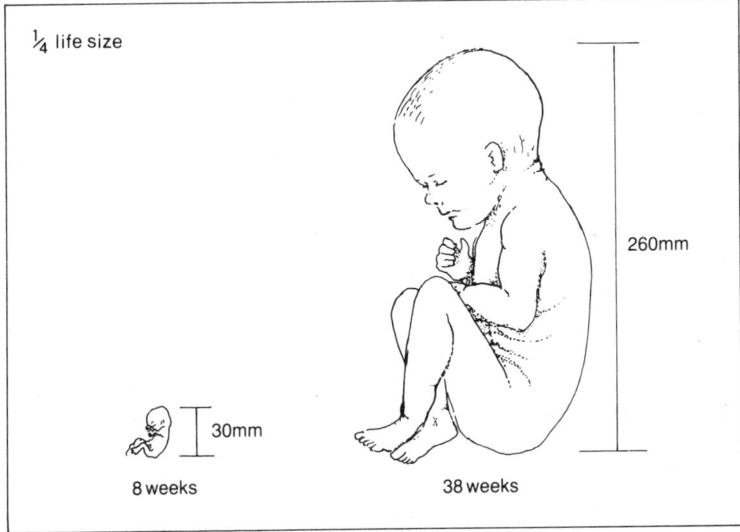


5 FROM EMBRYO TO FOETUS
The relative size of an early embryo and a baby at birth. An 18-day old embryo is only just visible with the naked eye. At the end of the eighth week the embryo has recognisable human features and from here on is known as a foetus until birth, 38 weeks after fertilisation.

Soon after ovulation, one sperm will penetrate an egg and fertilisation begins to take place. This is one of the most important stages of development and regarded by many people—possibly the majority—to be the beginning of the new life. There is no such thing as 'the moment of fertilisation', it is a gradual process that takes about 22–24 hours from insemination and involves the joining, or *fusion*, of the nucleus of the sperm and of the egg. As each nucleus contains 23 chromosomes, the new cell has a full complement of 46 chromosomes and for the first time it has all the genetic material necessary for a human being to start developing.

Fertilisation produces what is loosely called an embryo but is, strictly speaking, a zygote or conceptus which then begins to cleave or divide in half, to form two identical cells, each with a nucleus. They are encased in a membrane and form a two-cell conceptus. After 12–14 hours, each cell divides, creating four identical cells or a four-cell conceptus. Another 14–20 hours later, or about 54–60 hours after fertilisation, an eight-cell conceptus is formed.

At the fifth division (64–cell stage), about five days after fertilisation, it develops an outer layer and an inner cell mass and is known as a blastocyst. Later, the outer cells are needed for the conceptus to imbed in the uterus. The inner cells become the embryo proper. These are the first recognisable parts within the conceptus and the first sign of the embryo itself. Should this be regarded as the beginning of life?

The blastocyst continues to divide and on day six or seven begins to imbed in the uterus. This process, *implantation*, takes about a week, so implantation is usually complete at 12–14 days after fertilisation. It is the second most important event after fertilisation, and to some people this marks the point where the individual begins.

Others believe life begins at the next stage, when the inner cell mass forms what is called the embryonic disc and then the primitive streak, a band of cells that marks the spot where the embryo begins to develop. By this time all the cells have a defined function and it is no longer possible for the embryo to split, producing identical twins, although in extremely rare cases the primitive streak can partly split resulting in Siamese twins. The primitive streak appears 14–16 days after fertilisation and scientists describe this as the 'first true rudiment of the embryo' and say 'biological individuality emerges only after implantation and the emergence of the [primitive streak]'. Many scientists argue this marks the beginning of an individual.

At 17 days the first signs of the nervous system appear and by the end of the fourth week it is possible to see the rudiments of all the major organs and the cardiovascular circulation has begun. At about six weeks, the brain and genital ridge, or sex cells, begin forming. The higher parts of the brain do not show any electrical activity or nerve-cell connections until about 12 weeks. But the embryo has the identifiable features of a small baby at about eight weeks and from then on is known as a foetus until birth.

Generally, we talk about an embryo as the product of conception but technically it is one of many parts of the conceptus and it forms out of *some* of the cells of the conceptus. As British reproductive scientist Anne McLaren of the Medical Research Council said: 'It seems preferable to use the term "pre-embryo" or "conceptus" up to the end of the implantation stage and "embryo" for that small part of the pre-embryo or conceptus, first distinguishable at the primitive streak stage.'[2] Another term often used is 'pre-implantation embryo'. 'The main argument for the term pre-embryo is that most of the public believe an embryo has arms, legs, body and head,' said Carl Wood.

While there are various stages in the early development of the conceptus and embryo, they are continuous. As the British Goverment's Warnock Report said: 'There is no particular part of the developmental process that is more important than another; all are part of a continuous process ... Thus biologically there is no single identifiable stage in the development of the embryo . . . However we agree that this is an area in which some precise decision must be taken, to allay public anxiety.' The committee decided the cut-off point for research should be 14 days after fertilisation because that is the end of implantation and before the primitive streak appears.[3]

Not everyone agrees there is a cut-off point, and even among the medical profession there is lack of consensus. Professor Richard Lovell, representing the ethics committee of Australia's National Health and Medical Research Council, told the Senate Select Committee on Human Embryo Experimentation: 'Implantation is a definable landmark in the development of the foetus. It is now in place, it is latched on. It is a biological landmark. It can now go ahead.' But Jerome

Lejeune, Professor of Fundamental Genetics at the University of Paris, who discovered the chromosome abnormality that causes Down's syndrome, told the Senate hearings, 'There is no special landmark that we could use to tell us that there is a change in the status of the embryo, there are only stages of its development.'[4]

Britain's Professor Ian Donald, pioneer of ultrasound diagnostics and former Professor of Midwifery at Glasgow University, who died in 1987, said a cut-off point is a 'fatuous inconsistency seeking to differentiate the rights of a 13-day embryo from those of a 15-day-old one,' and added, 'As if any scientist would obey such a limit if he felt he was on the trail of something interesting.'[5]

The Senate Committee recognised implantation as an 'event marker' but said it 'could see nothing which marked it as other than a significant event in a continuum of development until birth' and concluded that, 'the respect due to the embryo from the process of fertilisation onwards requires its protection from destructive non-therapeutic experimentation'.[6]

The committee was against non-therapeutic destruction of a single-cell conceptus, yet the Australian Senate, like legislatures in most countries, allows abortions and the free use of contraceptives such as inter-uterine devices (IUDs) which prevent implantation and are non-therapeutically destructive. It should be remembered that at fertilisation the conceptus is a single cell and at implantation it is a spherical collection of 200–400 cells encased in a membrane, and that the primitive streak which denotes the site where the embryo will develop has not yet appeared. In contrast abortions are legal up to at least the 18th week in most countries—the 28th week in Britain—when the conceptus is a fully formed foetus with well-developed features including eyelids, genitals and toes.

Some authorities say the 'marker' is fertilisation. The New Zealand Commission on Contraception, Sterilisation and Abortion commented: 'From a biological point of view there is no argument as to when life begins. Evidence was given by eminent scientists from all over the world. None of them suggested that human life begins at any time other than conception.'[7]

Australian Senator Brian Harradine agrees, and told the 1985

Australian and New Zealand Association for the Advancement of Science (ANZAAS) congress: 'As soon as the egg is fertilised a new, separate human life begins. Its genetic characteristics have been set, once and for all, and its development proceeds on its own account. These are matters of scientific fact.' He pointed out that scientists never doubt the time the life of a mouse begins, nor have any qualms about referring to the fertilised mouse egg as an embryo, but 'they become strangely coy when it comes to the human species'.[8]

Some people, including British scientist Professor Robert Edwards and Australian philosopher Professor Peter Singer, argue that as the definition of 'brain dead' is the end of life, 'brain life' could be regarded as the beginning of life. As the nervous system does not start to develop until day 17, it could be considered then. Or, as the embryo is not sentient, does not have any feeling, before 28 days, maybe 'brain life' starts then.

It is obvious that if research on embryos is to end after a certain period, a cut-off point is needed and if that is to be based on the beginning of life, there are several possibilities:

* Fertilisation, the joining of the two nuclei containing the chromosomes.
* Implantation, when the conceptus imbeds in the uterus.
* The formation of the embryo proper, at the primitive streak stage.

A confused reader may be tempted to let the scientists decide when an individual's life begins and what experiments are reasonable. Or the lawyers or the religious leaders. The problem is that all three groups have different definitions and there are differences within each group.

## THE RELIGIOUS STATUS OF THE EMBRYO

The discussion so far has concentrated on the scientific point of view. But over the centuries, societies and various religions have established their own definitions of when life begins and what status the unborn child has, although few have considered the status of the embryo. All the major religions have a different view of what an embryo is and what constitutes the beginning of life, according to Professor John Bowker, Dean of Chapel at Trinity College, Cambridge, and former professor of religious studies. He told a 1985 conference on human embryo research organised by the Ciba Foundation in London:

> Each religion contains a totally different reflection on what human nature is and on when it begins . . . According to Western religions, human life is constituted through the union of sperm and ovum [and] endowed by God with a 'soul' . . . In the East it is entirely different. All Eastern religions believe that there are long sequences of continuity . . . Hindus believe that the enduring, continuing, indestructible continuity in all things is Brahman, the unproduced producer of all that is.[9]

The Catholic Church believes that a human being is formed at conception.

In most religions, 'life' is derived from the seeds of the man and woman and a third force, often interpreted by Christians as a soul or spirit. In Buddhism it is the *karma*-energy, or 'ghost', which, according to Buddhist writer Mahathera Nyanatiloka, is sent like a flash of lightning from a dying person to a woman's womb ready for conception. The general view in Islam is that a foetus receives a soul at about the end of the fourth month and it then becomes a person.

Although abortion is opposed by most Western religions, it is still carried out legally. According to Bowker, the majority of jurists in the four main Moslem schools of law agree that there can be no abortion after a foetus has been given a soul, at the end of the fourth month, 'unless it is reliably established that to continue the pregnancy would endanger the life of the mother. But they failed to reach a consensus on abortion before that time [although] abortion is accepted with contraception as a form of birth control.'

He pointed out that abortion is an offence at any stage for most, although not all, Moslems. But the degree varies and he quoted the Islamic writer al Ghazali:

> Abortion is a crime against an existing being. The first stages of existence are the setting of the semen in the womb and its mixing with the secretions of the woman. It is then

A "supermouse" (right) that has been injected with human growth hormone, next to a normal one. Gene manipulation in mammals has led to suggestions that the same could be done to humans to correct diseases—and to produce "super-athletes".

CSIRO workers with their first transgenic lamb that has an extra gene for growth hormone. When an egg is injected with an extra or altered gene, then fertilised, that gene is passed to all subsequent generations. Some countries have banned this type of research on humans.

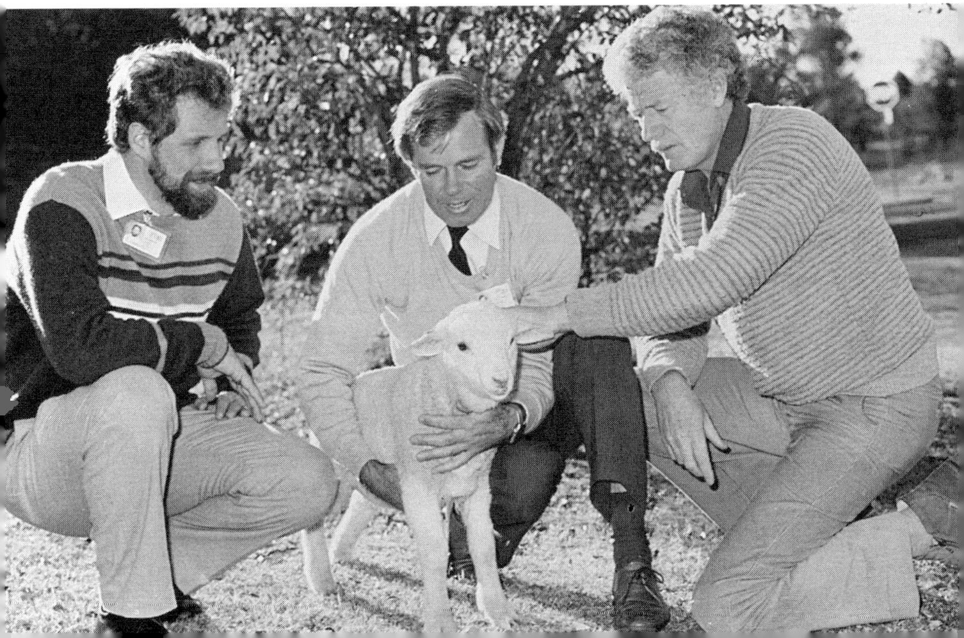

At the University of California, Davis, a 'geep' or sheep/goat chimera gestated a lamb embryo, as part of the study into immunology, reproduction, genetic abnormalities and cancer. In theory, the chimera technique could also lead to a half-human, half-animal creation.

Micromanipulation is used manually to inject a sperm into an egg to fertilise it. The egg is held by a pipette (left) while the sperm is passed through its outer shell on the end of a long, thin needle (right). The same technique is used to inject a gene into an egg in gene manipulation.

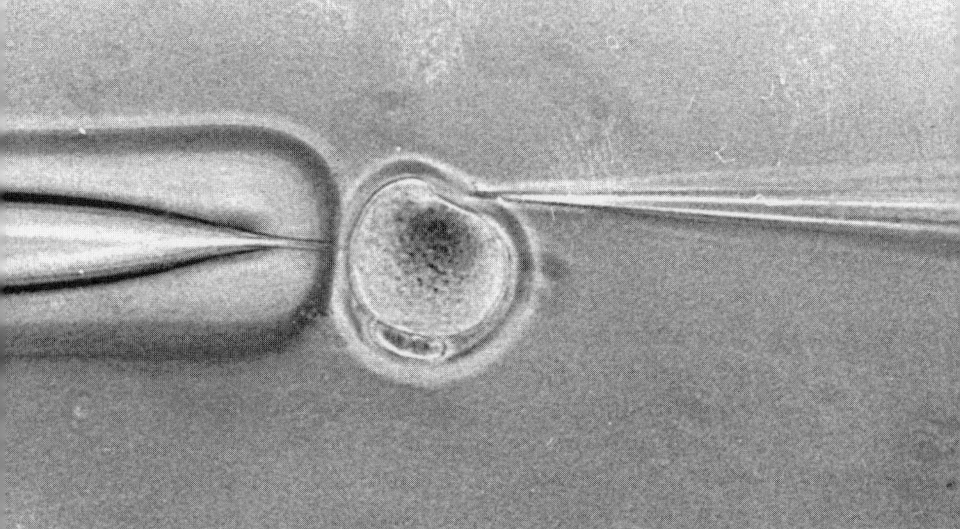

> ready to receive life. Disturbing it is a crime. When it develops further and becomes as a lump, aborting it is a greater crime. When it acquires a soul and its creation is completed, the crime becomes more grievous. The crime reaches a maximum seriousness when it is committed after it is separated alive [from the mother].[10]

Obviously, the embryo is assigned a degree of respect and entitled to special protection, but does it have the same status as a child? The Catholic Church thinks so. 'Human beings have a right to the same respect that is due to the child already born.' According to Bowker, 'The Zaydis maintain that the unformed (unensouled) foetus is in the same condition as semen, that is without human life. The Malikites (Moslem) agree that it is not a human being but it should never be disturbed or interfered with, except in the most exceptional circumstances.' He quotes a Buddhist writer, Domyo Miura: 'Buddhism takes the stand that the right to life for all beings must be respected. Buddhism regards it as a life from the very instant . . . when life is produced in the womb at conception . . . the instant the sperm joins with the egg.'[11]

Moslem and Jewish leaders have made statements about their views on artificial insemination and IVF but few of the religions have issued position papers on embryos. The most prominent exception is the Catholic Church's *Instruction* which states: 'To use human embryos for experimentation constitutes a crime against their dignity . . . keeping alive human embryos *in vivo* or *in vitro* for experimental or commercial purposes is totally opposed to human dignity.' For the same reason, the Church opposes operations, freezing and manipulations involving embryos.

## THE EMBRYO'S MORAL STATUS

When it was reported at a recent medical conference in Hong Kong that doctors in Shanghai, China, were using pancreas tissue from seven-month-old aborted foetuses for diabetic patients, the room was filled with uncomfortable murmurings. Forced abortions are common under China's policy of one child per family and the use of foetal pancreas tissue—by Western and Chinese doctors—is a promising cure for diabetes, but clearly even doctors do not approve of aborting foetuses at seven months in the name of research. What about an embryo at seven days?

One of the main discussion points is whether the embryo should be accorded the same status—the rights and respects—as a person, and if not, where should the line be drawn? If an eight-cell embryo in a laboratory dish is not a person, is an eight-day-old embryo in the womb? Is an 18-week-old foetus a person, or does a baby have to be born to have that status?

Some people argue that as it is not immoral to destroy individual eggs and sperm it should not be regarded as immoral to destroy the cell that results when they join together, and that the embryo before implantation is no different to any other collection of cells in the body.

A more realistic argument is that an embryo should be given more respect than other human cells because it has the potential to become a person and is genetically unique. However, it should not be regarded as a person because it has not yet gained the physical and mental features of a person. Therefore, it should be treated with special respect but not the same level of respect as a person.

After considering 270 submissions, the Australian Senate Committee on embryo experimentation concluded: 'Until the contrary is demonstrated beyond reasonable doubt, the embryo of the human species should be regarded as if it were a human subject for the purposes of biomedical ethics.' However, it added: 'The committee has not attempted to attribute the status of "person" to the embryo in either the philosophical or legal senses.'[12]

The Warnock Committee, on the other hand, did not attempt to define the moral status of the embryo, but instead drew up guidelines on how the human embryo should be treated which included recommendations on donating, freezing and culturing embryos.

Peter Singer, Professor of Philosophy at Monash University, draws a parallel between the early embryo and the common garden lettuce. He rejects the suggestion that embryos must be protected just because they are of the human race. He told a recent Office of Technology Assessment seminar in Washington:

> If we ask why humans should have some right to life above rights possessed by dogs or pigs or marmosets, the difference is our superior mental powers, our self-awareness, our rationality, our moral sense, our autonomy, which make us 'truly human', make us *persons*. A human embryó is not a human being in this sense. The early embryo has no mental qualities, no brain, no nervous system. So far as its mental life goes, it has no more awareness than a lettuce. 'Human' means 'a being with certain mental qualities' [also] 'human' means 'member of the species *homo sapiens*'. Surely we must look at its actual characteristics, not just the species to which it belongs. If ET and similar visitors from other planets turn out to be sensitive, thinking, planning beings, who get homesick just like we do, would it be acceptable to kill them simply because they are not members of our species?[13]

Singer, who is also director of the Centre for Human Bioethics in Melbourne, caused an outcry at the 1986 Health, Law and Ethics conference when he suggested that early embryos could be regarded as having the same status as animals, and that because they do not feel pain they could be used instead of rabbits for certain experiments.

> Up to the point at which the embryo has not developed [a nervous system] it has not developed the capacity to feel pain or feel anything, has no degree of consciousness and no sensory awareness. I believe, in terms of its rights or moral status, it doesn't even reach the level of the standard laboratory mammal. It's more like a vegetative existence.[14]

At the same conference, George Annas, Professor of Health Law at Boston University, replied: 'If you really believe there is no difference between a rabbit and a human embryo you should be happy to bottle human embryos in a jar and sell them to gourmets to eat,' at which point he stunned the audience by eating some unidentified matter from a glass jar. 'You could go down to the corner store and buy a roasted rabbit—most people wouldn't have any trouble with that—but I suggest most of the people in the world would have a lot of trouble eating human embryos.' Annas argued that the embryo needs to be protected but does not have any rights, and he drew a parallel with protection of Australia's Great Barrier Reef marine life: 'The human embryo is worthy of protection but you can't say it is worthy of having rights, just like the Barrier Reef cod—he is worth protecting but he doesn't have rights.'

## THE EMBRYO'S LEGAL STATUS

In February 1985 the British MP and former Health Minister Enoch Powell introduced the Unborn Children (Protection) Bill to the House of Commons in an attempt to ban donation and research involving embryos. It was not passed, but the bill aroused considerable public debate and three other MPs prepared similar bills. The name 'unborn children' reflects the stand taken by many people, although it begs the questions; can a two- or four-cell conceptus be regarded as a child? Should it have the same protection, respect, dignity and legal status of a child?

Generally, a pregnant woman knows she has life in her womb when she first feels the baby move, or kick. Gerard Wright, a Queen's Counsel (QC) who fought for index-linked compensation for Thalidomide victims in Britain, points out that under criminal law an offence can be committed if the child is 'quick', meaning alive, 'In the seventeenth century a foetus was thought to be alive, and therefore protected by the law, when its mother experienced the physical sensation known as "quickening" [which] was accepted as evidence of life.'[15]

Sir Cecil Clothier, a member of Britain's Voluntary Licensing Authority and former health service commissioner, says that at the time parliament passed the Offences Against the Person Act in 1861 it was common to ask a woman if she was 'quick with child'. He told the opening of the Ciba Foundation seminar:

> It is slightly shocking that we still have in force a law that only reflects our state of knowledge in 1861 of how and

> when life begins. This illustrates how far science has travelled while the law has almost stood still. The notion of protecting an embryo didn't enter the minds of the draftsmen at the time.[16]

Under American, British and Australian law, neither the embryo nor foetus is seen as a *person*, nor is it given the same status as a child or adult.

The ethics committee of the US Department of Health, Education and Welfare in its 1979 report on research and IVF said: 'The human embryo is entitled to profound respect; but this respect does not necessarily encompass the full legal and moral rights attributed to persons.'[17]

The American Fertility Society takes a similar view: 'Currently, the pre-embryo is not a legal subject in its own right and is not protected by laws against homicide or wrongful death ... the pre-embryo is not yet individual, because twinning can still occur. Thus, it is not surprising that the law does not recognise the pre-embryo itself as a legal subject.'[18]

In its July 1987 report, *Artificial Conception*, the New South Wales Law Reform Commission stated the position of English law as used in Australia: 'Traditionally, it is the event of live birth which confers legal personality and the rights associated with being a human person. The statutory offence of murder requires the victim of such a crime to have "breathed and been wholly born into the world".' It pointed out that the regulation covering abortion is aimed at protecting the mother's health and life, not the foetus. And the same applies with miscarriage—a person can be charged with attempting to cause a miscarriage whether or not the foetus the woman is carrying is dead, and even if the woman is not pregnant.[19]

According to the Warnock Committee the human embryo *per se* has no legal status. 'It is not, under law in the UK, accorded the same status as a child or an adult, and the law does not treat the human embryo as having a right to life ... Nevertheless, we agreed the embryo ought to have a special status ... We recommend that the embryo of the human species should be afforded some protection in law.'[20]

In Western society, a baby born alive after a 40-week pregnancy is given the full status of a person. So is a baby born prematurely if he lives. However, if a baby was born prematurely at 30 weeks and was the next day killed, the assailant would be charged with murder, but if a 30-week pregnant woman and her unborn baby were killed, the murder charge would be for the mother only.

There have been attempts to give an unborn foetus similar status to a child, for example, if a foetus is injured or killed when a pregnant woman is assaulted. In Connecticut, US, in March 1986, a 28-year-old woman who was six months pregnant was shot dead and her baby died. The killer, a woman, was charged by the State Attorney with murdering the mother and causing the death of 'baby boy Amos'. But the Superior Court judge dismissed the second charge, saying that state law did not recognise an unborn child as a person.

In England and Wales, damages can be recovered, in certain circumstances, when an embryo or foetus is injured in the womb by someone other than the mother, under the Congenital Disabilities Act. Under this law, the embryo *in vivo* is given certain protection. But there is no such law covering embryos *in vitro*.

One prominent case that tested the legal status of the embryo was in the US in July 1978. Doris and John Del Zio of Fort Lauderdale, Florida, sued New York's Columbia-Presbyterian Medical Center and its chief of obstetrics and gynaecology, Dr Raymond Vande Wiele, for $1.5 million for the deliberate destruction six years earlier of an embryo that had been created *in vitro* from their own gametes by Landrum Shettles (see p 171). They sued for wrongful deprivation of property and claimed they suffered severe mental and physical pain after Wiele destroyed the laboratory culture, ending their only chance of having a child. 'I couldn't believe he had murdered my baby. I lay in bed all night thinking how could a man do this to another person,' the mother-to-be told the court. The jury awarded damages for psychological harm but dismissed the property claim.

Ruth Hubbard, Professor of Biology at Harvard University, reports that the supervisor of the Santa Clara Juvenile Court Unit in California drafted legislation that would 'make the foetus a dependant of the juvenile court system in situations where the mother's behaviour is judged to be harmful [and] if a pregnant woman is not willing to follow court orders, she should be placed in a medically controlled environment—possibly against her will—where she and her foetus could be supervised.'[21]

Even where there is a law covering the status of the foetus, it does not extend to the embryo. One exception—possibly the only one—is the law enacted in the Australian state of Victoria in 1984, specifically to protect the embryo against laboratory manipulation or experimentation. It carries a four-year imprisonment for anyone conducting a 'prohibited procedure' on embryos outside the body.

## TO RESEARCH OR NOT TO RESEARCH

George Bernard Shaw once wrote, 'Atrocities are not less atrocities when they occur in laboratories and are called medical research,' and the crux of the decision whether or not to allow embryo research is that the very nature of experimentation involves the loss of embryos. Many people argue that using embryos for research knowing they will be destroyed is not the same as the accidental loss of an IVF embryo intended for a pregnancy, and they oppose embryo research because they see it as deliberately destroying innocent human life which cannot defend itself, as a person can in a life-and-death situation. Teresa Iglesias, of Britain's Roman Catholic Centre for the Study of Health Care Ethics, points out, 'It is never normally permissible for you to take a person's life.'

French geneticist Professor Jerome Lejeune believes there is no need for embryos to be grown for research. He says genetic research can be done with existing techniques or by using aborted foetal tissue, and certain genetic diseases can be prevented by giving vitamins to pregnant women who are at risk.

Many of the objections to embryo research are on religious and moral grounds, as discussed. However, support for research is just as strong as opposition, although it is generally less vocal. Prominent physicians, scientists, lawyers and philosophers have all publicly discussed whether or not research should be allowed, and generally those who support the idea cite four main reasons for allowing research: to improve IVF and other infertility treatments; to improve understanding of natural conception and why it sometimes fails; to detect genetic diseases; and to develop contraceptives.

Australian gynaecologist and IVF pioneer Carl Wood says the ability to carry out IVF means that for 'the first time man can study his early development in the laboratory and I believe the future benefits to man of research in this area will dwarf all the research hitherto done on man's degenerative process.'

French expert, Professor Jean Cohen, Head of Obstetrics and Gynaecology at the Hôpital de Sèvres, Paris, believes research involving embryos is essential for improving IVF, and reducing miscarriages, ectopic pregnancies and multiple pregnancies in both IVF and natural conceptions.

British scientist Dr Anne McLaren, who was also a member of the Warnock Committee, outlined some of her reasons for allowing research:

> To improve the success rate of IVF, to look at chromosome abnormalities, testing new compounds for contraception and the prevention of genetic and chromosome defects. Chromosome studies is an area of critical importance because chromosome abnormalities are one of the criteria that will indicate damage to the conceptus. And there are a number of research projects on male infertility including micro-injection.

She said a recently developed compound blocks the maturation of eggs and offers a promising new approach to contraception, but it may allow a few eggs to be fertilised which could then develop abnormally and this could be tested on laboratory-cultured embryos.

Soon after the release of the Warnock Report in June 1984, Robert Edwards explained in a newspaper interview why he and other members of the committee recommended that embryo research should be allowed: 'To place an embryo in a woman without knowing that everything has been done to make sure that it is as normal as we can possibly make it, is far more unethical than studying embryos in the first place. It is the interests of the child that is eventually produced that must come first.'[22] Edwards and several other experts have since expressed concern that egg freezing was developed, and babies born, without the technique being tested scientifically—the resultant embryos were transferred to women without being analysed.

He added: 'All this research is not designed to produce ogres. It is designed to help human life, to put things right, to provide new treatment and to help patients. The losers, if it is prevented from happening, will be patients, not doctors and scientists.'

The losers will be fertile people as well as those who are childless. As the Ontario Law Reform Commission said in its 1985 report on artificial reproduction: 'Research on human embryos should be encouraged in order to further our knowledge of embryonic development so that all persons, fertile and infertile, might benefit.'[23]

It would be unethical *not* to carry out embryo research, according to Dr John Loudon of Edinburgh University, a member of Britain's Voluntary Licensing Authority. He believes banning research on embryos when foetuses up to 20 weeks are aborted and disposed of without ceremony is 'ethically absurd'. Speaking at the 1986 World Congress on Fertility and Sterility, he said research was necessary to improve the success rate of IVF and to increase understanding of why pregnancies fail. 'To accept a take-home baby rate of 17 per cent, without making every effort to improve it, is unjust for the couples concerned. Defined and approved research is also needed to unravel the causes of pregnancy failure and chromosomal abnormalities. It is entirely ethical and should be encouraged.' He said the legislation in Victoria that banned certain research was 'tragic'.[24]

The Victorian legislation was based on recommendations of the Waller Committee, two members of which disagreed with a ban. In their dissenting report the two Melbourne University Professors, Priscilla Kincaid-Smith (Medicine) and Roger Pepperell (Obstetrics and Gynaecology) said that preventing attempts to improve IVF would be inhumane and that it would be 'contrary to the value of human life', especially if it restricted research on abnormalities and attempts to improve IVF pregnancy rates.

Melbourne embryologist Alan Trounson believes prohibition is contrary to medical ethics. 'It is ludicrous that the prevention of embryo experimentation may result in increased risk of genetic abnormality and birth defects. Medical ethics argue that we be as certain as possible about the techniques we develop and use. The prevention of embryonic research promotes the opposite.'[25]

John Bowker says research could be seen as a sacrifice on the part of the embryos:

> If we ask young people to die in a just war, might we ask embryos to die in a just war against a genetic defect? . . . I ask whether it makes moral sense to say, 'Greater love hath no embryo than this, that it lay down its life for the more abundant life of others'—life on the other side of the healing of infertility, genetic defects, and the like?[26]

Alexander Capron, Professor of Law at the University of Southern California, believes embryo research is acceptable as long as there is no harm to the baby born.

> My major concern is the welfare of the child that is to be born. To be discarded is one thing, to be possible to be born is something else. An experiment that occurs on a six or seven-month-old foetus is a greater risk than a two-week old embryo, not because of the difference in age but because the two-week-old embryo in a petri dish in a laboratory is not going to be born.

Some authorities have warned that IVF might cease if embryo research is not allowed. It is hard to imagine IVF disappearing, but it has been claimed that unless the success rate is improved, health authorities will give it less priority, the public will lose faith and eventually IVF researchers will be forced to abandon their projects. Mary Warnock believes it is not only legitimate but essential that research be allowed: 'If the techniques of treating infertility through IVF are to continue, research is necessary.'

Peter Singer told the OTA meeting: 'Without the prospect of such improvement, it may be doubted if IVF is worth the resources now being allocated to it.'[13] The New South Wales Law Reform Commission said in its 1987 report on IVF: 'Legislative prohibition of important IVF research may bring to an end IVF as a part of medical practice.'[27] The National Health and Medical Research Council's ethics committee expressed a similar view: 'We question whether it would be ethically acceptable for the practice of IVF to continue if research critical for its improvement was made unlawful.'[28]

In some cases research can be done with animal, rather than human, embryos and a basic principle of medical research is that all possible experiments be conducted on animals before transferring the technique to humans. However, this is not always possible, nor does it give the best results. Animal studies for the contraceptive pill, for example, did not reveal all the risks, nor benefits, which only emerged after 25 years' use by millions of women.

A frequently expressed concern is the lack of controls over such research and the fact that often the general public does not know exactly what is going on in the laboratories. However, most IVF centres affiliated with a hospital or university are governed by that institution's ethics committee which decides what procedures should be allowed. Several authorities, including the Warnock Committee, have suggested embryo research be licensed and controlled by an independent body. In November 1987, three and a half years after receiving the Warnock Report, the British Government announced it would set up a statutory licensing authority to regulate IVF and embryo research.

## THE PUBLIC'S VIEW ON RESEARCH

Until scientists discovered the stages of early human development in the 1940s, and reproduced them in the laboratory in the 1970s, the community had no reason to question the religious, moral or legal status of a two- or-eight cell embryo. Although there has been considerable public discussion on IVF, there have been few surveys to gauge public opinion on the use of embryos in the laboratory. However, four important surveys have put the question to three distinct groups: couples on an IVF programme, women of reproductive age and the general public.

The first was in Australia in 1982, when IVF was still in its infancy. Patsy Littlejohn of the Phillip Institute of Technology in Melbourne gave detailed questionnaires to couples on the Queen Victoria/Monash University IVF programme and of the 114 patients who replied, 68 per cent said it was all right for any embryos not transferred in IVF to be used for research, although they were not told what type of research. Twenty-four per cent said 'no' and 8 per cent were unsure or did not answer. Those who replied were predominantly professionals with secondary level education or higher. More than 40 per cent were of no denomination, 22 per cent were Catholic and 20 per cent Church of England.[29]

A larger study by M.E. Adler of Edinburgh University, published in 1986, questioned women of reproductive age, including more than 1,000 attending a family planning clinic, more than 500 at an antenatal clinic and a smaller number at an infertility clinic. Women in the three groups expressed almost identical views: 60–70 per cent approved of research on embryos up to 14 days if the aim was to improve understanding of congenital abnormalities or improve IVF technique; and less than 10 per cent opposed embryo research, regardless of the aim. About 12 per cent of the women were Catholic and 20 per cent Church of England. Although those questioned were women of reproductive age and therefore not representative of the whole community, this is the age group most likely to benefit from embryo research.[30]

In July 1984, a few weeks after the Warnock Report was completed, the British public were asked their opinion on embryo research and a poll commissioned by the Order of Christian Unity, which found 51 per cent believed human embryo experiments should be banned by law, 85 per cent said there should be a law to control experimentation, and 92 per cent opposed cross-species fertilisation.[31]

A year later, while Enoch Powell's Protection of the Unborn Child Bill was being debated, in another public opinion poll more than half of those questioned (52 per cent) said they approved of the use of embryos in research work to improve knowledge of the cause of disease and handicap in newly born children; a quarter (26 per cent) disapproved and less than a quarter (22 per cent) said they had not thought about it enough to say.[32]

Of those who approved, there was very little difference between the age groups up to 64, and the highest disapproval rate was among those over 65 and women. More men than women approved of embryo research (57 per cent compared with 48 per cent). Although much of the research would apply to women, more men than women felt they had given it sufficient thought to form an opinion. People most confident about expressing an opinion were those (men and women) in the 35–64 age group, which represents women in the latter half of, or beyond, their reproductive age.

## THE GOVERNMENT'S VIEW

Several national and state governments in Europe, America and Australia have set up committees to consider whether embryo research should be allowed, and if so, under what circumstances. The Victorian Government in Australia was the first, and at the time of writing the only one, to pass legislation on embryos created in the laboratory. Recommendations or draft legislation in some countries, such as Austria, have been shelved because of a change of government. Other governments, such as those in Britain and Spain, have debated legislation in their respective parliaments without enacting law.

The Victorian legislation was based on the final report of the Waller Committee, set up by the Goverment in 1982 and headed by Law Reform Commissioner and Professor of Law Louis Waller. It recommended embryo research be limited to excess embryos produced by IVF patients but not used; that the research be immediate and in an approved project; and that the embryos not be allowed to develop in the laboratory beyond 14 days after fertilisation. All these recommendations, except the last, became law in November 1984. Three years later, after considerable public debate and criticism that the legislation was too strict, it was amended to allow scientists to carry out research on a specially created conceptus before the nuclei of the sperm and egg fuse, which occurs about 22–24 hours after insemination.

In 1979, the US Department of Health, Education and

Welfare's ethics committee released its report on IVF in which it approved of embryo research in principle and said it would be permissible to culture embryos *in vitro* for up to 14 days. However, embryo research in the US has been restricted by a ban on the use of federal funds for foetal research, which has been taken to include embryo research. The ban has effectively stopped all embryo research in the country because it indirectly affects even private institutes, which do not want to risk losing federal funds for other research projects by doing embryo research.

In addition, 25 states have statutes restricting foetal research and most of them would apply to embryo research, according to Lori Andrews of the American Bar Association.

> The Missouri statute, for example, applies to 'the offspring of human beings from the moment of conception until birth'. Others neglect to define the term foetus. The Maine statute applies to 'any live human foetus whether intrauterine or extrauterine' without defining this. Legally, embryo research is allowed in almost all states if it is to benefit that particular embryo. Non-therapeutic research is allowed in 25 states that have no laws on foetal research. In most states non-therapeutic embryo research *is* allowed, but physicians and scientists are overwhelmingly deterred from undertaking it because of a lack of funding, perceived social opposition and the lack of clarity in rules governing foetal research.[33]

In other countries where there are no laws or government guidelines on embryo experimentation, the rules have been left to ethics committees or medical bodies. Doctors and scientists in West Germany, for example, are prohibited by the Board of Physicians from creating more embryos than would be transferred to the woman at one time. Under the guidelines, imposed in 1986, the freezing of embryos is not allowed, which is why several centres are developing pronuclear egg freezing which is considered ethically more acceptable. Non-therapeutic research on embryos is allowed if it has been approved by an ethics commission which lays down strict prerequisites and conditions.

All IVF centres in Australia are asked to follow guidelines

on embryo research laid down by the Federal Government's National Health and Medical Research Council. Centres that do not comply will not be registered by the Fertility Society of Australia, but there is no legal compulsion to comply.

In 1985, the Ontario Law Reform Commission recommended to the Government that research be allowed on pre-implantation embryos, provided it was at research centres that had an ethics committee and the project had been approved by the Ministry of Health. So far, none of the LRC recommendations have been made into law.

In Austria, a committee of doctors, scientists, lawyers and religious representatives, set up by the Ministry of Health, drafted a 28-point protocol on IVF and the use of gametes and embryos in which it approved of research involving embryos within 14 days of fertilisation but recommended embryos not be used for routine tests or commercial purposes.

A similar committee in France, the National Consultative Ethics Committee, is strongly against research involving embryos unless it is to treat the infertility of a particular couple—a stand which prevents research aimed at helping other couples and future generations.

And in Britain, the non-government Voluntary Licensing Authority's guidelines allowed embryos to be used for research, provided they are not cultured for more than 14 days, that they are not later transferred to a woman and that the gamete donors had given signed consent. In November 1987, the government released its proposed legislation on IVF and embryo research which gave two options: MPs could vote to ban all embryo research or they could legislate to allow research on embryos up to 14 days.

## THE 14-DAY LIMIT

Several committees decided there should be a limit to the time embryos are kept in the laboratory, and most recommend 14 days because that is when the primitive streak appears, implantation is complete, the cells of the embryo proper have lined up and beyond this point it is not possible for identical twins to form (except Siamese twins). Opponents of research say the line should be drawn at day zero, while others, mainly scientists, say 28 days would be more beneficial as some disorders that could be prevented are not detectable until then.

Four major British medical institutions suggested three different times to the Warnock Committee: the Royal College of Obstetricians and Gynaecologists favoured 17 days because that is when the nervous system begins to develop, the British Medical Association opted for 14 days and the Royal College of Physicians and the Medical Research Council suggested the end of implantation, at about day 12.

The 14-day limit was first proposed by the US Department of Health in 1979 and has since been adopted by the American Fertility Society, the Royal College of Obstetricians and Gynaecologists and the Ontario Law Reform Commission in Canada, the Warnock Committee and the Council for Science and Society in Britain, the Waller Committee in Victoria, the Dutch Health Council and Spain's Special Commission on IVF. The French National Ethics Committee recommended a seven-day limit and Germany's Benda Committee only allows embryos to culture up to the first cleavages, about 6–12 hours after fertilisation.

Robert Edwards suggests a movable line, and told the Ciba seminar:

> The danger of drawing a line is that it may have to be modified later. Once the line is drawn, there could be far more difficulty in modifying it than if it had not been drawn in the first place. A better alternative is to establish a powerful ethical authority which demands justification for every piece of research. The 14-day rule is too generous for some research; for example the study of chromosomes can largely be done at day five. Studies on the haemopoietic (blood forming) system would require embryos at day 14 or perhaps later. For the myocardium (heart tissue) it would be necessary to go to day 20. Each of these is a legitimate study, yet if an arbitrary line is drawn some of them are excluded [and] a 14-day rule would allow some scientists to let embryos grow for too long.[34]

Bob Williams, Professor of Biochemistry at the University of London, disagreed and replied:

> Drawing a line is the only way of reassuring people. The more medical researchers say it would be very interesting to do more experiments later, the less reassured the public will be, and the more need there is for a line. I agree it is difficult to change the line—that is part of its point—but it is not unchangeable. Your objection to this line seems to be that it makes things slightly more difficult for your colleagues. But that is what it is for . . . The rule says 'at most 14 days', not that every experiment has to go till 14 days.[35]

Sir Cecil Clothier, Britain's former health service commissioner, concluded: 'It is workable, it is observable, it has a quality of certainty about it—there is an important change at 14 days.'[36]

Alan Trounson agrees with Edwards that the line could be movable if necessary, and he told the Senate Select Committee in Australia, 'I accept that it [14 days] is a reasonable time [but] if suddenly we get the answer to cancer or every debilitating disease by studying 200 28-day-old embryos, I would be prepared to put that to the appropriate ethics committee and allow it to make a decision.'[37]

This argument for a flexible line has drawn criticism from Australian Senator Brian Harradine whose controversial Human Embryo Experimentation Bill led to the Senate Select Committee's enquiry in 1986. He told parliament, 'Society will start off with 14 days and then there will be a demand for an extension and we will see it creep up until 20 days and then 28 days and so on—all for the purpose of satisfying these scientists who can see the opportunity to experiment with more mature cells or tissue.'[38]

Harradine's argument is shared by many other people who see the culturing of embryos—for whatever purpose—as the beginning of the slippery slope, with no end in sight.

At the time the American, Canadian, British, Dutch, Spanish and Australian committees recommended a 14-day limit, the longest an embryo had been officially cultured in the laboratory was nine days. However, two teams—one in England and one in Sweden—are now reported to have grown an embryo for 12 days. This is one of the few cases where guidelines on reproductive technologies have come ahead of the scientists' ability.

## SPARE EMBRYOS AND CREATED EMBRYOS

In some types of research the embryo can be studied without harming it. Sometimes one or more cells can be removed and analysed without jeopardising the embryo's chance of developing. But at this stage most research ends with the destruction of the embryo. In the discussion so far there has been no distinction between embryos that are left over from IVF treatment and those created specifically for research. Indeed, several of the major committees and reports on embryo research have not made a distinction, but many people say there is a very important difference.

Before scientists developed a method of freezing embryos for later use, 'spare' embryos were common. Doctors would retrieve and fertilise as many eggs as possible to give the couple the maximum chance of a pregnancy, but often not all were transferred for fear of a multiple pregnancy. This left 'spare' embryos, and depending on the policy of the clinic and the wishes of the couple, they were discarded, used for research or donated to another infertile couple. This is still the procedure in clinics where freezing is not yet used. When eggs or embryos are defective and not suitable to be transferred they are often used for research and are usually included in the group of 'spare' embryos, but these embryos are limited in number and most proposed research requires 'healthy' embryos.

The alternative is to create embryos specifically for research. The sperm and egg have to be donated by people other than patients wanting to receive embryos. Obtaining the sperm poses little problem as the men who donate sperm for artificial insemination or IVF can state whether or not they agree to it also being used for research. But obtaining eggs is much more difficult. There are three main sources: women who have more eggs retrieved for IVF than are needed, which is rare because they can all be fertilised and in most cases frozen for later use; non-IVF women who are having their tubes tied or ovaries removed; and women who volunteer to have eggs retrieved for a friend or relative.

The main argument against creating embryos for research is that there is no intention to transfer the embryos and give them a chance to develop, therefore 'life' is created for the purpose of destruction.

The use of spare or created embryos is a significant ethical question, yet there is no consensus. The decisions of three major committees made up of doctors, scientists, theologians, psychologists, lawyers, social workers and representatives of parents and parents-to-be give some idea of how the community is split over the issue: the Waller Committee approved experiments on spare embryos but not those created specifically for research; the Ontario Law Reform Commission did not make a distinction between the two; and the Warnock Committee approved the use of both spare and specially created embryos.

In arguing against creating embryos, the Waller Committee concluded: 'This individual and genetically unique human entity may not be formed for any other human purpose however laudable.'[39] One of the committee's nine members presented a dissenting report in which he recommended limiting research to pronuclear fertilised eggs. Dr the Reverend Francis Harman, Presiding Judge of the National Tribunal of the Catholic Church, said:

> To bring embryos into existence and freeze them is to derogate grossly from their intrinsic worth; it reduces them to a level of objects for the satisfaction of others while placing their vital continuance in serious jeopardy. To bring them into existence solely for the purpose of experimentation would be still more reprehensible, giving grimmer meaning than he ever contemplated to Thomas Hood's lines: 'Oh God! that bread should be so dear, and flesh and blood so cheap!'[40]

But Barbara Burton of the Infertility Federation of Australasia says infertile patients take the opposite view: 'It is perhaps ethically preferable for embryos to be created specifically for research, rather than using spare embryos generated in IVF programmes, as infertile couples would prefer to see all spare embryos frozen for use in a later treatment cycle.'[41]

Not everyone agrees that there is a difference between spare and specially created embryos. David Baird, Professor of Obstetrics and Gynaecology at Edinburgh University and a former consultant to the WHO steering committee on infertility, says as far as the embryo is concerned there is no difference. He told the Ciba seminar, 'I can see no difference, from the embryo's point of view, between whether it is brought into being for the purpose of being experimented on or whether it happens to be surplus to requirements for therapeutic purposes.'[42] Added Antonia Gerard, lecturer and specialist in family law, 'Provided scientists produce the results quickly, it doesn't really matter whether one uses spare embryos or deliberately created ones. It is the time limit which is of overwhelming importance.'[43]

Gordon Dunstan, Professor of Moral and Social Theology at the University of London and a member of the Voluntary Licensing Authority, commented, 'I could not say that the creation of embryos *ad hoc* is morally illicit. If we accept research on "spares" we can accept the others too.'[44] The Warnock Committee expressed a similar view: 'If research on embryos is to be permitted at all, it makes no difference whether these embryos happen to be available or were brought into existence for the sake of research.'[45]

Dr Robert Jansen, obstetrician/gynaecologist of Royal Prince Alfred Hospital, Sydney, pointed out to the Senate Select Committee that the books can be fiddled:

> It is a fallacy to distinguish between surplus embryos and specially created embryos . . . any intelligent administrator of an IVF programme can, by minor changes in his ordinary clinical way of going about things, change the number of embryos that are fertilised. There would be no purpose at all in enshrining in legislation a difference between surplus and specially created embryos.[46]

The Senate committee concluded that it found any difference 'ethically unsound and practically most unlikely to be maintained'.[46]

Even if creating embryos is permitted, there are logistic problems in getting enough eggs. Some women who have had IVF treatment say they would be prepared to donate their eggs for research as a thank you, whether or not they were successful. Margaret Irving, for example, is a 40-year-old Melbourne woman who did not become pregnant after three

IVF attempts but says the least she can do for the programme is give the research team some of her eggs. British scientist Anne McLaren of the Medical Research Council said: 'If I was being sterilised I would feel it was inherently wasteful for the oocytes (eggs) not to be used if they could be.'[47]

## WHAT TYPE OF RESEARCH?

Shortly after Louise Brown was born, Robert Edwards wrote: 'One day all the secrets of this early development may be known, and these same secrets may help us to repair the ravages and defects in the tissue of sick and ageing men and women.'[1] Now Edwards and several other scientists are working towards solving the mystery of inherited diseases and blood disorders. In many cases they are limited to using spare embryos and progress is slow. Others are testing the safety of micro-injection and egg freezing. In addition, several groups are working on being able to determine genetic abnormalities and the sex of embryos before a pregnancy is established. And some are trying to find ways to transplant embryonic cells into infants and children to cure diseases such as leukaemia.

To date, scientists have the ability to biopsy, split, sex and grow embryos. In most cases it is to detect genetic and chromosomal abnormalities and it is necessary to look at what these abnormalities involve before discussing what the research entails. It is worth remembering that one in 50 babies in the Western world are born with an abnormality and in most cases this is due to a genetic problem.

British geneticist Professor David Weatherall recently described searching for a gene, known as gene probing, as like looking for an ant standing on Mount Everest. The reason? A single gene, which directs a single feature or function such as eye colour or production of an enzyme, is encoded in about one part in six million of the *DNA* (deoxyribonucleic acid) which is in the nucleus of each cell and contains all the information needed by a cell to replicate and grow. This long double strand of DNA that looks like a twisting ladder is cut into 23 sections, or 23 pairs of chromosomes, each of which is made up of thousands of genes, or units of DNA. The number of genes varies with each species but man is thought to have as many as 100,000.

Abnormalities can occur in genes or chromosomes and they are either passed from parent to child as inherited disorders or result from a mutation, a change, at any time, either as a freak of nature or because of environmental factors such as exposure to drugs, chemicals or radiation.

Women have 44 chromosomes plus two X chromosomes and men have 44 plus an X and a Y. An egg divides to produce two identical halves, each with 22 chromosomes and an X. The sperm cell divides to produce one sperm with 22 and an X, and one with 22 and a Y. If the X-carrying sperm fertilises the egg, the embryo that results has 22X + 22X i.e., 44XX, so a girl will be born. Fertilisation with the Y-carryng sperm produces 44XY, and is therefore, a boy.

Occasionally two sperm fertilise an egg, producing an embryo with 69 chromosomes, known as a *triploid* embryo. It usually either fails to implant or ends in a spontaneous abortion, although in extremely rare cases such children have been born but have never lived more than a few hours. When they first developed IVF, Robert Edwards and Jean Purdy analysed more than 100 embryos to check that the chromosomes were normal and they did not find any triploids, but their fourth IVF pregnancy, just after Louise Brown was born, ended in a miscarriage and subsequent analysis showed it was a triploid.

Sometimes an embryo has 45, 47, 48 or 49 chromosomes, instead of 46 and the result is usually a miscarriage and occasionally a birth. The most common example is Down's syndrome, or mongolism, where there are 3 chromosomes at position 21, instead of a pair.

When the extra chromosome is an X or a Y it usually leads to an intersex abnormality. The affected person's sexuality is understated or they show slight traits of the opposite sex. One example is Klinefelter's syndrome where men have an extra X (female) chromosome which leads to exceptionally small testes, almost no facial or chest hair and occasionally small breasts. The sufferers are almost always infertile.

Sometimes one of the sex chromosomes is missing, giving

just 45 chromosomes. No Y (male) chromosome produces all women, with Turner's syndrome. The women usually have short stature and immature reproductive organs including a small uterus and sometimes no ovaries.

The chances of an abnormality occurring in the egg increase as a woman gets older, which is why in Western countries women over 36 usually have genetic screening.

Certain genetic defects can be detected in the foetus by amniocentesis, which involves withdrawing cells from the amniotic fluid around the foetus at about the 16th week of pregnancy and by chorion villus sampling (CVS), by analysing a portion of cells from the embryo's outer membrane at about eight weeks.

## EMBRYO BIOPSYING

Now the biological clock is being turned back further—to detect genetic diseases in embryos before they implant in the womb, in the first few days after fertilisation. CVS was a major emotional advance over amniocentesis because it is far less traumatic for a couple to have a termination at eight weeks than at 16 weeks if an abnormality is discovered. Testing for defects in the embryo makes it even less traumatic as it is done before a pregnancy is established.

Routine genetic screening of women at risk could be done at the embryo stage as it is now done at the foetal stage. Since 1984 almost all the pregnant women among the Cypriot population in Britain, for example, have undergone CVS for *thalassaemia*, almost completely eliminating the possibility of a child in that community being born with the disease.

Embryo biopsying will be used to check for incorrect numbers of chromosomes such as triploids and Down's syndrome, intersex abnormalities as in Klinefelter's and Turner's syndrome, and single-gene disorders such as cystic fibrosis. In future it may also be used to test for multiple-gene disorders such as heart disease and diabetes.

The embryo can be flushed out of the uterus before it implants by lavage (see p. 192) or the embryo could be cultured *in vitro,* as part of standard IVF. Part of the embryo is removed and examined in the laboratory and, if all is well, transferred to the womb for implantaton. If an abnormality is found the embryo is not transferred, and is either discarded or used for further research. Both lavage and IVF are already used to treat infertility and they are now being combined with pre-implantation embryo biopsying for fertile couples who know they are at risk of passing on a genetic disease to their children.

One or two cells can be removed from a cluster of cells without jeopardising the embryo's chances of implanting and developing into a normal baby. The cells are separated by gently pipetting, or pulling, the embryo in a special calcium-free solution that reduces the adhesion of the cells. There is no need to use a scalpel.

If, for example, one cell is removed from an eight-cell embryo, it is then analysed while the other seven are either left in the petri dish to continue growing, or frozen until the results of the biopsy are known, depending on how long the analysis takes.

To find the abnormality, scientists run a DNA probe that picks up the gene with a specific abnormality, such as cystic fibrosis. DNA probes are pre-coded markers which latch on to the gene if it is there, like a trained sniffer dog searching for drugs. If the gene for cystic fibrosis is not found, the embryo can then be transferred.

DNA probes can be used in CVS to identify the gene for several hereditary diseases including cystic fibrosis, haemophilia, thalassaemia, some muscular dystrophies and cleft palate. About half-a-dozen teams are working on being able to detect these diseases in embryos. They include Robert Edwards's at Cambridge, Robert Winston's at Hammersmith in London, Gary Hodgen's at the Jones Institute, Virginia, and the Carl Wood-Alan Trounson team at Monash, Melbourne.

Drs Marilyn Monk and Anne McLaren at the Medical Research Council have developed a method of detecting Lesch-Nyhan syndrome in an embryo. This condition is caused by a missing enzyme HPRT and affects males who suffer from spastic cerebal palsy, engage in self-mutilation and usually die before reaching their teens. Women carry the gene but do not develop the syndrome. There are 25 known couples in the UK in which the woman carries the gene. If and when they want to have children, they could first have their embryos biopsied, and this is being tried by Dr Alan Handyside at Hammersmith. The first woman to approach the Hammersmith team had undergone two abortions after she was found to be carrying an affected foetus.

Trounson's team is taking a different approach. It is developing methods for culturing biopsied cells to detect genetic defects and has developed a cell-sampling technique which does not affect the embryos.

Although Lesch-Nyhan syndrome is rare, the ability to identify it in embryos is the stepping stone to detecting other inherited diseases such as thalassaemia, the most common genetic disease in the world, and cystic fibrosis, the most common in Western countries.

One of the criticisms of genetic screening is that it does not indicate the extent of the abnormality. Not all of these disorders are life-threatening, some appear in varying degrees, and many patients with mild forms are able to lead near-normal lives. Some people, especially those in the Right to Life movement, believe that no (embryo) lives should be disposed of unless the test can indicate how severe an abnormality would be if a child was born.

## SPLITTING EMBRYOS

Splitting embryos in half to create artificial identical twins is a form of cloning that has been used in the sheep and cattle industry in many countries since the early 1980s to increase the number of top-line breeders. In Australia it has increased sheep production by 50 per cent when used. And the technique could also be used in humans.

In theory, doubling the number of embryos by splitting them in half could increase the chances of an infertile couple having a baby, as it does in livestock. As Carl Wood, head of the Monash IVF team, explained at the 5th World Congress on IVF: 'If we did it, we would increase our pregnancy rates, particularly for those couples who only have one or two embryos because we would split them into four. Some women on IVF don't produce a large number of eggs after they are stimulated for ovulation and it would be suitable for them. But I don't know that it has a big application.' The danger is that in the process of trying to increase the number of embryos, some may be destroyed, as they are in freezing.

Embryo splitting may also be used to detect genetic diseases because one half could be analysed and the other half kept in culture or frozen until the results are known, as with embryo biopsying.

Splitting embryos to create identical twins poses more ethical than medical barriers. Wood says the first problem is the fact that complications with naturally produced identical twins is higher than for non-identical twins:

> The idea of artificial identical twins worries ethics committees because the data is not as good as for non-identical. But it would be better in IVF because we could separate the two embryos completely. Most of the problems with natural identical twins is cross-circulation in the womb which could result in the death of one twin. And when they are not completely split they have a single sac and you can get a twisted cord and locked twins. If you split them artificially you would not have those problems, and it decreases the chance of loss compared to natural identical twins.

Although embryo splitting could be done, Wood believes there are more important projects to concentrate on at present. 'I see it as an advantage for a few patients, but I don't think it's worth taking the step because it would involve another detailed ethical debate.'

With embryo splitting it would be possible for one half of the embryo to be transferred and the other half frozen for, say, 20 months then transferred, so the identical twins would be born 20 months apart. If they were frozen for 20 years, a generation could be skipped so that a woman could give birth to her own identical twin. It would also be possible to split the embryo several times, creating not two, but four, 16 or even 32 identical twins and this is one form of 'cloning'.

Some physicians and scientists are concerned that splitting embryos is taking science fiction too close to reality. Dr Zev Rosenwaks, head endocrinologist at the Jones Institute in Norfolk, Virginia, is uncomfortable with the idea:

> It smacks of Brave New World and I don't think we are ready for it—the public, nor the profession. It needs a lot more debate and understanding. Embryo splitting in animals may be desirable but not in humans. Our mission as physicians is to advance medicine and to do no harm and we must not do harm to society when society is not ready.

Wood said his team at Monash and two other centres, one in the US and one in Britain, have the know-how to do it, though no one yet has. However, scientists are working on creating identical twins in rhesus monkeys, the non-human primate closest to man. One of them is Barry Bavister who, along with Robert Edwards, fertilised the first human egg *in vitro* and was later responsible for the first reported rhesus monkey IVF birth. Now, at the Department of Veterinary Science at the University of Wisconsin-Madison, US, he is working on producing identical rhesus monkeys.

The benefits of this are two-fold, he says:

> In the past the rhesus monkey has been *the* model for human behaviour but identical twins don't occur in nature so you don't have a control, and biomedical researchers are hindered in doing psychological/behavioural research and in testing medical treatments. Secondly, if you were able to split a two-cell rhesus monkey embryo you would have a perfectly matched control embryo which is important because we desperately need to improve our culture conditions for monkey embryos, and that will extrapolate directly to human IVF. This is a more immediate advantage because of the poor success rate with IVF—only 10 per cent of embryos give rise to a pregnancy and I strongly suspect it is due to the culture.

## SEXING EMBRYOS

Some diseases only occur in men and others only in women, and are known as sex-linked diseases because they are distinguished by the X (female) or Y (male) chromosome. If scientists could tell whether an embryo was carrying the X or Y chromosome they could determine the sex of the embryo and tell the parents-to-be whether or not the disease will be passed on to their baby. If a couple knows that one of them has, or may have, the gene for a sex-linked disorder, such as haemophilia or muscular dystrophy, their embryo would be fertilised *in vitro* or removed from the uterus by lavage, then one or two cells would be removed and checked for the X or Y chromosome. If it is a male disease they are worried about and the Y chromosome is found, the embryo would not be returned.

It may appear simple, but the DNA probe is highly sophisticated and time-consuming. Nevertheless, a team at Edinburgh University, under Professor David Baird, has succeeded and become the first in the world to develop a technique of sexing pre-implantation human embryos by analysing the chromosomes. Researchers have been able to detect the Y chromosomes by using DNA probes and will use them to select against sex-linked diseases such as haemophilia. The new test will be available in about three years' time for thousands of affected couples who want to have a child. Meanwhile, other scientists, including Handyside, have also started sex selecting human embryos using a similar technique for Y probing.

The most common sex-linked disease is the blood disorder haemophilia which, like Lesch-Nyhan syndrome, affects males, although females are carriers and can pass the defective gene on to their boy babies. Ideally men who are haemophiliacs and women who are carriers will be able to have children without passing on the disease if they have their embryos biopsied before a pregnancy.

In theory, if embryo biopsy was carried out for everyone in a particular country who has the gene for, say haemophilia, and wants children, it would mean the end of haemophilia in that country—without the need for abortion. This is feasible in Western, but not developing, countries.

As with embryo biopsying, embryos found to be defective will be discarded or used for research, a move which has brought criticism from religious and Right to Life leaders. One of the strongest arguments comes from the Vatican which says embryo therapy is only acceptable if the aim is to transfer the embryo to the womb. 'Simple observation of the embryo would become illicit were it to involve risk to the embryo's physical integrity.' The Vatican says destruction of embryos is to be condemned and 'corpses of human embryos must be respected just as the remains of other human beings'.[48]

Nicholas Tonti-Filippini, director of the St Vincent's Bioethics Centre in Melbourne, compared the scientist's domination over the embryo's destiny to that of a master over his slave, both of which he said are unacceptable.[49]

The possibility of routinely sexing sperm and embryos raises numerous ethical problems, as discussed in the next chapter.

## GROWING EMBRYOS

Researchers are also working on ways to transplant embryonic tissue into children to treat immune and blood disorders. The secret is to remove stem cells, which are in the part of the conceptus that later develops into specific cells, for example, for the blood system or certain organs. The ability to transplant stem cells may prove to be an alternative to bone marrow transplants for leukaemia patients, and the technique may eventually be suitable for victims of nuclear accidents.

A team in Lyons, France, reported at the European Society of Human Reproduction and Embryology conference in Cambridge in June 1987 that it had treated 12 children with severe immunodeficiency disease by giving them cells from aborted foetuses. The children were born without white blood cells and because they had no immune system, they lived in isolation 'bubbles', but according to project leader, Dr Jean Touraine of the Hôpital E. Herriot, the transplanted stem cells were accepted by the infants and grow into normal white blood cells. After four to five months' treatment a new immune system had developed and the children were able to leave their isolation bubbles.

The cells were taken from the developing liver of eight-to 12-week-old foetuses because these are the cells that go on to produce red and white blood cells. The French researchers then injected the cells into the children. This is similar to the technique, mentioned earlier, of transplanting cells from the pancreas of foetuses to diabetic patients in the hope that the cells will grow into insulin-producing cells in the adults. The next stage is to use embryos rather than foetuses, which is what Edwards and his team at Cambridge University are working on. They are attempting to produce stem cells from embryos in the hope of finding a treatment for leukaemia.

The French team is also performing foetal stem-cells transplants for other disorders including severe aplastic anaemia and metabolic problems. And there have been suggestions that embryos could be grown for treating diabetes in the same way.

If these techniques prove successful, embryos will have to be grown in culture, specifically for cells to be removed and transplanted. While the possibility of curing childhood disorders is highly desirable, the ability to grow embryos in the laboratory leads to suggestions of embryo farms where embryos are also grown for toxicology tests and for human spare parts.

# 13
# THE FUTURE: SCIENCE vs ETHICS

'In research on man, the interest of science and society should never take precedence over considerations related to the well-being of the subject.' *The Declaration of Helsinki, passed by the World Medical Association, Helsinki 1964 and Tokyo 1975.*

It is only 12 years to the year 2000. Twelve years ago, the first test-tube baby, Louise Brown, was not even conceived. Scientific advances in the distant future are hard to predict, given the enormous strides that have been made in the last few years, especially since the advent of DNA technology and the increased understanding of embryology. As British geneticist Professor David Weatherall said in 1986, 'If you had told me 10 years ago that a spot of DNA could be taken out of a foetus at eight weeks to identify genetic diseases, I would have thought it crazy,' but this is now routine in chorion villus sampling. However, some of the social and ethical issues are easier to foresee.

Not all these future developments can be seen as 'advances' and not all are aimed at producing healthy babies—some are by-products of existing babymaking techniques.

## SEX SELECTION

The normal proportion of boy and girl babies is about the same, 106 boys are born for every 100 girls. Some people believe more males are conceived than females, with a higher proportion of males lost in miscarriage or stillbirth, but this has not been substantiated.

An increase in reproductive technologies, including techniques for sexing sperm, has brought with it an increase in demand. When surveyed in 1968, 26 per cent of US students said they would like to choose their firstborn's sex; in 1970, 39 per cent of married women in a national survey said the same and in 1977, 66 per cent of Californian students said sex-selection technology should be available for parents-to-be.

Studies show if people are given a choice the majority in most countries would choose a boy as their first child. Due to social and religious traditions in several Asian and African countries, many families prefer all or most of their children to be males. Because of the high infant mortality rate in many of these countries, a woman is forced to keep having children until there are enough boys to ensure at least one will survive through adulthood to inherit the family name and property and to look after the parents in their old age. Under the law in some Asian countries, inheritance can only be left to sons.

The desire for a boy is particularly strong in India, China, Taiwan and Korea, and as a result the social pressure on women is enormous. According to tradition, a wife is not accepted by her husband's family or the community unless she bears a male, preferably as the first born. A girl is considered a social let-down and an economic burden. There is little chance of her getting work and her parents must provide a large dowry when she marries. Although female infanticide was outlawed in India in 1890, baby girls are still either 'accidentally' killed or allowed to die through malnutrition or medical neglect. And there have been recent reports from Korea of baby girls being allowed to die and of women having abortions after discovering they are carrying a girl.

The preference for males is not restricted to Asia and Africa. Numerous US studies in the last 30 years have shown the majority of people—single and married—would choose a boy as their firstborn, if they could. A 1970 study found 48 per cent of women wanted a son, 18 per cent a daughter and 32 per cent said either. Thirteen years later, another study showed 62 per cent of students preferred their firstborn to be a son and 34 per cent would be happy with either sex.

For centuries, people have advocated numerous methods to produce one sex or the other. The Bible tells us that, 'If a woman emits semen and bears a manchild . . .'[1] And according to the Talmud, 'One who desires all his children to be male should co-habit twice in succession.'[2]

The belief that the type and timing of intercourse determines the sex of the baby has always been, and still is, popular—but also unproven. The Talmud suggests, 'To have a son, a man should conduct himself with modesty at the time of marital intercourse. As a reward for containing oneself during intercourse in order that one's wife may emit the semen first, the Holy One gives one the reward of the fruit of the womb,' i.e., a son.[3]

Historically, suggestions for sex preference have included timing intercourse to coincide with events such as temperature changes, rainfall, wind direction or phases of the tides and the moon, and according to Dr Gabor Kovacs, medical director of the Family Planning Association of Victoria who published a review of sex-selection methods in 1987, 'Other methods have recommended that various apparel be worn during intercourse.'[4]

The ability to determine sex in the unborn is a highly valued tool in the livestock industry. The fastest way to build up new or valuable stock is to have a lot of breeders, so females are favoured. Bull calves born to dairy cows end up being grown for beef although they are not bred as beef cattle. It is not uncommon for a prize cow to be sold in calf and to fetch a price according to whether she is carrying a bull or heifer calf. So veterinarians set out to find a way of sexing embryos before implantation and they now have an 80 per cent success rate in cattle, sheep and pigs. One way is to detect what is known as an H-Y antigen which appears on the surface of male embryos, but not sperm. Many of the sexing methods being developed in medicine today are based on veterinary techniques.

The main medical reason for allowing sex selection in the future is to avoid the birth of a child with a sex-linked disease, such as haemophilia. A social reason would be to balance the ratio of boys and girls in a family.

In theory there are four main ways to alter the sex ratio: to change environmental factors; to separate the male and female sperm before fertilisation; to sex the embryo before implantation; and to sex the foetus. The first two might influence the sex ratio before conception, but these methods have not been scientifically proved by independent researchers to make any significant difference. The second two methods enable scientists to determine the sex of an embryo or foetus, and only subsequent destruction will alter the ratio of boy and girl babies born.

*The environment* . Changes in the vagina during the menstrual cycle are thought by some physicians to favour male or female sperm (as discussed in Chapter 5). Based on this, in the mid-1950s, American gynaecologist Landrum B. Shettles, who later became one of the first in the US to attempt an IVF pregnancy (see p. 171), released his now famous formula for producing the baby of choice. He suggested the couple had more chance of a boy baby if they refrained from sex up till, and for two days after, ovulation; if the woman had an orgasm before her partner; and if the man ejaculated high into the vagina, near the cervix. The opposite applied for girl babies: refrain from intercourse after ovulation, no female orgasm and ejaculate low in the vagina.

Another popular practice, first suggested in the 1930s and repeated by Shettles and others—and still unproven—is to douch the vagina with an alkaline solution for a boy, or vinegar for a girl. This is because the vagina is acidic and it is assumed the male sperm are less likely to survive in an acidic environment, which can be toned down by the alkaline solution. Just before ovulation and during orgasm the vagina becomes more alkaline, and therefore more receptive to male sperm, so if the woman douches with alkaline, has intercourse just after ovulation and has an orgasm, she is more likely to have a male baby—in theory.

The success of this method is controversial: Shettles's studies showed the technique is 80 per cent successful in producing the desired sex, while other studies show it makes no difference. A study in Singapore in the 1970s found only 45 per cent of couples who wanted a boy were successful—a ratio that is less than in nature.

However, the Shettles formula is now sold in the US as a $50 do-it-yourself kit that comes in pink for girls and blue for boys, and is widely available to anyone who believes it will influence the sex of their child.

Various researchers have tried to create an environment that kills or incapacitates female sperm with alkaline or a chemical solution, either in the vagina or the laboratory. This quest for a 'manchild' pill has been so far unsuccessful.

Another do-it-yourself technique is diet. According to Gabor Kovacs:

> The suggestion that the sex of offspring depended on the time of intercourse during the menstrual cycle was probably first suggested by Empedocles from Greece. The possible effect of nutrition on the sex of offspring was first put forward by Schenk in 1898 in Vienna. He recommended a high-protein diet that would promote maturation of the ovum and result in a male child.[4]

Research by doctors in Canada and France suggests the sex of a baby is influenced by certain minerals in the mother's diet. Israeli researchers reported in 1981 that a diet high in salt and potassium and low in calcium was more likely to lead to boy babies and the opposite produces girl babies. They claim it is 80–84 per cent successful. Two other studies found that a diet low in salt and high in alkaline resulted in girls being born in 81 and 86 per cent of cases, respectively. None of these studies have been reported by other researchers.

*The sperm.* The first methods that took selection out of the bedroom and into the laboratory were those that tried to separate the male and female sperm; however few of them have been successful. Numerous techniques have been attempted, all based on the fact that the X-bearing (female) sperm look and act differently to the Y-bearing (male) sperm, allowing them to be separated. As discussed in Chapter 5, these include spinning sperm in a centrifuge, swimming them through certain solutions, filtering them through special filter papers and identifying their different electrical charges. The most popular is the Ericsson method of 'swimming' sperm through layers of albumin. The success rate in separating the X and Y sperm ranges from less than the natural rate to claims of more than 80 per cent.

Ronald Ericsson says that in the US couples do not use his sperm sex-selection method to start a family but to complete their childrearing, if, for example, they have three daughters and want a son. Or if they only want two children and the first was a daughter, they can use sex selection rather than rely on nature's 50:50 chance to produce their boy.

If a couple in a Western country end up with the 'wrong' sex it causes little more than a passing disappointment. As Ericsson said, 'Most of the sex selectors already have children, and before they undergo the process, they are told clearly that it's not absolute. If they're not willing to be parents again, they should not use it.'

In his comprehensive review of all methods of selecting sex before conception, Kovacs concluded, 'There is no worthwhile method of preconceptional sex preselection available.' He believes an 80 per cent or more success rate is needed to alter the chances of a couple having a baby of the desired sex.

There obviously needs to be considerable improvement to make sperm separation reliable and repeatable if it is to be used in the future as a method of sex selection. However, its use can be justified on medical and social grounds when a scientifically accepted method is available.

Sperm screening could be combined with amniocentesis or chorion villus sampling. If a woman knew she carried the gene for a sex-linked disease, but was unhappy about the 50:50 chance of having to face an abortion after amniocentesis or CVS, she might be able to reduce her chances of having a baby of that sex by having sperm sex selection before AI.

It can also be combined with IVF. The first such baby, Justin Spencer, was born in New Orleans in January 1986. His father's sperm had been separated then used to fertilise his mother's egg in standard IVF.

*The embryo* . As seen in the previous chapter, an embryo can be either flushed from the uterus before it implants using lavage, or created in the laboratory using IVF. The embryo is then 'sexed' by looking for its X or Y chromosome. So far, the aim of developing embryo sexing is to eliminate sex-linked diseases, but when the technique becomes well established it could also be used in the future for family planning. The use of lavage or IVF will make it an expensive procedure. Added to that is the fact that both these techniques carry certain risks to the mother and the embryo and they currently have a low success rate. However, these problems could be offset by the fact that the sexing is done before a pregnancy is established, and there is no need for an abortion if an abnormality is found. This is a major consideration for the parents, and is generally considered more acceptable by the anti-abortion lobby, although the Right to Life movement opposes the destruction of pre-implantation embryos as well as those established in a pregnancy.

*The foetus.* According to one women's magazine there are several ways to tell whether a pregnant woman is carrying a boy or girl: for example, 'If you have patchy skin on your face then it will be a boy,' and 'View the mother-to-be from behind, late in the pregnancy. If she looks pregnant, the child is a boy.' These myths have been replaced by the more sophisticated methods for assessing the sex of a foetus: amniocentesis and the more recent CVS. Whether others will be developed in the near future remains to be seen.

Amniocentesis and CVS are usually only carried out to identify a genetic abnormality in a foetus when the mother is known to be at risk, but the tests also reveal the sex of the baby and this information can be used for non-medical reasons. Some parents-to-be want to know the sex of their unborn child out of curiosity, so they can start identifying with him/her during the pregnancy, or so they know whether to decorate the nursery in pink or blue. Occasionally the information is used to terminate the life of a baby of the 'wrong' sex. This is not uncommon in India, although it is illegal. However, terminating a 'wrong' sex pregnancy is not restricted to developing countries. For example, a report released by a Sydney hospital in October 1987 revealed that of the first 300 women who had CVS to identify a foetal abnormality, five had their pregnancies terminated because the baby was not the sex they wanted.

Cases such as this in Western countries are likely to be minimal, according to the author of the report, Dr Tom Boogert of the Foetal Medicine Unit at Prince Alfred Hospital:

'It's an ethical issue no doubt, but I honestly don't think it's likely to get out of hand while it's performed by an accredited unit.' He believes women who have CVS have a right to know the sex of their baby and the right to decide whether or not to have an abortion. 'My personal feeling is we have no right to withhold that information. Obviously I'm not happy about people terminating pregnancies, but largely it's up to the patient.'

## THE ETHICS

Few people can argue that reducing sex-linked diseases and foetal abnormalities is not a justifiable use of sex-selection methods, but should couples be allowed to use them to have a child of one sex or the other? The main argument against this is that it is contrary to nature. There have also been concerns expressed that if sex selection were widespread, the world would become overpopulated with men. On the other hand, some people have suggested the preference for males could eventually become a form of population control because with fewer females, there would be fewer babies born. However, it would take several generations for a sex imbalance to be noticeable and the fear of too many men is unrealistic.

However, there are emotional, or social, reasons for allowing sex selection other than for sex-linked diseases. In *Test-Tube Women*, Viola Roggencamp describes the case of a young Indian woman who had a backyard abortion after amniocentesis showed she was carrying a baby girl. She had been sent by her husband and his family to have the test because she had already borne three daughters. The abortion was obviously traumatic and afterwards she said, crying:

> Each child is sent by God. But why doesn't he give me a son? Will he never give me a son? How shall I continue? Maybe I will never have a son? Maybe it is my fault? Who knows, only God does. But what do I have to do? What should I do? I am so afraid. I will do it [again] if only my body will take it. And I am afraid that my husband will divorce me and take a new wife who will give him sons. He is the man. He had a right to a son.

She continued:

> You just don't know what I've been going through in the last seven years because all I gave birth to were girls. Again and again it was a girl. I carry her for nine months. The family prays to God, the priest pays a visit, the family undertakes *puja* [a religious ceremony]. Then finally the birth. And again—nothing. After my second and third delivery all they did was to send my little brother-in-law to see me at the hospital. It would be so much easier for me with a son. My husband and his family would respect me more.[5]

It is pleas like this that could be answered by sperm or embryo sex selection before pregnancy. However, if sex choice were allowed in China without government interference, in theory, it could result in a nation of almost all men—in one generation. A boy child is of great importance to the Chinese but under the current population control programme, generally only one child is allowed per family. If parents were given a choice of sex, the vast majority would undoubtedly opt for a boy, leaving few females to produce the next generation. It is conceivable that there would then be a greater demand for girl babies in the next generation, and the balance could be redressed.

When a proven and reliable method is found there is an obvious and urgent need for sex selection to help reduce the number of sex-linked diseases, and there are also compelling arguments for it to be used in social cases such as helping to balance the sexes, for example by adding a son to a family after many daughters, which would relieve social stigma and emotional strain without upsetting the male-female ratio. It could be argued that in extreme cases the failure to produce a son borders on being a 'medical' reason for allowing sex selection.

However, the practice is open to abuse, especially in traditional male-oriented countries, but also in Western societies. If authorities in India, for example, cannot control abuse of the more sophisticated technique of amniocentesis, there is little chance they will regulate unproven, and possibly unsafe, backyard sperm separation schemes. Ericsson predicts sex selection will be part of life, 'just as radio, calculators and microwaves are now', but if that is the case, there is cause for concern among health workers in many Asian countries. The greatest danger is that thousands of unsuspecting people will eagerly part with their meagre savings for unscrupulous entrepreneurs who claim they can produce a boy or girl based on a method that is not scientifically proven. In the majority of cases the result will be heartbreak and more social stigma.

## CLONING

*Cloning* means cutting, from the Greek *klon*, and is used routinely in horticulture and occasionally in animal husbandry. It involves reproducing plants and animals with the same genetic structure without them mating, known as asexual reproduction. Every time a gardener takes a cutting from a bush and grows it, he is cloning—he is creating another individual that is genetically identical, without fertilisation. A common form of cloning in the animal world is when an earthworm is cut in two and each half becomes a new worm. It happens naturally in humans when an embryo in the uterus splits in half to form identical twins, but the prospect of artificially cloning man presents difficult and controversial decisions.

Cloning is often portrayed as the ultimate in science fiction come true, the evil of all scientific evils. To clone man sounds an outrageous suggestion that creates images of identical, mindless armies or of everyone in the same town looking and acting alike. Cloning has been condemned as the ultimate dehumanizing act and some people charge that it is the lowest form of incest. However, there are some sound medical reasons for wanting to clone humans.

There are two ways to clone artificially. As mentioned in the previous chapter, splitting an embryo in half in the laboratory to create two identical embryos is cloning. Each half could then be split again to produce more identical embryos—up to the sixth cleavage division, after which an embryo is programmed to form to a blastocyst irrespective of the number of cells it has. This could be done at the two- to

32-cell stage, before the cells in the embryo become specialised. If all these split embryos were transferred to various surrogate women, they could in theory develop into a small group, or 'army', of human clones. But all this is speculative.

The alternative to splitting is nuclear transplant. In one suggested method an unfertilised egg would be removed from the ovaries and its nucleus (which contains 23 chromosomes) surgically removed or wiped out by irradiation. In place of the original nucleus, a scientist would insert the nucleus of another cell that has been taken from the body of an existing animal, say a rabbit. Because the egg receives a nucleus with a full set of 46 chromosomes it thinks it has been fertilised and then, without a sperm, it would develop into an exact carbon copy of the rabbit that the nucleus came from. In natural fertilisation, the young rabbit would have half its chromosomes from the egg and half from the sperm but in cloning it has neither, and the egg simply acts as a nurturing sac in which the new cell grows. In practice, the inserted nucleus is most likely to come from the cells of embryos, athough some people have predicted that these cells may one day come from any cell in an adult, for example from the skin or a muscle, and that it will develop into an exact replica of the animal it came from. Unlike clones made by splitting, these offspring only have one 'parent'.

Transplant cloning was first developed in frogs. In 1952 Drs Robert Briggs and Thomas King of the Institute for Cancer Research in Philadelphia reported they had performed nuclear transplant, as part of their cancer research, to produce tadpoles. Fourteen years later, Oxford University biologist Dr J.B. Gurdon cloned toads after destroying the nuclei of eggs with a narrow beam of ultra-violet radiation. From 707 attempts he produced 11 clones, although only a fraction of them were normal. In 1975 another Oxford biologist, Dr Derek Bromhall, reported that he had done it in rabbits, using cells from rabbit embryos. However, no one has repeated Bromhall's work. Because rabbits are warm-blooded and their eggs are about the same size as human eggs, the scientific world and the media buzzed with the possibility of cloning humans. Bromhall predicted cloning would be used in the livestock industry, but not in humans: 'With cloning you could take a top cow and produce exact replicas to propagate any desirable characteristic you want, such as exceptional milk yield,' and he added, 'No one in their right mind would clone humans.'[6] Soon after his research was published in *Nature*, he said, 'Cloning grabs the imagination. I've spent sleepless nights over this, but not from worry—I've been kept awake by excitement. We've done all these things with frogs before, but there is a tremendous gap between cold-blooded frogs and live mammals. I've shown that gap can be narrowed.'[7]

Why would anyone want to clone man? Cloning has several possible medical and social uses. Bromhall, who abandoned cloning in 1976, said cloning should be used to help in cancer research, medical genetics and natural reproductive biology. The Warnock Committee outlined one therapeutic future use of nuclear transplant: 'It has been suggested that one day it might be possible to produce immunologically identical organs for transplantation purposes to replace a diseased organ, for example a kidney. The cloned replacement organ would be grown in an embryo in which the nucleus had been replaced by one taken from the person for whom the replacement organ was intended.'[8]

The main problem with conventional organ transplants is that the recipient's body rejects the donated organ because it is foreign, but this would not happen with a cloned organ because it would come from the recipient and have the same genes. If it became possible, cloning would make all tissue and organs available, whereas existing methods are generally limited to cornea, kidney, heart, lung and liver transplants.

Splitting could in the future also provide 'spare parts', as long as it is done at the time of conception. In theory, an embryo could be split into two, four or more cells. While one is transferred for a pregnancy, the others are frozen until needed by the person born as a result of the transfer. When he grows up, he will effectively have a bank of spare parts. If, for example, his pancreas started to deteriorate, the frozen embryos (his unborn identical twins) could be thawed. Pancreatic cells could be removed from the embryos and grown in culture, then transferred to the patient, hopefully to grow into replacement organs. This would overcome the current problems of rejection and problems of a shortage of donor organs. A simpler version of this is already being done experimentally for diabetic patients who have foetal pancreatic tissue placed in their forearm or abdomen in the hope that it will grow into an insulin-producing pancreas.

Cloning has another important role as far as research is concerned. It offers scientists an opportunity to study the growth of cells, which may give a better understanding of what causes foetal abnormalities, how cancer cells act and how cells change during ageing. Researchers say that ultimately cloning could lead to cures for both cancer and childhood disorders.

If a woman wanted to clone herself, she could do so without her child having a father. There are at least three occasions when she may want to do this: if she has no eggs herself and does not want to use an egg donated by another woman because it would have the donor's genetic material; if her partner has a serious inherited gene and they prefer not to use donor sperm; and if she is single and does not want a male contribution to her baby.

Should cloning be banned for these uses? The first two are obviously medical indications that side-step infertility and avoid genetic diseases, and although there are alternatives (donor egg and sperm) it would be hard to deny women or couples the use of the technology if it were available. It could be argued that single women should not be having babies without a father, but it must be remembered that there are many single women who deliberately become mothers by natural means and others who do so with artificial insemination. If they are allowed AI should they also be allowed to have a child by cloning?

Cloning has social advantages in that it allows a couple to choose the sex of their child—all boys would come from a cell from their father and girls from a cell from their mother.

Socially, although not medically, nuclear transplants are in some ways similar to elite sperm banks, such as the Nobel Prize-winning one discussed in Chapter 5. If famous scientists and athletes are willing to give up their sperm for a woman to have one of their offspring, maybe they will be willing to give up cells for nuclear transplants too. However, there is an important difference: when sperm is used the outcome of the offspring is left to the chances of natural reproduction since the father's genes are mixed with the woman's. But with nuclear transplant, the outcome is already predetermined—the child would be genetically identical to the cell donor.

Many writers, mainly in newspapers, have suggested that cloning could lead to thousands of copies of famous scientists or athletes. Even if one clone were made the offspring would not necessarily turn out to be a famous scientist or athlete. Although the clone will be genetically the same as that of the original, he may not have the same personality because environmental influences will not be the same. His childhood will be different, as will the social, cultural and political climate in which he must exert himself as an adult.

In *The Reproduction Revolution*, Australian Professor of Philosophy Peter Singer and lawyer Deane Wells argue that by the time a genius has made his mark on the world and is cloned (which may take 20–40 years) he will no longer be the best in his field:

> A nation which cloned its best runner would have to wait about 20 years for its gold medals. At best, the cloned athletes would, for a while, win all the track events their progenitor would have won [but] sooner or later the random processes of sexual reproduction will throw up a person with a physical constitution superior to the person from whom the clones were taken. The situation would be similar if a nation decided to clone its best scientist or thinker.[9]

However, that would not stop couples or single women wanting a clone of the genius, even if it were 20 or 40 years after his heyday, just as the sperm of a 70-year-old Nobel Prize-winner is still sought after by couples in America.

As with 'Nobel sperm bank' children, clones may have difficulty living up to their parents' expectations. They would be pressured into thinking they had to excel and might feel guilty if they failed, especially as their parents had gone to unusual lengths to produce them artificially.

Australian Professor of Obstetrics and Gynaecology William Walters suggests, in *Test-Tube Babies*, that cloning may lead to a loss of identity and a lack of sense of uniqueness or self when surrounded by identical clones. He also suggests that as only one partner would be needed 'this could reduce men to a feeling of being castrated or women to a feeling of being mere incubators'. And he expresses concern that clones may have less chance of surviving:

> There is a danger that cloned people may not be as adaptable with the passage of time to a changing environment as their fellows originating from sexual reproduction [which] is an important means of ensuring genetic adaptability. If cloned people chose to return to sexual reproduction after several generations of cloning, there is a risk of an accumulation of deleterious recessive genes and mutations being introduced into the human genetic pool with an increase in various diseases and malformations.[10]

More than 20 years ago Nobel Prize-winning American geneticist Joshua Lederberg said combining asexual and sexual reproduction offered the best of both worlds, where cloning gave uniformity, better understanding and proven excellence, and sexual reproduction added diversity and innovation. 'A mix of sexual and clonal reproduction makes good sense for genetic design. Leave sexual reproduction for experimental purposes; when a suitable type is ascertained take care to maintain it by clonal propagation.'[11] However, Lederberg later retracted from his stand on cloning.

Several experts have suggested that it is possible there would be better communication between clones because they would understand each other more easily than people with different genes. This would apply equally between clones of the same generation produced by splitting an embryo or between mother and daughter or father and son produced by nuclear transplants.

Lederberg once suggested jobs that required close team effort would be best served by clones who understand each other and communicated easily. They could include astronauts, deep-sea divers and surgical teams. A few years later, American theologian Joseph Fletcher suggested clones with certain characteristics, such as shortness, could be bred for specific roles, such as space flight to which short people would be better suited. But in *The Biological Time Bomb* scientist

Gordon Rattray Taylor suggested that armies of aggressive people could be developed by cloning, as could a race of submissive slaves.

It is probably the suggestion of cloned armies that worries most people, yet it is the most impractical use of cloning and the least likely to occur. As Singer and Wells said, 'Cloning would be a grossly inefficient way of raising armies. It would take at least 18 years. Few mad dictators are so patient. Most would prefer to train existing 18-year-olds.' And they point out that an army of clones would not be any more susceptible to brainwashing than anyone else.

> They would be separate individuals. Their own brains, not the brain of their progenitor or the scientist, would control their behaviour. Identical twins are not more susceptible to brainwashing techniques than single births, and no more would cloned individuals be. Mad dictators will brainwash whoever they get their hands on.[12]

It must be remembered that cloning does not make better babies, it simply reproduces, gene for gene, the good and bad of the parent. So ideas of producing super-humans by cloning is nonsense. Gene manipulation may in time produce super-humans, but that is another story. Cloning could be used to increase the number of high achievers in the world but the effect would be a drop in the ocean, as the Nobel sperm bank has been.

In fact, if everyone were cloned, there would be no improvement in the human race because that only comes with the chance mixing of genes in sexual reproduction. Excluding drugs and technology, the only reason runners run faster is because nature has selected those qualities. In cloning there is no selection, it is all repetition.

In summary, it is important to take into account that cloning could be a way of saving, or simply lengthening, lives by providing an alternative to existing organ transplants. And it may be an alternative to using donor egg and sperm where one partner is infertile or has a hereditary disease. Cloning may be justified if it is limited to one clone per person, avoiding the unacceptable concept of factories or armies full of clones.

## EMBRYO 'FARMS'

*For spare parts.* As mentioned, French scientists have successfully removed stem cells from aborted foetuses to produce white blood cells in children (see p.301), and it may be possible in the near future to use cells from laboratory embryos to treat other diseases or to replace a degenerating organ such as a pancreas or kidney.

Payment to organ donors is banned in most countries to discourage people from donating, for example, one of their two kidneys or eyes, and to discourage premature deaths for the sake of selling organs. Nevertheless it is not uncommon in India for people to want to sell a kidney, and a racket in Sao Paulo, Brazil, reported in May 1987, caused international concern. It was claimed that 11 doctors were involved in removing and selling organs including kidneys, corneas, livers and hearts from patients before they died.

The same week, reports that two abnormal babies in West Germany were kept alive in their mothers' wombs so that their kidneys could be used for transplants caused further outrage. One of the mothers had been expecting twins but an ultrasound at 16 weeks found one had no brain. It could have been killed without affecting the healthy twin but the parents agreed to wait until 36 weeks when it was delivered and the kidneys removed. In the second case a baby was discovered with a brain problem at 36 weeks and the mother agreed to keep the baby in her womb for another two weeks. The kidneys were removed in a 45-minute operation after the birth. While some people find this abhorrent, it could be seen as a generous act of giving, a way of saving the life of another baby. And it undoubtedly helped the parents' grieving at the loss of their own baby which would have died anyway. What if a woman deliberately became pregnant and had an abortion at seven months so that the foetus's kidneys could be given to her husband who was dying of kidney failure? This could be extended to the suggestion—and fear—that some women might be encouraged to get pregnant and give up their aborted foetus for money.

If removing organs from adults and foetuses under such circumstances causes concern, would the use of embryonic tissue be more acceptable? It has been suggested that cells from laboratory-cultured embryos could be transplanted to patients to grow into replacement organs. It may be possible to grow embryos in the laboratory until nervous tissue is formed, then transplant that tissue to adults suffering from nervous disorders, including paralysis. In theory, heart muscle cells could be removed from three-week-old embryos and transplanted to patients.

It may be necessary to grow large quantities of embryos to get enough cells to transfer to a patient. Alternatively, the cells could be removed from the embryo and grown in culture.

French geneticist Professor Jerome Lejeune of the University of Paris says ideas of growing spare parts for repairing children or adults 'are so far-fetched that no critical analysis can be made. Conceivably, grafts of stem cells could be of theoretical interest [but] specialised tissues are not yet detectable in pre-implantation embryos'.[13] Other scientists are optimistic that it will become a reality in the near future.

*For drug tests.* Large numbers of laboratory-produced embryos could also be used for testing drugs. Philosopher Peter Singer is well known as an animal liberationist and has taken his embryo-versus-animal argument to the international arena. He told the Office of Technology Assessment meeting in Washington that the long-term prospects for embryo experimentation included, 'quicker and more reliable methods of testing whether new drugs taken by pregnant women are likely to lead to deformed infants. The use of embryos could also provide an alternative to present methods of safety testing which involve considerable animal suffering.'[14]

Singer suggests that early embryos would be a more realistic alternative, as they do not feel pain at the early stage of development.

> Up to the point at which the embryo has not developed a nervous system is has not developed the capacity to feel pain or feel anything, has no degree of consciousness and no sensory awareness. Up to the point at which it can feel pain

> or experience something I believe experiments on the embryo, with the consent of the donors of the gametes, is justifiable.[15]

He believes that point is at least six weeks after fertilisation.

The Warnock Committee opposed the use of embryos for testing, except in special circumstances.

> This is an area that causes deep concern because of the possibility of mass production of *in vitro* embryos, perhaps on a commercial basis, for these purposes. We feel very strongly that the routine testing of drugs on human embryos is not an acceptable area of research because this would require the manufacture of large numbers of embryos. We concluded however that there may be very particular circumstances where the testing of such substances on a very small scale may be justifiable ... subject to very close scrutiny.[16]

The committee said the decision would be made by a licensing authority, according to the merits of each particular project.

Alexander Capron, Professor of Law at the University of Southern California, disagrees with Singer and says the feeling of pain should not be the sole criteria.

> I don't think pain is the issue. There is a respect for the human form, for humanity. The notion that you have this potential human being is to me more important. I cannot agree with using embryos rather than animals because there is a legitimate ethical argument that differentiates human beings from other animals.

George Annas, Professor of Health Law at Boston University, dismisses Singer's suggestion as bizarre.

> The notion that we have to choose between putting drops in a rabbit's eyes and putting them in human embryos seems to me to be bizarre. We have no need to experiment with either. We can look for another way to develop our cosmetics and do our toxicology testing—there is no necessity to do it on either one. You can develop a third method or not do it at all.[17]

## EMBRYOS IN ANIMAL RESEARCH

*Chimeras.* When a 'geep' was born in the US in the spring of 1985 it attracted worldwide attention. It was produced by Professor Gary Anderson's research team at the University of California, Davis, and had both sheep and goat features, with patches of sheep and goat hair. It was in fact a sheep/goat chimera, the result of fusing, or joining, a sheep embryo and a goat embryo. In Greek mythology a chimera was a fire-breathing she-monster having a lion's head, a goat's body and a serpent's tail, according to Anderson. In reality, a chimera is a plant or animal that contains two or more sets of cells from two or more different embryos. A chimera animal is produced by combining three- to seven-day-old zona-free embryos from the same or different animal species in a laboratory. The new embryo is then transferred to a surrogate and ideally develops in a normal pregnancy. The first reported animal chimeras were mice produced in the US and in Poland in the early 1960s, followed by rabbits in 1980 and sheep in 1986. A mule is a hybrid, not a chimera, because each of its cells contains some horse chromosomes and some donkey chromosomes. A hybrid is unable to reproduce but generally chimeras can. And when they do, about 75 per cent of the offspring are males, according to Anderson.

The UC Davis researchers started working on chimera mice and sheep in the mid-1970s as a way of preserving endangered animal species and studying reproduction. As one officer said, 'We are not striving to produce better farm stock, we are trying to develop better immune responses and prevent immune rejection, and to understand why the mother's uterus accepts an embryo. Chimeras give us a model for studying the role of the placenta in preventing rejection of the foetus.' If scientists prevent rejection between species it will be possible for a domestic animal to act as a surrogate to the foetus of an endangered species.

Chimera research has also helped in studying embryos, genetic abnormalities and cancer. 'Analysis of results from chimeras has led to the conclusion that only a few cells of the blastocyst contribute to formation of the embryo proper.' Anderson said, 'Chimeras have also been useful in the study of certain developmental anomalies,' including muscular dystrophy. 'An extreme example of the ability of normal cells to direct development of abnormal cells in a chimera is the reversal of malignancy of embryonal carcinoma cells.'[18]

All this sounds a plausible reason for allowing chimera research, but could it one day be extended to humans? Jerome Lejeune asks: 'What about an "artistic" embryo, an "athletic" embryo and a "scientific" one fused together? Would not that create a kind of superman?' He dismisses such suggestions as 'fictional experiments' that do not deserve discussion. 'These nursery tales for grown-ups can be rejected easily. To devise a man wiser than we are, we should be already wiser that we can be!'[13]

And could human embryos be fused with the embryos of another species to produce half-man half-animal? For example, humans and monkeys, as they are the closest species to man? This is unlikely unless there is some medical reason, but it is still a possibility.

*Surrogates*. Individual breeds of cattle have given birth to other breeds and donkeys have given birth to horses as a result of biological experimentation. Recently researchers proved that a horse can be a surrogate to a zebra. The foal born to a quarter horse mare in Louisville, Kentucky, in May 1984, was a zebra foal from a rare breed. Twelve months earlier the zebra embryo had been transferred to the mare's womb and then developed normally. Veterinarians Drs Bill Foster and Scott Bennett who were responsible for the cross-species surrogacy said the experiment was part of research to build up numbers of vanishing and endangered equine breeds such as Grevey's and Chapman's zebra. Earlier, a sterile mule gave birth to a healthy thoroughbred foal after Dr Douglas Antczak of New York State College for Veterinary Medicine transferred a horse embryo to the mule. And Dr W.R. Allen of the London Zoo proved a domestic mare could give birth to a Przewalski horse, which is extinct in the wild.

On the success of these experiments it has been suggested that a baboon could act as a surrogate for a human embryo in a life and death situation. In 1984 Californian doctors transplanted the heart of a baboon into 'Baby Fae' who survived three weeks with the animal heart. Could the same thing be done in reverse with a foetus in an emergency? If a woman died part-way through a pregnancy, could the embryo be removed from her womb and transferred to the womb of a hormonally-prepared baboon in an attempt to save the embryo? This is hypothetical, but should we allow scientists to even consider it?

*Cross-species fertilisation.* It may also be possible in the future to fuse the gametes of two different species, in what is known as cross—species fertilisation. The egg of a sheep, for example, may be fertilised by the sperm of a goat. When the hamster-egg test is used as a fertility test (see p 30) a man's sperm fertilises a zona-free hamster egg and the resultant embryo may develop to the two-cell stage, but no further. One reason is the difference in chromosome numbers between humans and hamsters. However, fertilisation with an animal that has close to 46 chromosomes might be more likely to develop further.

Britain's Warnock Committee was concerned about the possibility that other similar cross-species fertilisation tests could be developed in the future and that they could result in an embryo which developed for considerably longer than the two-cell stage. 'Both the hamster tests and the possibility of other trans-species fertilisations, carried out either diagnostically or as part of a research project, have caused public concern about the prospect of developing hybrid half-human creatures.' The committee approved of cross-species fertilisation as part of a recognised infertility programme, to assess or diagnose subfertility, provided the programme is licensed and the resultant hybrid is terminated at the two-cell stage. 'Any unlicensed use of trans-species fertilisation involving human gametes should be a criminal offence.'[19]

## GENETIC ENGINEERING

British scientists James Watson and Francis Crick made one of the most important contributions to science when they discovered the 'double-helix' structure of DNA in 1953, and since the early 1970s scientists have been able to produce new combinations of DNA molecules. Sections of the DNA strand can be cut out, discarded, replaced or inserted elsewhere in the DNA chain, in what is known as recombinant DNA technology. This heralded the new era of genetic engineering which is being used today in many fields including medicine for the production of drugs and vaccines.

The ability to inject new genes into a molecule is the most recent and high-tech advance in biology and seems like science fiction coming true. It also holds the key to improving crop and animal production. By altering the genetic structure of plants—and by borrowing genes from other organisms—scientists will be able to develop crops that are resistant to the environment, diseases and predators such as drought, fungi, viruses and insects. Researchers say that eventually it will be possible to combine animal, plant, microbe and human genes into animal embryos to develop made-to-order animals.

Gene transplanting in bacteria and yeast are almost commonplace and now scientists are moving to plants and animals. The first genetically engineered material used in environmental tests was in the US to control frost damage in plants, the second was in South Australia for the control of crown gall, a disease that ravages fruit crops. Some plants will even be made with inbuilt organic insecticides which will do away with chemical insecticides. Belgian researchers reported in June 1987 that they had successfully transferred an insecticide gene from bacteria into tobacco plants to produce a plant that kills leaf-chewing caterpillars. Gene transplanting requires micro-injection and the new plant is known as a *transgenic* tobacco. As Dr Jim Peacock of Australia's Commonwealth Scientific and Industrial Research Organisation (CSIRO) said, 'It is no longer a dream, no longer science fiction. The first blush of the biological bio-engineering crop species in plant production is at hand ... we are able to construct entirely new genes.'[20]

The world's first transgenic animal was a mouse that had been injected with a rabbit gene. The procedure was carried out by Professor Thomas Wagner of the Ohio University's Edison Animal Biotechnology Centre in 1980. Soon afterwards, mice were injected with a rat growth-hormone gene to produce giant mice, known as 'super-mice', which are produced at several centres around the world. Scientists are now working on transgenic pigs and sheep. The world's first genetically engineered sheep with extra growth hormone was developed by the CSIRO to produce a faster-growing, larger and leaner sheep. A one-cell sheep embryo was injected with the gene for growth hormone and the first lamb was born in April 1986. Researchers at the University of Adelaide, South Australia, and Ohio's Edison Center are inserting growth-hormone genes into pigs and the Agricultural Institute in Galway, Eire, is producing transgenic salmon by injecting an extra gene for growth hormone into the fish eggs. They are also transplanting pig growth hormone into cow eggs.

However, the technique is still fraught with problems. When researchers at the US Department of Agriculture's research station in Maryland inserted a human growth-hormone gene into pig embryos the result was pigs that suffered from several defects including severe arthritis, crossed eyes and susceptibility to disease.

When all goes as planned, genetic engineering in sheep, cattle and pigs has obvious advantages for food production worldwide. As Wagner said in 1987, 'We can enhance the growth rate of mice by 100 per cent and cut by 30 per cent the amount of feed they require to gain a given unit of weight. And their body fat ratio is reduced by as much as 70 per cent—which has positive implications for human health.'[21] But is gene transplanting possible, and acceptable, in humans? It certainly is possible and several research teams in the US are working on using it to correct genetic diseases, although no one has yet reported a success. The priority is immune deficiency disease due to the lack of one enzyme expressed in blood cells, and the race is on to find a genetically engineered cure. As David Weatherall commented, 'There are more people in the US working on this than there are patients with the disease—they are wanting to be the first to correct a human genetic disease.'

There are two approaches to treating inherited diseases with genetic engineering: to insert the missing gene, known as gene therapy, or to isolate and remove the defective gene and replace it with one taken from another embryo or person as in organ transplants, known as gene transplant. Both of these could be done in an infant found to have a genetic abnormality, but if the new gene is injected into gametes (eggs or sperm) it is passed to all subsequent offspring, eliminating the defect in future generations. Both will allow scientists to cure inherited diseases which may eventually include the most common such as cystic fibrosis, thalassemia and haemophilia.

Gene therapy and transplant require painstaking work and a special genetics laboratory with micro-injection equipment. Although they will be used for valid medical reasons such as correcting genetic defects, the ability to transplant genes for growth hormones or enzymes raises the possibility of, in the future, inserting genes for specific human traits such as height or eye colour. In the future it may be possible to order a baby of choice by selecting the genes for desired features: tall, brown-haired, blue-eyed, pimple-free etc. Today's scientists dismiss this as science fiction, but tomorrow's scientists may prove them wrong—the technology is available, it's just a matter of whether society allows it to be used for non-medical reasons.

Although several centres in the US are working on genetic engineering in humans, the US Government has put a temporary ban on patenting the results. Genetically engineered plants and animals will have enormous commercial value and the US Patent Office decided in April 1987 to allow new forms to be patented, but Charles Van Horn, director of organic chemistry and biotechnology, said, 'The decision says higher life forms will be considered, and it could be extrapolated to human beings, but for the time being, we are not going to consider applications involving human life.'[22] The decision to include animals brought a storm of protest from religious and moral leaders. Dr Robert Nelson, director of the Institute of Religion at the Texas Medical Center, Houston, said, 'It removes one more barrier to the protection of human life. Good God, once you start patenting life forms, is there no stopping?' Dr Michael Fox, scientific director of the Humane Society, added, 'One can infer from this decision that the entire creative process in higher forms of life, including human life, is going to be redirected or controlled to satisfy purely human ends . . . We are not only playing God, we are assuming domination over God.'[22]

In November 1987 Australia's National Health and Medical Research Council issued what is thought to be the first set of guidelines on human gene therapy. No such research in Australia can be done without permission of the council; gene therapy on eggs, sperm and embryos is banned; but research on other human cells is allowed under strict controls. The council decided it would be highly unethical to allow therapy on reproductive cells because not enough is known about the risks for future generations. The decision means only people affected by a genetic abnormality will benefit from a gene injection. The first experiments expected to be approved in Australia will be to correct the rare inherited diseases caused by severe deficiences of the immune system such as ADA (adenosine deaminase) deficiency and PNP (purine nucleoside phosphylase) deficiency, which cause mental retardation, multiple infections and early death. Chairman of the NHMRC's ethics committee, Professor Richard Lovell, praised the scientists who had asked the council for ethical guidance several years earlier and were responsible for initiating the new guidelines, which were drawn up by a committee of doctors, scientists, lawyers, theological and lay members after a two-year enquiry.

## ARTIFICIAL WOMBS

An artificial womb may sound like science fiction but many people, including the scientists most likely to develop it, predict it will be a reality in two to three decades.

Babies born 20 weeks prematurely, half way through a pregnancy, can in rare cases be kept alive in incubators, and embryos have been cultured in the laboratory for up to 12 days. It is only a matter of time before scientists discover the secret of how to grow embryos longer, and the age at which a premature baby can be incubated is coming down all the time. The two ends are gradually coming closer together. When they meet, we will have *ectogenesis*, the ability to grow outside the body.

Dr Gary Hodgen, scientific director of the Jones Institute in Virginia, says:

> It is not a deliberate attempt to create an artificial uterus but a case of two groups working at opposite ends of the scale, doing their own thing. Paediatricians are bringing down the time premature babies can survive, and working completely independently scientists have the ability to culture embryos in the laboratory. And I will be surprised if the two do not meet within the next 25 years.

Ectogenesis will allow scientists to study the development of embryos and foetuses and to compare normal and abnormal growth. It may well lead to better understanding of implantation and embryonic growth and may possibly lead to ways of overcoming some abnormalities. On the other hand, it could eventually be a new way of having babies for certain women. The womb as we know it would be eliminated. This would allow women who do not have a uterus to have a baby without the emotional, ethical and legal complications of using a surrogate mother. But is it morally acceptable?

The 1982 US President's Commission on foetal research cited several early attempts at developing an external life-support system, what it called an artificial placenta. The first, published in the US in 1963, involved 9-24-week-old aborted foetuses. Fifteen of them were immersed in salt solution containing oxygen at extremely high pressure, in an attempt to force oxygen to the foetus through the skin. The longest survived 22 hours. In an earlier study in Scandinavia, seven aborted foetuses were perfused with oxygenated blood through the umbilical vessels, and the longest survived 12 hours. English researchers used a similar method on eight foetuses removed after hysterectomy and the longest survived five hours.[23]

Attempts are now being made to culture a human uterus in the laboratory. A team at the University of Bologna, Italy, under Professor Carlo Flamigni, has succeeded in keeping several uteri alive for up to 48 hours outside the body. The uteri are surgically removed from women having hysterectomies, often because of cancer, and placed in a specially built machine, similar to an incubator. In 1986, the Bologna researchers reported they removed nine uteri and kept them 'alive' for up to 12 hours.[24] Ten months later, in January 1987, they reported that 25 uteri had been retrieved and incubated for up to 48 hours.[25]

The machine, or cabinet, the uterus is kept in is quite simple and similar to an artificial kidney machine that pumps in tissue culture, oxygen and carbon dioxide. It is constantly moist and kept at body temperature. Monitoring the hormones given off by the uterus indicates if and when it is functioning. When cellular activity ceases, it is deemed to be 'dead'. This pumping of fluids through the uterus, known as perfusion, is similar to the temporary preservation of organs, such as hearts and kidneys, before a transplant operation goes ahead.

The initial aim of the Bologna research is to measure what gases, hormones and enzymes the uterus needs in order to function and which substances are given off. This tells scientists about the function of the uterus and the endometrium. The longer-term aim is to study abnormal growths in the endometrium, which will greatly increase understanding of uterine cancer, and also to study embryo implantation, which will help improve the success rate of IVF.

In the Bologna team's second report, chief researcher Dr Carlo Bulletti said it is not yet possible to keep a uterus outside the body for very long but it would be useful for medical studies. 'At present, medium-term preservation (for days or even weeks) is required only under specific conditions, but this would become much more relevant with the development of studies [of the] endometrium, or for *in vitro* embryo implantation in the endometrium. At present long-term preservation (for months or years) is possible only with single cells.'[25]

Bulletti is keen that the research should help improve IVF and suggests studying mice embryos implanting in the incubated uterus. 'The critical problem in the IVF programme is the implant in the endometrium, which is difficult to study *in vivo* (in the body). A new approach to examining closely the mechanism of the embryo implant *in vitro* could be the implantation of a mouse embryo in a human perfused uterus [and] 48 hours are sufficient for a free blastocyst to complete implantation.'

How long before any of this will lead to an external womb capable of nine months' gestation is anyone's guess. Ultimately, an artificial womb may be a cross between Bulletti's human uterus and a machine, similar to a humidicrib that transfers blood and nutrients at a constant rate, at controlled temperature, possibly with computerised rocking to imitate the mother's body movement and an artificial heartbeat! One of the main problems will be preventing impurities getting into the foetus's blood supply.

Patrick Steptoe was one of the many people who oppose the idea of an external womb. He dismissed the possibilities of an entirely artificial womb, with embryos developing wholly outside their mother's body. 'No, for me there has first to be a medical justification before an artificial womb should be developed.'

The Warnock Committee considered ectogenesis so futuristic it declined to make a judgement except to reaffirm its recommendation that embryos should not be cultured in the laboratory for more than 14 days.

## MALE PREGNANCY

It is not beyond the realm of possibility for modern medicine to create a male-mother, although the idea horrifies many people. Male pregnancy is technically possible, but it would be extremely dangerous, both for the man and the foetus. There have been numerous jokes, cartoons and skits on pregnant men—including Australian comedienne Sue Ingleton's one-woman show 'Bill Rawlings, The Pregnant Man' which won acclaim at the 1985 Edinburgh Festival—all implying it is such an extraordinary concept that it will never happen. However, some American scientists predict it might happen within five years, although others say 15–20 years is more realistic.

Several groups of men have expressed interest in taking on 'the childbirth experience'. The men most likely to want a pregnancy include homosexuals in long-term monogamous relationships, as a child would complete the family and give them the same—or similar—experience as other couples. Many transsexuals, who have changed from man to woman, feel they would be 'completely woman' if they could carry and deliver a baby. And there are single heterosexual men who want to fulfil a strong maternal urge to experience childbirth. There is also a group of men who might want a pregnancy on medical grounds because their wives cannot have a baby, for example, if the woman is infertile or post-menopausal or if a pregnancy would be a danger to her health, in which case her husband might want to carry their child. In this context male pregnancy could be seen as an infertility procedure, similar to conventional surrogacy.

Some people see male pregnancy as the next logical step after IVF and surrogacy. Gynaecologists have discussed it in theory, although many have dismissed it on medical and ethical grounds. One problem would be finding a place for the embryo to imbed and nurture for nine months. In theory, a man with a large abdomen could carry a baby to term, and an embryo fertilised in the laboratory, presumably with his own sperm, could be transferred to the abdomen through an incision in the abdominal wall. The foetus's life support for nine months is the placenta which transports nutrients from the mother to the foetus and at the same time removes waste products. As the embryo produces the placenta itself, it would not be necessary for a man to have an endometrium, although it may be useful to transplant some endometrial tissue to the site where the embryo is going to implant.

Some people have suggested the embryo could implant in the abdominal wall, others say the liver or kidney where it would have a good supply of blood, and even the bowel has been suggested. Before and during pregnancy the man would have to be given estrogen and progesterone, the hormones that are normally produced by the ovaries after ovulation and by the endometrium during pregnancy.

However, even if an embryo implanted and developed, it would be difficult to sustain the pregnancy for the whole nine months. If he did manage to go full term, the man would then face the biggest risk: the delivery, which would have to be by Caesarean section. The main problem would be detaching the foetus from the abdomen. The uterus is designed to withdraw its blood supply at the time of delivery by contracting, but abdominal muscles cannot contract and doctors would face a massive haemorrhage if they severed the placenta. It would have to be left in the man's abdomen to wither and be absorbed by the blood system, but that carries the risk of infection developing.

Breastfeeding may not be a problem for transsexuals. One American psychiatrist claims one of his patients was able to share breastfeeding with his wife because he was given hormone treatment.

Male pregnancy has been achieved in animals. The first and one of the most successful was in the US in the mid-1960s when a male baboon was implanted with an embryo that grew for four months at which point researchers terminated the pregnancy. It attached itself to the omentum, a fatty fold of membrane between the stomach and colon. Since then scientists have also tried male pregnancy in rodents, mice, fowl, salamanders and other amphibians. In one experiment, in the 1960s before IVF was developed, embryonic tissue is said to have been removed from a female mouse and transplanted to the testes of a male mouse where it turned into cancerous cells rather than an embryo.

The equivalent to male pregnancy has occurred accidentally in women. There have been more than 1,000 reported cases of an embryo implanting in the abdominal wall, although only 10 per cent have resulted in live births. There are at least 24 known cases of women carrying a foetus after having a hysterectomy but only one has delivered a healthy baby, a 29-year-old New Zealand woman in 1979.

However, if a male pregnancy was well planned and closely followed by physicians throughout it might not be as dangerous as an ectopic pregnancy which is unexpected and uncontrolled. In male pregnancy the implantation site could be prepared, the hormone levels regulated and the pregnancy could be monitored for the full nine months.

Some gynaecologists, including Professor William Walters, Chairman of Obstetrics and Gynaecology at the University of Newcastle, Australia, are considering pregnancies for women who have no uterus. An IVF embryo could be transferred to the omentum, possibly after an endometrial tissue transplant.

> I have been involved with about 20 patients who don't have a uterus. We [doctors] have discussed it in theoretical terms

> and if it worked for them, in theory it should possibly work in men as long as you could make the hormone environment equal to the female, which I think you can. A lot of things would have to be quite experimental. Abdominal pregnancies occurring naturally are almost unheard of in other primates and there are no other animal species that we know of so it is no good saying it seems to work in sheep or dogs or mice.

Walters says a pregnancy for a woman without a uterus is medically feasible and ethically acceptable but he believes it will be a long time before it is extended to men. 'My view is that society is not ready for that at present and it would take a great change in public opinion to have it accepted. I doubt that will happen in the next 20 years.' He says it would be ethically wrong to assist in such a pregnancy unless the child born as a result was accepted in the community and that doctors should not go against a society's view. 'As doctors we are just members of that society, we have to live in that society, and it is important that we conform to certain social norms and as such we should not be going completely counter to society's view. When they change and are ready, that would be the time to look into it.'

The social and legal consequences of male motherhood would be complicated. Would the man be mother or father, or both? Under some laws a DI child born to a single woman does not have a legal father, although he has a genetic father. Conversely, a child born to a man-mother would have a legal father but no legal mother, although the woman who donated the egg would be the genetic mother. The definition of 'mother' is female parent, but perhaps in the future we should invent a new term for male-mother.

In her questionnaire on reproductive technologies, New York psychiatrist/lawyer Judianne Densen-Gerber presented some of the questions raised by male pregnancy:

> Should a male ever be allowed to gestate a child? Would this be in the child's best interest? Should all the rights and/or obligations that applied to a female gestational provider (a surrogate who uses her own egg) apply to a male? Should anyone doing work in this field be required to report

> directly to the controlling state agency? Should there be any special rules governing male pregnancy? Should a male be allowed to carry a child from an egg donor and his own sperm? Who is to be considered the mother—the egg donor or gestational donor? If it is the latter, can a male be considered both the mother and father if he is the gestational provider and sperm donor?[26]

George Annas, Professor of Health Law at Boston University, sees no justification for male pregnancy: 'I think male pregnancy and transsexual pregnancy is one of the craziest things I have ever heard in my life. I do not believe it would be a major medical advance or a major social advance for men to have babies—it's just crazy. It serves no useful human purpose and could create problems.'[17]

# 14
# REGULATION AND CONTROL

'If war is too important to be left solely up to the generals then biology is too important to be left to the biologists alone.' *American theologian Joseph Fletcher.*

Who should it be left to, if not the biologists? The public, the church, the lawyers, the medical profession, the politicians?

Medical advances are almost always several steps ahead of the law-makers, but new developments in reproductive technology are streets ahead. As the *Straits Times* of Singapore said, 'Recent advances in biology have created concepts of birth and parenthood faster than the standard English vocabulary can define them.'[1] I commented recently to an IVF expert that advances are moving so fast the public cannot keep up with them. 'Half the people in the field can't keep up with them!' he replied. If doctors and scientists cannot, can lawyers? Lori Andrews of the American Bar Association says there is a simple reason why law is always behind medical advances: 'Medicine looks forward, while the law gazes backwards. Medicine will readily embrace an innovative technology [but] common law cannot assimilate a new technology unless it has legal precedents to draw upon.'[2]

So what happens until the laws *are* made? Who is watching the doctors and scientists, who is controlling them? So far few countries have legislation on assisted procreation, and—strange as it may seem—it is largely controlled by the doctors themselves. The medical and scientific profession has always had an extraordinary system of self-regulation that does a fairly good job of ensuring that professional standards are met and ethics are maintained.

Most countries have one or more governing medical bodies—such as the British Medical Association or the Medical Research Council of Canada—and most of these associations have an ethics committee that draws up guidelines and monitors activities. In addition most universities or research institutes have an ethics panel that researchers have to receive approval from for research projects, and generally if they go outside those guidelines they lose their funding. Only one of the six Australian states has legislation on reproductive technologies but since 1982 all six have been controlled by guidelines imposed by the National Health and Medical Research Council (NHMRC). Centres that breach the guidelines will lose Federal Government funding for research. This also applies in the US if any medical or research centre becomes involved in embryo or foetal research. In theory this does not stop funding from a commercial company but in practice it usually does, because companies—and researchers—do not like to be associated with a project that has already been declared unethical.

Unfortunately, not all countries have such controls. For example, Dr Roberto Nicholson of the Centre for Studies in Gynaecology and Reproduction in Buenos Aires says there are no rules, regulations or legislation in Argentina covering assisted reproduction, and his centre is the only one that has an ethics committee to consider IVF cases.

In the 1950s and 60s several people were trying to fertilise human eggs in the laboratory, includng Landrum B. Shettles and John Rock in America, Daniele Petrucci in Italy, Steptoe and Edwards in England and reportedly scientists in the USSR. Very few people knew what they were doing until they published their work. Those in the profession say that today it is almost impossible for anyone to create 'brave new world' techniques without colleagues knowing, and if they are breaching ethical guidelines they would not get the necessary scientific funding. Dr. B.N. Saxena of the Indian Council of Medical Research speaks for many in the profession when he says: 'No doctor can work on this alone. You require a team of doctors backed by a good laboratory. Since in India the government is funding research in this area, there is no immediate danger [of exploitation].'

Patrick Steptoe believed research can be controlled:

> You would have to have a very corrupt team, and teams doing this not only need a licence, but every person involved has to be licensed and everybody can see what is being done. I see no reason why there should not be a licensing authority with powers to inspect and discover what is going on, and any research is something an ethical committee and licensing authority has to approve.[3]

However, having visited many IVF centres, I can see how a small group of people, who agreed among themselves to maintain secrecy, could do their own experiments without the hospital or university administration or ethics committee ever knowing. Even if a hospital administrator walked into a laboratory unannounced he is unlikely to know exactly what was in a particular test-tube or incubator—whether it was a two- or 12-day-old embryo, whether it was derived from an infertile woman or a donor, or whether it had been subjected to a biopsy.

We can never be sure that somewhere along the way someone is not going to deviate from their accepted research, out of curiosity rather than medical need. However, if someone wants to follow curiosity, they will do it whether there are rules or not.

Two recent, quite famous, examples show how easy it is for a research project or a new technique to be known of by only a few people. In Texas in 1984, Ricardo Asch only told his colleagues the night before he attempted his first successful GIFT operation. And when the world's first frozen-egg babies were born in Adelaide in 1986, only three people in the hospital at the time knew that the twins born to a 29-year-old Adelaide woman had been frozen before conception. In both cases these techniques were world firsts and each is now considered a substantial contribution to assisted reproduction.

It is generally assumed that peer pressure and ethical guidelines may be tight enough in Western countries, but this is not true in all countries. I visited Thailand's first IVF programme in Bangkok in 1987, and asked the director of the infertility clinic and the head of obstetrics and gynaecology what happened to the spare embryos in their programme. In the 12 months they had been operating, no one had asked them this question, not even the hospital's ethics committee which gave permission to start the programme. 'Because they didn't have the knowledge to ask,' was the chuckled explanation.

Doctors and scientists worldwide say there are reasonably good controls within the profession itself, and there is ample evidence of that, but 'reasonably' may not be good enough.

When the Warnock Report was released British researchers agreed to a voluntary moratorium on embryo research but it still continued, according to one London obstetrician/gynaecologist involved in IVF, who wrote: 'The Warnock report has been taken to be a useful piece of whitewash, diverting attention from what is really going on. The experimental work on cloning, genetic manipulation and human embryos is, of course, continuing. The disastrous effect of the prohibition is that it has been driven underground and will not be published.'[4]

Every now and then, those who want to see reproductive practices under stricter control remind us of the horrific Nazi 'experiments' on concentration camp inmates done in the name of medicine, or the killer bees that accidentally escaped during an experiment at the University of São Paulo, Brazil, in 1957 and now invade South and Central America. Australian Senator Brian Harradine, who introduced the Human Embryo Experimentation Bill in 1985, believes reproductive research should be controlled by law:

> Just as in the 1940s the development of nuclear weapons posed a threat to mankind as a whole, so in the 1980s human embryo experimentation poses a similar threat. All my bill seeks is to prevent human embryos from being created to be destroyed or experimented on. In other words to stop the creation of a race of laboratory disposable human beings.[5]

The urge to be first is tempting for all scientists, especially those involved in the fast-evolving world of reproduction, and some members of the profession are concerned that the technologies are moving ahead too quickly. Alan Trounson warned colleagues at the 1987 World Congress on IVF that they should be approaching their research prospectively, rather than retrospectively, otherwise it may be too late.

At the same conference the highly respected French reproductive specialist Jacques Testart called for a two-year moratorium on research. But American endocrinologist Zev Rosenwaks of the Jones Institute is not in favour: 'Moratoriums only stagnate the mind. What we need is lots of public debate. It is a public decision so doctors and scientists have to get out of their clinics and laboratories and tell the public what they are doing and what impact it will have in the future.' Ian Kennedy, Professor of Medical Law and Ethics at King's College, London, says the public must be given time to consider all the issues.

> We ought not to be hustled into making hasty decisions by the doctor or researcher anxious to get on with things. Science seems to be in a hurry but we can properly ask for time to catch our breath and consider. It is our right to deliberate on issues which touch the deepest values of our culture. And public opinion needs time to prepare and educate itself.[6]

Scientific director at the Jones Institute, Gary Hodgen, says he will not go ahead with research projects until society approves of the work. He has the ability to test for genetic abnormalities in pre-implantation embryos but says he will wait for public approval before doing it. 'We want their understanding and a degree of permission that comes from saying, this is an important enough gain that it deserves undertaking the risk with you.'

An editorial in *The Times* in 1984 warned: 'The thrust of scientific curiosity in laboratories seems to be outpacing society's ability to ask questions.'[7] And advances in reproductive technologies are moving faster now than in 1984. Testart, Kennedy, Hodgen and *The Times* have all warned that science has to slow down and allow the public time to digest its new work and decide on the issues.

Hodgen says the medical and scientific professions must be more open and more willing to discuss their plans.

> We need to work very hard, much harder than we did in the past, to communicate with our publics, to assist them to understand what our motives are and to make decisions. We must endorse and encourage participation. We cannot justify basic research in the old classical ivory tower way

> where we say the only thing that I have to justify is the need to know. It is not just them understanding us, we must also understand the public. There must be interplay that is at least based on trust on both sides. Historically, scientists and physicians lived in an era where they regarded this as their private domain and it was none of the public's business. Scientists have not in the past felt a real obligation to communicate to the lay public.[8]

But, he says, at the same time the public must appreciate that the outcome of research is not always foreseen. 'Waxman was an agronomist studying organisms that grow in the roots of plants when he discovered streptomycin. What is the likelihood that he would have made one of the largest medical discoveries in the twentieth century and received the Nobel Prize in 1952?' The public must also appreciate that with research it is important to look and plan ahead.

> For what we are going to need in the twenty-first century, the seeds must be sown now. You cannot put a quarter in a candy machine, pull a lever and the answer drops out. It is much more like forestry where we plant the seedling knowing we cannot harvest the tree for 20–30–40 years. The public must understand that basic research is not a candy machine.
>
> A hundred years ago the interval from observation to exploitation was very long. Today we have the opposite. Most new observations are applied within one to three years and because the changes are happening so fast there is little time for dialogue and understanding, among peer scientists and between scientists and the public. Scientists must agree to limits, they must be flexible. I will allow, and agree with, society in putting a fence around me at some level as long as society works with me to move that fence back in directions that we can both agree are in the public interest. Some of the most urgent needs of the public will be served by trust. In order to get that trust we must have to trade a degree of public supervision, and insight. I invite it, I want it, I enjoy it.

Hodgen had resigned as chief of the Pregnancy Research Branch at the National Institutes of Health in Bethesda in 1983 because his work was restricted by a 10-(now 15) year ban on federal funding for foetal research. After 14 years at NIH, Hodgen left saying his 'patience is worn out', and he moved to the private Jones Institute. *Science* magazine commented at the time: 'It may prove a serious mistake to drive scientists out of federal institutions, where research is done openly and its consequences may be debated while the work is progressing. When research must be done in the private sector, debate usually is postponed until results are announced.'[7] The point is very valid, although in this case both Hodgen and the Institute have been open in discussing their research projects and inviting public debate.

When the Victorian Government prohibited certain embryo research, some members of the Monash IVF team threatened to take their expertise overseas.

Brian Harradine points out that some of the physicians and scientists who talk of the need for public debate later pass less than academic criticism when parliamentary representatives make decisions that they do not agree with.

> On the release of the Waller Committee's report the community was treated to such statements as: 'It's a nonsense. Either they allow us to experiment or they don't. It is ridiculous from a scientific point of view' (Ian Johnston); or 'Inconsistent both ethically and scientifically' (Carl Wood); or 'Some of us would be prepared . . . to give up work and go to London or wherever to do the necessary embryonic research' (Alan Trounson).[5]

Hans Jochen Vogel, chairman of the Socialist Party in the German lower house and former Federal Minister of Justice, also calls for more public debate, but is not in favour of legislation.

> This discussion must begin and produce results before the railroad switches are shifted, before the decision is made about where the trains are going . . . I prefer this form of opinion-making to the prohibition of research and development . . . Legal prohibition must, of course, not be excluded from the start, but it must be the last resort.[9]

His counterpart in Austria, C. Broda, former Federal Minister of Law, is also against prohibition.

> Legislation hindering a person from availing himself of the medical methods for reproduction would not be humane but, rather, inhumane—so inhumane that we should have to protest against legislation in the name of humanity ... On the other hand, it is unmistakable that new medical methods raise difficult legal questions, especially in civil law. The need for provisions must be recognised. Those who want to use the new medical methods to have a child must be given safety about their decision rather than making them insecure; they must be helped to determine their actions on the basis of clearcut social advice instead of being frightened by horrible visions of imaginary medical possibilities.[10]

Broda quotes Professor Kurt Weinke of the Philosophical Institute, University of Graz: 'In the field of human artificial reproduction, an insecurity of values and, therefore, of attitude by the public legislator, runs right through all denominations down to the doctors (and their professional bodies) as well as to the patients ... You sometimes get the impression that more problems are induced by the decision-makers.'

The security of, and the effect on, people using assisted reproduction, and the children born as a result, must be given consideration, Broda said.

> Partnership relations between two persons must not be exposed to vexing incrimination by an unfriendly and irresolute legal system; they must, rather, enjoy any possible assistance and encouragement by an understanding community ... children who owe their existence to medically aided reproduction must grow up free from any shadow of discrimination or even of some legal prejudice ... Experience ought to warn us against general criminalisation of an intimate sphere of life. Again it is only the weakest, above all, women, who might become the victims. It cannot be the legislator's task to stipulate to the partners how they are to live together and how they are to have the children that they have not been able to have. Law must not regulate this at all. Let us not forget that it is precisely those who are eagerly awaiting children who deserve our care.

The Women's Reproductive Rights Information Campaign in Britain says that licensing and restricting AI centres will give women less control over their bodies and that allowing embryo research gives scientists the opportunity to perfect and perpetuate the race. However, it is concerned about the effect of new technologies on Third World countries, particularly surrogacy, as poor women in Africa, Asia and South America would be paid 'a pittance' for the use of their wombs by Westerners who would not consider asking other Western women to do the same, and says that without restrictions, Third World countries could become bases for 'manufacturing' embryos.

Many of those involved in the new reproductive technolgies agree that some regulation is needed, especially for IVF, embryo research and gene therapy. Ideally this would unravel the ethical problems and ensure that standards in training and facilities are upheld.

However, most in the profession are against legislation because technology changes faster than legislation can be amended. 'We don't need laws,' says French infertility expert Professor Jean Cohen, a member of his country's National Consultative Ethics Committee. 'By the time you make the law, there will be new techniques. If there had been a law two years ago forbidding the freezing of embryos there would be no frozen-embryo babies today.'

Australia's Russell Scott, chairman of the New South Wales Law Reform Commission, strongly opposes legislation: 'Passing a law on something as complex as IVF is about as wrong as you can get.' Robert Edwards agrees laws are unnecessary: 'Voluntary guidelines are better than legal rules. The Voluntary Licensing Authority (in Britain) puts out certain rules that can be changed if there is a very important clinical reason.' And scientist Anne McLaren, a member of the VLA and of the Warnock Committee, argues for regulation, not legislation, because she says it is too hard to 'undo' laws.

In 1977, a year before the first IVF baby was born, Russell Scott was the first in Australia to call for parliamentary regulation of IVF, but he told the 1986 International Conference on Health Law and Ethics that times have changed. 'Today in Australia there are over a hundred operating local institutional ethics committees. We also have state government committees. In addition there are two national organisations ... [providing] an effective non-legislative system of regulating IVF and related research.' He argued for regulation but not legislation, saying 'legislation is proving to be an awkward if not inappropriate medium'.[11]

> The New Biology has exhibited the capacity to arouse storms of public debate and to paralyse politicians or impel them towards unwise legislation ... A reading of the critical provisions of the Victorian statute will show that some of them plainly amount to moral statements in legislative form ... In my view it is unlikely that resort solely to traditional legislative forms and criminal sanctions will or can provide effective regulation or will serve the public interest.

He said some legislation will be needed. There is also a definite place for guidelines, which have the advantage that they can easily be amended. Consideration should also be given to statutory guidelines such as the existing legislation on brain death. Sensible control of purse strings can be justified—an example being the US Government's threat to withhold funds from hospitals in the 1970s to prevent IVF. There is also a place for self-regulation, which he believes is highly developed in the medical profession in Western communities. 'There is a growing opinion that resort solely to legislation in traditional form may not be adequate.'

Scott concluded:

> Research and other activities in biomedicine can obviously be prohibited by means of legislation and criminal sanctions. However, it would not be wise for a parliament in a pluralist society, in response to a disputed moral opinion, to outlaw research in important areas of developmental medicine such as IVF, unless there existed evidence of actual or possible abuse on the part of the research community. Effective regulation, on the other hand, could be both creative and beneficial.

Although it is important that each country draw up laws to suit its particular society, some standardisation is needed, and one of the problems with regulating assisted reproduction is the lack of uniform rules in different states and countries. Broda told the Austrian enquiry that within the European Council's 21 member countries there were no legal regulations on IVF or surrogacy, 'although the vast majority of such states consider a European harmonised legal regularisation in this field necessary and the current ethical regulations for doctors and scientists inadequate'.

He advocated uniform regulation but said it will be hard to achieve because already different countries have adopted opposing stands. 'While the Warnock Report advocates the donor's absolute anonymity in Britain, and France also favours this anonymity, the Federal Republic of Germany mainly shares the Swedish view that the child has the right to obtain all the information on his or her genetic descent when he or she has reached maturity.'[10]

In the US, each state may have a different law and if there is a dispute, several important, but conflicting, principles could be applied: contract law, genetic inheritance or what is in the best interest of the child. If surrogacy, for example, is allowed in one state and banned in another, patients will simply cross the border. States can determine their own laws on AI, IVF and surrogacy as these do not come under federal jurisdiction. To cope with the complexities of the new reproductive technologies many states are relying on interpretations of existing laws. Others have passed new laws. According to Lori Andrews, laws in six states in the US ban research on embryos and 29 states have artificial insemination laws providing that the child is the legal child of the sperm recipient and her consenting husband. Payment for a human embryo is specifically banned in Florida and may be indirectly forbidden in 11 other states. In at least 24 states, laws prohibit payment to a woman who gives up her baby for adoption, but states differ in whether this also applies to payment for surrogates. In Arkansas, a couple who contracts an unmarried surrogate mother are by law the legal parents. Idaho recently passed a law making it compulsory for hospitals and sperm banks to 'use all reasonable means' to detect the AIDS antibody in sperm donors.[2]

Some of this fragmentation could soon be consolidated as Congress is considering a comprehensive report prepared by the Office of Technology Assessment with the help of 13 experts including physicians, scientists, lawyers, ethicists, geneticists and representatives of infertile patients, veterans and pharmaceutical and insurance companies.

The lack of consistent regulation obviously facilitates 'across the border' practices. Indeed people will cross continents to fulfil their dreams, as seen by the number of Arab, Indian, Turkish and European couples attending the main IVF centres in Britain. Swedes, especially single women, who find IVF and AI regulations in their own country restrictive go to Denmark for treatment. A recent law in Denmark prohibits embryo research so some Danish scientists are working in Sweden. The ban on commercial surrogacy in Victoria has not stopped Victorian surrogates advertising their services in other states. And to avoid the British ban on commercial surrogacy, some women are going to the Netherlands to have their babies then returning to the UK.

*Who* should decide on regulations is complex. If it is left to committees, there is rarely total agreement on sensitive issues such as surrogacy, embryo research and gene therapy. Seven of the 16 members on the Warnock Committee disagreed with recommendations on the use of embryos in research, and three filed a dissenting report on surrogacy. The American Fertility Society's ethics committee was not unanimous on the use of donor sperm, eggs and embryos. The Victorian legislation might have been completely different if the composition of the committee had not been as it was.

Patrick Steptoe believed the public, especially the patients, should decide on how eggs and embryos are used. 'It is up to society to decide,' he said.

> With eggs, the whole thing is in the hands of women because they provide the eggs which involves an invasion of their bodies. I think women should be a little more knowledgeable and a little more vehement about it. The embryos must belong to the parents, the husband and wife who give the sperm and eggs, and they are the ones who should have the say in what happens—whether they should be used for research, frozen or destroyed. It is for them to decide, not for a government or society. The government

doesn't say you can't have an abortion, and there you have a much more developed thing, so the government should not interfere with the much earlier stage.

In some cases politicians have decided. Since the 1970s, several countries have enacted laws defining the legal status of AI children, Britain and Victoria have banned commercial surrogacy, and Denmark has banned embryo research, but few other countries have legislated on assisted reproduction, although many have set up committees to recommend on regulation.

The Victorian legislation is the most comprehensive, yet less than three years after enacting it the government was forced to amend part of it to allow certain embryo experiments. Depending on your view, it could be said that the legislators showed lack of foresight, or that they were responsive to public demand. In that three years, research was held up while scientists, lawyers and the public debated why there should, or should not, be a change in the law. Advances in reproduction are moving so fast it could be argued that it does not really matter if research is held up for three years while an important ethical issue is being debated. If rules are too easily changed, there is little value in having them.

Before the amendment, Alan Trounson's research on the safety of egg freezing and micro-injection was prohibited. About 20 per cent of infertile men could father children for the first time with micro-injection, and IVF experts Professor Lars Hamberger of Sweden and Professor Shlomo Mashiach of Israel believe micro-injection babies would have been born by early 1987 if the research had not been held up. 'It is one of the breakthroughs we were really waiting for because there are few ways of dealing with male infertility in IVF,' said Mashiach. Although the work is important, does it matter enormously that those 20 per cent of infertile men had to wait another three years for a technique that had not been available previously? Three years is not long in a lifetime, compared with the importance of regulating science involving human life.

In some cases legislation could work against the best interests of the people it was designed to protect. By making certain research a criminal offence, the Victorian Government prevented Trounson analysing embryos derived from freeze-thaw eggs. Ironically there is no law to prevent doctors transferring such embryos to potential mothers, and several babies have already been born without the technique being proved to be safe: 'Threatening to put them in jail is not the way to treat scientists doing this sort of work,' he said.

Most of those involved in assisted reproduction say legislation is needed to define the legal parents in surrogacy, embryo flushing, and the donation of sperm, eggs and embryos. On a more practical level, the American Fertility Society is concerned that there is quality of services and that all physicians involved are trained and experienced. It also suggests physicians and programmes be certified and that annual assessment be mandatory. Some infertility experts argue for a limit on the age of the woman patient, for example 40, because the chances of pregnancy decline dramatically after that. Others have called for a limit on the number of eggs or embryos transferred. In Britain, the Voluntary Licensing Authority decides on these finer points, and any centre not prepared to follow VLA guidelines loses its licence. At the moment the VLA has no legal power but under the government's proposed legislation a statutory licensing authority will be established to control all aspects of IVF and embryo research.

Possibly the best compromise in this complex debate is for governments to lay the foundations—and the most important is to legally define mother and father—and to leave the month-to-month decisions to a statutory commission made up of representatives from the medical, legal, welfare, religious and political fields, patients requiring services and agencies providing them. This would allow a more flexible approach to change than legislation; the commission would be receptive to, and influenced by, public opinion; and a government that did not agree with the commission's general attitude or certain decisions could always change the representatives on the commission, which would be preferable to giving politicians total power.

Australian law reformer Mr Justice Michael Kirby, who was responsible for innovative legislation on tissue transplantation, believes the issues should be dealt with by a national law reform agency.

> Unless it is solved by a law reform agency, it will not be solved by parliaments. It will be solved by busy doctors and infertility assistants dealing with the crisis and pain of infertility by simply providing the materials, and when problems arise, by judges. And we will have to resort to principles developed in village England years ago to solve absolutely different questions. That is why it is important that society consider these questions aided by the best experts in the land and that they give close attention to questions of morality, medicine, science and the law which are posed by these new remarkable developments.[12]

Kirby, who is now President of the Court of Appeal of the Supreme Court, said it is easy for the law to wrap these problems up as what is in the best interests of the child, but that leaves a great deal to judicial discretion, and it would be preferable for politicians to give guidance.

> And they should do it with the knowledge that 15 per cent of marriages are infertile and that having a child is an important part of marriage, that it's important for society. There are new and special problems in our community with the growing level of infertility, particularly because of sexually transmitted diseases. We must face realities that many couples can produce eggs and sperm but in some cases the wife cannot carry a child and if science provides the solution there are many who say it is a solution that should be permitted in properly monitored conditions.
>
> If we have rules and guidelines it would be good for the profession and society and above all it would be good for the infertile couples who suffer. It is all very easy for people who have children to adopt a high moral stance without understanding the problems of people who don't have children. People who adopt an insensitive approach to this should speak to more infertile couples and understand the very strong force that exists.

In her questionnaire sent to professional, religious and social leaders Judianne Densen-Gerber started by asking:

> Should the government have the right to regulate the application of the new reproductive technologies? If your

answer is No, should there be a right to reproduce for some adults only (such as denying the right to the retarded, the impoverished, etc)? If your answer is Yes, should government intervention be influenced most by: the recognition of a right to reproduce for adults; the best interests of the child; societal concerns, such as population control, religious freedom, property rights, etc; all of the above?[13]

What should be allowed, who should decide, and who should control them? That's what all the fuss is about.

# GLOSSARY

*abortion* Spontaneous or induced expulsion of an embryo or foetus from the womb before it is viable.
*adenomyosis* Condition where pockets of endometrium (uterine lining) appear in the muscle wall of the uterus: a form of endometriosis.
*adhesions* Scar tissue that often appears after infection or surgery and binds organs together.
*amniocentesis* Procedure in which amniotic fluid is withdrawn from the womb at the 16th–18th week of pregnancy to diagnose certain genetic diseases, or later in pregnancy to diagnose foetal lung maturity.
*amniotic fluid* Liquid produced by the foetus and placenta surrounding the foetus in the womb.
*andrologist* Physician who specialises in the study of male reproduction.
*anovulation* Condition where woman fails to ovulate.
*artificial insemination* Procedure whereby semen is injected into a woman's vagina, cervical canal or uterus, usually done with a needleless syringe, either with her husband's sperm (AIH) or donor sperm (donor insemination).
*azoospermia* Condition where men produce no sperm in their semen.
*biopsy* Procedure in which a piece of tissue is removed for examination in a laboratory.
*blastocyst* An early embryo consisting of many cells that form about five days after fertilisation, just before the embryo implants in the uterus.
*capacitation* A chemical transition in the membrane of the sperm head which must occur before it is able to penetrate the egg membrane.
*catheter* A long, thin, hollow instrument that is inserted into the body to remove fluid (as in egg collection) or deposit fluid (as in GIFT),

or to determine whether a passage in the body (such as fallopian tube) is open.

*cervix, or cervical canal* The neck (entrance) of the womb (uterus).

*cervical mucus* Fluid produced by cells in the cervical canal.

*chlamydia* A micro-organism, usually transmitted sexually in adults, that often causes inflammation in the male and female genital tract, frequently without symptoms.

*chorion* Outer membrane produced by the embryo and surrounding an embryo in the womb.

*chorion villus sampling* Procedure in which chorionic cells are withdrawn from the womb at the 6th–8th week of pregnancy to diagnose certain genetic diseases.

*chromosomes* Strands of protein that contain genes. Every cell in the human body has 23 pairs of chromosomes, except that eggs and sperm before they are released have 23 chromosomes.

*clomiphene* Drug given to women to stimulate the ovaries to release one or more eggs, used for superovulation in IVF and as a fertility drug for women with ovulation failure.

*cloning* Process that results in one or many cells that are identical to each other and the original source.

*conception* Process involving the fertilisation of an egg by a sperm, the union of egg and sperm.

*conceptus* The product of conception—a group of cells resulting from the fertilisation of an egg by a sperm.

*congenital* A feature (such as an abnormality or a disease) that exists at birth, although it may not be detected at birth.

*cryopreservation* Preservation by freezing. Sperm, eggs and embryos are frozen in liquid nitrogen.

*cryoprotectant* Substance used to treat sperm, eggs and embryos before they are frozen.

*cumulus cells* surround the egg.

*cycle* See menstrual cycle.

*cystic fibrosis* Hereditary disease affecting boys and girls characterised by defect of numerous glands, resulting in severe digestive disorders, lung infections and breathing difficulties. Most sufferers die before the age of 20.

*DES* Diethyl stilboestrol—synthetic estrogen (hormone) used to prevent recurrent miscarriages, mainly in the US in the 1950s–70s.

*dilation and curettage (D&C)* Procedure in which the cervix is dilated and the uterus is scraped (curettaged), usually done for a biopsy, after a miscarriage or to terminate a pregnancy.

*DNA* Deoxyribonucleic acid—the chemical units forming chromosomes in the nucleus of each cell. It carries the genetic or hereditary material, appears as a long double strand, like a twisted ladder.

*DNA probing* Technique of seeking out and identifying a gene with a specific DNA code, eg. the code for cystic fibrosis.
*DNA technology* The science of identifying and altering DNA.
*Down's syndrome* (mongolism) A congential defect caused by a chromosome abnormality—three chromosomes appear at the 21st position instead of the usual two (known as trisomy 21)—resulting in mental retardation and various physical defects.
*ectogenesis* Development of a foetus outside the body; bodyless babymaking.
*ectopic pregnancy* Dangerous condition whereby an embryo develops outside the uterus, usually in one of the fallopian tubes.
*egg* Female sex cell, matured in ovaries and released in ovulation, and when fertilised by a sperm develops into an embryo.
*egg collection* Procedure in which a physician removes eggs (in follicular fluid) from the ovaries before ovulation; also known as oocyte aspiration.
*ejaculation* Expulsion of semen from the penis during orgasm.
*electro-ejaculation* Process whereby male sex organs are electrically stimulated to produce semen, used mainly for paraplegics.
*embryo* A collection of cells (conceptus) from fertilisation to the end of the 8th week of pregnancy.
*embryo flushing* or *lavage* Procedure where an embryo is flushed from the uterus before implantation.
*endometriosis* Condition that occurs when the lining of the uterus appears outside the uterus on the surface of other pelvic organs, including the tubes, ovaries, outside of the uterus, bladder and bowel.
*endometrium* Lining of the uterus (womb).
*epididymis* A long, thin duct that sits tightly coiled on top of each testicle and carries sperm from the testes to the vas.
*estrogen* Hormone secreted mainly by the ovaries and necessary for female reproduction.
*fallopian tubes* Two tubes that extend from either side of the uterus to near each ovary where their open end collects eggs released after ovulation. Fertilisation takes place in the tubes and occasionally an embryo lodges here, resulting in an ectopic pregnancy.
*fertilisation* Process in which an egg and sperm are physically united.
*fibroids* Benign growths of muscle tissue in the uterine wall.
*fimbria* The open end of each fallopian tube that picks up eggs after ovulation.
*foetus* An unborn conceptus between the 9th week of pregnancy and birth.
*follicle* Fluid-filled sac in the ovary, from which an egg is released in ovulation.

*follicle-stimulating hormone (FSH)* Hormone released by the pituitary gland to stimulate growth of the follicle in women and sperm production in men. Used in infertility treatment artificially to stimulate the ovaries.
*follicular fluid* Liquid surrounding an egg in a follicle; removed during egg collection in IVF.
*fusion* Process in which the nuclei of an egg and sperm join together to form an embryo.
*gamete* Sex cell, i.e. an egg or a sperm.
*genes* Proteins which determine how bodies function and what physical characteristics we will have, eg, height, eye colour, foot size; found in the nucleus of all cells; humans have an estimated 100,000.
*gene manipulation* Technique of changing the structure of the gene to make a new gene that will produce different characteristics.
*genetic engineering* The science of manipulating genes.
*genetic-gestational provider* Woman who provides the genetic material (the egg) and gestates (carries) the baby—only used to distinguish between traditional and surrogate pregnancies.
*genetic parent* Man or woman who provided the sperm or egg that resulted in a child who may be brought up by another adult (a social parent); term used to identify parents in adoption and surrogacy births.
*gestation* The period of pregnancy.
*gestational mother* Woman (a surrogate) who carries the baby in pregnancy, after fertilisation with her own egg or another woman's.
*GIFT* Gamete intrafallopian transfer—technique that involves placing gametes (eggs and sperm) in the fallopian tubes.
*GnRH analog* A synthetic hormone that is a slight variation of the naturally occurring GnRH (gonadotrophin releasing hormone), used to control ovulation for egg collection.
*gonorrhoea* Sexually transmitted disease caused by gonococcus bacteria resulting in inflammation of the genital tract.
*haemophilia* Hereditary disorder resulting in abnormal blood clotting that usually affects men, although women may carry the gene for the disease.
*hirsutism* Condition caused by hormone inbalance resulting in excess body hair and obesity.
*human chorionic gonadotrophin (HCG)* Hormone produced by the chorion during pregnancy which can be extracted from the urine of pregnant women and used to stimulate ovulation in anovulatory women and in IVF.
*human menopausal gonadotrophin (HMG)* Hormone produced by the pituitary and extracted from the urine of post-menopausal women (usually nuns) and used to stimulate ovulation.

*hypospadias* Defect where urethra opens above or below the penis.
*hysterosalpingogram (HSG)* An X-ray picture which shows the shape of the uterus and tubes after dye has been injected into them.
*implantation* Process whereby an embryo imbeds itself in the endometrium; it usually takes a week and begins about seven days after fertilisation.
*incompetent cervix* A cervix that painlessly dilates, usually between the 10th and 20th week of pregnancy, often because it has been weakened or stretched; may result in a spontaneous abortion (miscarriage)
*insemination* in IVF—a procedure where sperm are added to an egg in the laboratory. Not the same as artificial insemination.
*in vitro fertilisation (IVF)* Literal translation is *in glass* fertilisation; generally it means fertilisation outside the body.
*laparoscope* Long, thin instrument with a magnifying lens and light source on the end, which is inserted through the abdomen to examine the female pelvic region, especially the tubes and ovaries.
*laparoscopy* Procedure in which laparoscope is used; usually requires general anaesthetic.
*leutinising hormone (LH)* Hormone produced by the pituitary in women in large amounts just before ovulation to give ovulation a final burst, and in men to stimulate the testes to produce testosterone.
*Lesch-Nyhan disease* Hereditary condition caused by the lack of an enzyme, results in mental retardation and self-mutilation, usually only in men, although women may also carry the gene.
*menarche* The beginning of female reproductive capacity, denoted by the first menstrual period, usually at age 12 in Western countries and 14 in Africa.
*menopause* The end of female reproductive capacity, denoted by the last menstrual period.
*menstrual cycle* Ideally a 28-day period in which follicles develop in the ovaries, an egg is released and the endometrium prepares to receive an embryo. If the egg is not fertilised the endometrium bleeds, breaks down and is passed out as a bleed, or period.
*miscarriage* Spontaneous abortion.
*nucleus* The core of each cell in the body, the part that contains the DNA.
*oligospermia* Condition where men produce lower than normal number of sperm in their semen.
*oocyte* Egg.

*ovary* Gland in the female pelvic which releases eggs and secretes hormones necessary to begin and sustain a pregnancy.
*ovulation* Process in which an egg is released from a follicle in one of the ovaries, on average every 28 days.
*parthenogenesis* Reproduction without sex, for example when an egg divides without being fertilised by a sperm.
*pelvic inflammatory disease (PID)* Infection in the pelvic region of a woman, usually affecting the tubes and ovaries and sometimes resulting in infertility.
*pituitary gland* A pea-sized gland in the centre of the skull, directly behind the bridge of the nose, that is responsible for the release of several hormones including FSH and LH.
*polyps* Small growths in the lining of the uterus.
*POST* peritoneal ovum and sperm transfer—procedure where eggs and sperm are injected into the peritoneum, the space behind the uterus.
*post-coital test* Test in which cervical mucus is examined after coitus for the presence of sperm.
*procreation* The production of offspring.
*progesterone* hormone secreted mainly by the ovaries after ovulation and by the placenta during pregnancy, essential for implantation and continuation of pregnancy.
*prolactin* Hormone secreted by pituitary gland in men and women, main role is to stimulate milk production, but increased levels reduce fertility.
*pronuclei* A portion of the nucleus that appears part way through fertilisation, after the sperm has penetrated the egg but before the egg nucleus and the sperm nucleus fuse together.
*PROST* pronuclear stage tubal transfer—procedure where a pronuclear stage pre-embryo is transferred to the fallopian tube.
*prostate* Gland at the base of the bladder in men, secretes fluid that makes up seminal fluid.
*salpingostomy* Operation to open fimbria-end of blocked fallopian tube.
*semen* Fluid produced in ejaculation, contains prostate and other fluids and sperm.
*scrotum* Pouch containing the testes.
*sperm* Male sex cell.
*sperm antibodies* Antibodies produced by the body against sperm in men and women; results in infertility.
*superovulation* Process where the ovaries are artificially stimulated by drugs to release more than the normal one egg.
*surrogate* Substitute mother, in particular a woman who

deliberately becomes pregnant with the intention of giving the baby to someone else, usually an infertile couple.
*testosterone* Hormone in men and women, mainly secreted by the testes for sperm production.
*thalassaemia* An inherited condition leading to anaemia, common in Mediterranean people.
*transgenic* Plant or animal that has an altered or extra gene, eg. transgenic mice have been given an extra gene for growth hormone resulting in 'super-mice'.
*triploid* Embryo with three sets of chromosomes within a cell, i.e. 69 chromosomes instead of the usual 46.
*two-cell embryo* A conceptus consisting of two identical cells (each containing 46 chromosomes) encased in a membrane. The two-cell embryo appears shortly after fertilisation when the conceptus divides. At the next division these two cells divide, resulting in a four-cell embryo.
*ultrasound* Technique involving high-frequency sound waves used for viewing internal organs, especially when investigating infertility in women.
*undescended testes* Condition usually diagnosed in infant boys where one or both testes fail to move out of the abdomen into the scrotum, resulting in permanent damage to sperm production if not corrected by surgery.
*uterus* Organ in women that nurtures a growing embryo and foetus, upper end opens into fallopian tubes and lower end into vagina, via the cervix. Lined by the endometrium. Occasionally the site of abnormal growths such as polyps and fibroids and adhesions which reduce fertility.
*varicocele* Swollen vein around either or both testes.
*vas* Male reproductive tube that transports sperm from each testis to the seminal vesicle.
*vasectomy* Operation in which the vas in both testes is 'tied' (surgically closed) to sterilise a man.
*womb* Uterus.
*ZIFT* zygote intrafallopian transfer—another name for PROST.
*zona pellucida* Outer layer of an egg which has to be penetrated by a sperm as the first stage of fertilisation.
*zygote* Cell resulting from fertilisation.

# REFERENCES

## CHAPTER 1

1 *Instruction on Respect for Human Life in its Origin and on the Dignity of Procreation. Replies to Certain Questions of the Day*, Congregation for the Doctrine of the Faith, Libreria Editrice Vaticana, 1987.

## CHAPTER 2

1 Quoted by Patricia Mahlstedt in 21 below
2 Genesis 30, 1
3 Harvey Sorkow in Baby M decision, New Jersey Superior Court, 31 March 1987
4 '*Infertility and Sexually Transmitted Disease: A Public Health Challenge*, Population Reports, Johns Hopkins University, Baltimore, July 1983, p116
5 Population Reports, p122; also Keith Edmonds et al, 'Early embryonic mortality in women', *Fertility and Sterility*, Vol 38 No 4, October 1982
6 Templeton and Penny, *Fertility and Sterility*, Vol 37 p175; Collis, Wrixon, Janes and Wilson, *New England Journal of Medicine*, No 309 p1201; Wood, Baker and Trounson, in *Clinical IVF*, Springer Berlin, 1984; Craven, Beadle and Lee, presentation to Fertility Society of Australia, Melbourne, 1985.
7 9, 12 and 14 below.
8 *Surrogate Motherhood: Australian Public Opinion*, Research Report, New South Wales Law Reform Commission, Sydney, May 1987
9 World Health Organisation, Special Programme for Research, Development and Training in Human Reproduction, 13th Annual Report, p70; also 14th Annual Report, p114

10 *Reproductive Health Hazards in the Workplace*, Congress of the US, Office of Technology Assessment, Washington, DC, November 1985, p9; also Sevgi Aral & Willard Cates, 'Increasing Concern With Infertility', *Journal of the American Medical Association* (JAMA), Vol 250 No 17, 4 November 1983, p2327–31
11 M.G.R. Hull et al, 'Population Study of Causes, Treatment and Outcome of Infertility', *British Medical Journal* Vol 291, 1985, p1693–7
12 Mark Belsey, 'The Epidemiology of Infertility: a Review with Particular Reference to sub-Saharan Africa', *Bulletin of the World Health Organisation* Vol. 54 (3), 1976, p319–41
13 Aral & Cates, 10 above
14 Willard Cates, Tim Farley & Patrick Rowe, 'Worldwide Patterns of Infertility: is sub-Africa Different?' *The Lancet*, 14 September 1985, p596–8
15 Population Reports, p115
16 Population Reports, p118
17 Population Reports, p117
18 Barbara Menning, 'The Emotional Needs of Infertile Couples', *Fertility and Sterility*, Vol 34 No 4, October 1980, p313–19
19 Kay Oke & Jan Aitken, 'The Implications of IVF for the Individual', Conference 'IVF: Problems and Possibilities', Melbourne, March 1982
20 Patricia Mahlstedt, 'The Psychological Component of Infertility', *Fertility and Sterility*, Vol 43 No 3, March 1985, p335–46
21 *Issue*, magazine of the National Association for the Childless (Britain), Autumn 1986
22 *Issue*, Winter–February 1987
23 *Issue*, Spring–May 1987
24 Diane & Peter Houghton, *Coping with Childlessness*, Unwin, London, 1987, p71
25 H.J. Brand, 'The Influence of Sex Differences on the Acceptance of Infertility', abstract, World Congress for Sexology, Heidelberg, 17–20 June 1987
26 Ellen Freeman et al, 'Psychological Evaluation and Support in a Programme of IVF and Embryo Transfer', *Fertility and Sterility*, Vol 43 No 1, January 1985
27 Cécile Ernst, 'Psychosocial Aspects of Artificial Procreation', presentation and debate, Colloquium on the Legal Regulation of Reproductive Medicine, Cambridge, 15–17 September 1987
28 Houghtons p84
29 *American Health*, May 1987
30 Houghtons p66

## CHAPTER 3

1 Jane Henderson et al, 'Occupational-related Male Infertility: A Review', *Clinical Reproduction and Fertility* (1986)4, p87–106
2 World Health Organisation, Special Programme for Research, Development and Training in Human Reproduction, 14th Annual Report, p114–24
3 *Infertility and Sexually Transmitted Disease: A Public Health Challenge*, Population Reports, Johns Hopkins University, Baltimore, July 1983, p128
4 Gordon Baker, 'Requirements for Controlled Therapeutic Trials In Male Infertility', *Clinical Reproduction and Fertility*, (1986)4, p13–25
5 Patricia Mahlstedt, 'The Psychological Component of Infertility', *Fertility and Sterility*, Vol 43 No 3, March 1985, p335–46
6 Robert Winston, *Infertility: a Sympathetic Approach*, Martin Dunitz, London, 1986, p27
7 Presentation to 12th World Congress on Fertility and Sterility, Singapore, 26–31 October 1986
8 World Health Organisation, Special Program for Research, Development and Training in Human Reproduction, 14th Annual Report, p114–24
9 Gordon Baker et al, 'Relative Incidence of Etiological Disorders in Male Infertility', Chapter 16 in *Male Reproductive Dysfunction*, Marcel Dekker, New York, 1986, p341–72
10 H.P. Azarian et al, 'Main Causes and Frequencies of Male Infertility in Infertile Couples,' presentation to Symposium on Diagnosis and Treatment of Infertility, Yerevan, Armenia, USSR, 20–21 May 1985
11 Gordon Baker et al, 'Testicular vein ligation and fertility in men with varicoceles', *British Medical Journal*, Vol 291, 14 December 1985, p1678–80
12 WHO 13th Annual Report, p79
13 Population Reports, p130
14 *Reproductive Health Hazards in the Workplace*, Congress of the US, Office of Technology Assessment, Washington DC, November 1985, p7–13
15 Henderson, p91
16 John Tyler, 'Reduced Testicular Temperature with a Cooling Device', presentation to Fertility Society of Australia 6th Annual Scientific Meeting, Sydney, 11–14 November 1987
17 Ellen Freeman et al, 'Psychological Evaluation and Support in a Program of IVF and Embryo Transfer', *Fertility and Sterility*, Vol 43 No 1, January 1985

18 Winston, p140
19 Baker et al, *Male Reproductive Dysfunction.*

## CHAPTER 4

1 *Infertility and Sexually Transmitted Disease: A Public Health Challenge*, Population Reports, Johns Hopkins University, Baltimore, July 1983, p124
2 Robert Winston, *Infertility*: a Sympathetic Approach, Martin Dunitz, London, 1986, p38–9
3 V Baukloh, 'Biocides in Human Follicular Fluid', *Annals New York Academy of Sciences*, Vol. 442, p240–50. Natural History Programme, BBC, 5 September 1987
4 T. Ya Pshenichnikova & A.M. Doshchanova, 'Clinical Picture, Diagnosis and Treatment of Infertility Associated with Minor Forms of Endometriosis', presentation of Symposium on Diagnosis and Treatment of Infertility, Yerevan, Armenia, USSR, 20–21 May 1985
5 Elsimar Coutinho, 'Recent Advances in the Treatment of Endometriosis', Infertility, Armenia
6 A. Rojanasakul, 'Lipid Profiles in Women with Polycystic Ovarian Disease', abstract, 12th World Congress on Fertility and Sterility, Singapore, 26–31 October 1986
7 David London, 'Prolactin Problems', Conference on Advances in Medicine, Hong Kong, September 1986
8 Donatien Mavoungou et al. 'Sexuality, Puberty and Sexually Transmitted Diseases (STD) in young African girls in Gabon', in press
9 Mark Belsey, 'The Epidemiology of Infertility: a review with particular reference to sub-Saharan Africa', *Bulletin of the World Health Organisation*, Vol 54(3), 1976
10 Lars Westrom, 'Effect of Acute Pelvic Inflammatory Disease on Fertility', *American Journal of Obstetrics and Gynaecology*, Vol 121, No 5, 1 March 1975
11 F. Holz, Scandinavia, 1930, quoted in 10 above.
12 Population Reports, p125
13 *Vogue* (US), May 1987
14 Robert Glass & Ronald Ericsson, *Getting Pregnant in the 1980s*, University of California Press
15 Edwards, et al 'Early Embryonic Mortality in Women', *Fertility and Sterility* Vol 38, p447–52
16 Winston, p35
17 *Issue*, magazine of the National Association for the Childless (Britain), Autumn 1986

18 *Issue*, Spring–May 1987
19 World Health Organisation, Special Program for Research, Development and Training in Human Reproduction, 14th Annual Report, p114–24
20 Population Reports, p119
21 Winston, p61

## CHAPTER 5

1 Peter Singer, 'Ethical Issues in Reproductive Technology: The View from 1987', presentation to the Office of Technology Assessment, Washington, DC, 27 April 1987
2 Margaret Brazier, *Medicine, Patients and the Law*, Penguin, 1987
3 Robert Winston, *Infertility*, p148
4 Mark Perloe & Linda Christie, *Miracle Babies and Other Happy Endings*, Rawson Associates, US, 1986, p227
5 Southern California Cryobank, Inc., Los Angeles
6 Lori Andrews, 'Legal Aspects of Assisted Reproduction', presentation to 5th World Congress on IVF, Norfolk, Virginia, 5–10 April 1987
7 Helen Bequaert Holmes, 'Sex Preselection: Eugenics for Everyone?', *Biomedical Ethics Review*, 1985, p40
8 *The Nation* (Bangkok) 30 January 1987
9 Holmes, p41
10 *Children Conceived by Artificial Insemination*, Summary of a report of the Insemination Committee, SOU 1983:42, p17
11 *Report on Human Artificial Reproduction and Related Matters*, Ontario Law Reform Commission, 1985, p180
12 *Human Artificial Insemination Report*, New South Wales Law Reform Commission, Sydney, 1986, 12. 4 and recommendations 28 & 29
13 Ontario LRC, p167
14 Associated Press, reprinted *San Francisco Examiner*, 2 March 1980
15 *Los Angeles Times*, 1 March 1980
16 *Washington Post*, 11 August 1982
17 Associated Press, reprinted *San Francisco Examiner* 2 March 1980
18 *San Francisco Chronicle*, 18 March 1980
19 *Washington Post*, 29 September 1982
20 *Sunday Times* (Singapore), 4 September 1986

## CHAPTER 6

1 Genesis 38, 8–10
2 Reuters, reprinted *Guardian*, 3 September 1987
3 *Instruction on Respect for Human Life in its Origin and on the Dignity of Procreation. Replies to Certain Questions of the Day*, Congregation for the Doctrine of the Faith, Libreria Editrice Vaticana, 1987
4 'Marriage and the Family', section VIII, 3rd draft of discussion paper by the working party of the Methodist Church (Britain)
5 *Report of the Committee of Inquiry into Human Fertilisation and Embryology* (Warnock Report), London, 1984, 4, 10–4, 12
6 Debate at colloquium on the Legal Regulation of Reproductive Medicine
7 R Jizuka 'The Physical and Mental Development of Children Born Following Artificial Insemination' *International Journal of Fertility*, No 13, p24–32, 1968, quoted by Ernst.
8 Cécile Ernst, 'Psychosocial Aspects of Artificial Procreation', presentation and debate at Colloquium on the Legal Regulation of Reproductive Medicine, Cambridge, 15–17 September 1987
9 Lori Andrews, 'Legal Aspects of Assisted Reproduction', presentation to 5th World Congress on IVF, Norfolk, Virginia, 5–10 April 1987
10 Warnock, 4.16, 4.22 and 4.26
11 *Human Procreation: Ethical Aspects of the New Techniques*, Report of a Working Party of the Council for Science and Society, London, 1984, p39
12 Robert & Elizabeth Snowden, *The Gift of a Child*, Unwin, 1984
13 Mark Perloe, *Miracle Babies and Other Happy Endings*, p231
14 *Report on Human Artificial Reproduction and Related Matters*, Ontario Law Reform Commission, 1985, p158
15 Hertzog quoted in McGuire and Alexander, 16 below
16 Maureen McGuire & Nancy Alexander, 'Artificial Insemination of Single Women', *Fertility and Sterility*, Vol 43 No 2, February 1985
17 Gerald Perkoff, 'Artificial Insemination in a Lesbian', *Archives International Medicine*, Vol 145, March 1985
18 *Human Artificial Insemination Report*, New South Wales Law Reform Commission, Sydney, 1986, p49

## CHAPTER 7

1 *New York Times*, 20 January 1987
2 American Fertility Society (AFS) Ethics Committee, 'Ethical

considerations of the New Reproductive Technologies', *Fertility and Sterility*, Supplement 1, September 1986, Vol 46, No 3, p62–67
3 Genesis 16, 1–6
4 Genesis 30, 1–24
5 *San Francisco Chronicle*, 18 November 1976
6 *Sunday Times* (London), 23 August 1987
7 *This World*, 2 November 1980
8 Kirsty Stevens, *Surrogate Mother, One Woman's Story*, Century, London, 1985
9 BBC TV, 14 October 1987
10 Kim Cotton & Denise Winn, *Baby Cotton, For Love and Money*, Dorling Kindersley Publishers, London, 1985, p37
11 *Sydney Morning Herald*, letter to the editor, 10 August 1984
12 Syndicated, reprinted *Daily Telegraph* (Sydney), 6 April 1984
13 *Health* magazine, reprinted *Sun-Herald* (Sydney), 18 August 1985
14 UPI, reprinted *San Francisco Examiner*, 20 February 1983
15 *Newsweek*, 19 January 1987
16 Handel (below) quoting 1981 study by Franks
17 William Handel, untitled paper on surrogacy, in press
18 Associated Press, reprinted *San Francisco Chronicle*, 7 September 1981
19 Stevens, p67
20 *Daily Star* (London), 27 January 1987
21 Cotton, p183
22 Stevens p182
23 *Daily Star* reprinted *Sunday Telegraph* (Sydney) 13 January 1985 and *Sun* (Sydney) 14 January 1985
24 As reported in the media 15 January 1985
25 *Newsweek* 19 January 1987
26 Press conference 31 March 1987
27 *US News & World Report*, 13 April 1987
28 *New York Times*, 1 April 1987
29 *Mail on Sunday* (London), 12 April 1987
30 *Instruction on Respect for Human Life in its Origin and on the Dignity of Procreation. Replies to Certain Questions of the Day*, Congregation for the Doctrine of the Faith, Libreria Editrice Vaticana, 1987
31 *In vitro Fertilisation and Surrogate Motherhood*, Summary of a Report by the Insemination Committee, SOU 1985:5, P66
32 *Report of the Committee of Inquiry into Human Fertilisation and Embryology* (Warnock Report), London, 1984, 8.1
33 AFS p64
34 As reported in the media
35 *The Australian*, 19 December 1986

36 Carl Wood and Peter Singer, 'Whither Surrogacy', *Australian Medical Journal*
37 *Glamour*, September 1981
38 Morgan Poll, published in the *Bulletin* (Australia) 16 November 1982
39 *Surrogate Motherhood: Australian Public Opinion*, Research Report, New South Wales Law Reform Commission, Sydney, 1987, p.xviii–xx
40 SOFRES poll, October 1984
41 Gallup polls, June 1983 & January 1987
42 *National Enquirer*, 7 May 1987
43 Lori Andrews, 'Surrogate Motherhood; Should the Adoption Model Apply?', Hastings Report, 1987
44 *Report on Human Artificial Reproduction and Related Matters*, Ontario Law Reform Commission, 1985, p241–2
45 Ontario LRC, p237
46 NSW LRC, p47
47 NSW LRC, p25
48 George Annas, 'Redefining Parenthood and Protecting Embryos: Why We Need New Laws,' *The Hastings Centre Report*, October 1984
49 Ontario LRC, p252
50 Susan Wolf, testimony to the Judiciary Committees of the NY State Legislature 10 April 1987
51 AFS guidelines, p13
52 Reprinted *San Francisco Chronicle*, 5 November 1980

## CHAPTER 8

1 Figures from numerous clinics and publications
2 John Rock & Miriam Kenkin, *Science* 100, p105, 1944; also Rock et al, 'The Human Conceptus During the First Two Weeks of Gestation', *American Journal of Obstetrics and Gynaecology*, Vol 55, No 1, January 1948, p6–17 & p440
3 Edwards in Robert Edwards & Patrick Steptoe, *A Matter of Life*, Hutchinson, London, 1980, p59
4 Steptoe, *Matter*, p70
5 Edwards, *Matter*, p94
6 Jean Cohen, 'IVF Pregnancies: Results of an International Survey', presentation to 5th World Congress on IVF, Norfolk, Virginia, 5–10 April 1987
7 Doug Saunders, 'The Australian Register', IVF, Norfolk

8 Paul Lancaster, 'Perinatal Deaths in IVF Pregnancies', presented to Fertility Society of Australia 6th Annual Scientific Meeting, Sydney, 11–14 November 1987

9 Saunders, debate, IVF, Norfolk

10 Linda Applegarth, 'Coping with the Stress of IVF', *Jones Journal*, Issue 3, Winter 1987

11 Haris Massouras, 'The Influence of IVF on the Sex Life of Couples', abstract, World Congress for Sexology, Heidelberg, 16–19 June 1987

12 Patricia Mahlstedt, 'The Psychological Component of Infertility', *Fertility and Sterility*, Vol 43 No 3, March 1985

13 Applegarth & Mahlstedt, 'The Psychosocial Issues of IVF', presentation to 2nd Annual Conference for IVF Nurse Co-ordinators, Norfolk, Virginia, 3–4 April 1987

14 Carl Wood & Ann Westmore, *Test-Tube Conception*, Hill of Content, Melbourne, 1985, p98

15 Lorraine Dunnerstein, presentation to 12th World Congress of Fertility & Sterility, Singapore, 26–31 October 1986

16 Ellen Freeman et al, 'Psychological Evaluation and Support in a Program of IVF', *Fertility and Sterility*, Vol 43 No 1, January 1985

17 *Report of the Committee of Inquiry into Human Fertilisation and Embryology* (Warnock Report), London, 1984, 3.4

18 Suheil Muasher, 'Daily IVF Routine for Physicians', nurse co-ordinators, Norfolk

## CHAPTER 9

1 Ricardo Asch, 'Results of the Multicentre International Cooperative Study of GIFT', presentation to 5th World Congress on IVF, Norfolk, Virginia, 5–10 April 1987

2 Ian Johnston, 'The Place of GIFT in Treatment of the Infertile Patient', IVF, Norfolk

3 Michael Ah-Moye & Ian Craft, 'The GIFT Technique—A New Fertility Option?', in press

4 Paul Lancaster, 'Perinatal Deaths in IVF Pregnancies', Fertility Society of Australia 6th Annual Scientific Meeting, Sydney, 11–14 November 1987

5 Congregation for the Doctrine of the Faith, *Instruction on Respect for Human Life in its Origin and on the Dignity of Procreation. Replies to Certain Questions of the Day*. Libreria Editrice Vaticana, 1987

6 John Yovich, 'Optimum Oocyte Numbers for Transfer in GIFT and PROST Programs', FSA, Sydney

7 Mary Warnock in *Moral Dilemmas in Modern Medicine*, ed. Michael Lockwood, Oxford, 1985, p141
8 *New Idea*, 22 March 1986
9 Alan Trounson, 'Microfertilisation', IVF, Norfolk
10 Jon Gordon, 'Enhancement of Fertilisation by Micromanipulation', IVF, Norfolk
11 *American Health*, June 1987
12 Robert Jansen & John Anderson, 'Catheterisation of the Fallopian Tubes from the Vagina', *The Lancet*, 8 Aug 1987, p309–10; also film 'Ultrasound-Guided Fallopian Cannulation for Gamete or Embryo Transfer', IVF, Norfolk
13 Claude Ranoux, 'The First Seven Births Using a New IVF Technique', IVF, Norfolk
14 Luca Gianaroli, Alan Trounson et al, 'Fertilisation and Culture in Physiological Fluids', IVF, Norfolk
15 Salim Daya, 'Production of Immunosuppressor Factor by Preimplantation Human Embryos—Correlation with Pregnancy', in press
16 Chris O'Neill, 'Embryo-Derived Platelet Activating Factor', IVF, Norfolk; also FSA, Sydney
17 Peter Rogers et al, 'Embryo Implantation in the Anterior Chamber of the Eye', IVF, Norfolk
18 Hossam Abdalla, paper in press

## CHAPTER 10

1 Alan Trounson et al, 'Pregnancy Established in an Infertile Patient After Transfer of a Donated Embyro Fertilised *in vitro*', *British Medical Journal*, Vol 286, 1983, p835–8
2 Comment by Steptoe at 11th World Congress of Fertility and Sterility, Dublin, 28 June 1983, reported in *The Australian* 29 June 1983; also *British Medical Journal*, Vol 286, 1983, p1351–2
3 LeRoy Walters, 'Ethical Aspects of the New Reproductive Technologies', presentation to 5th World Congress on IVF, Norfolk, Virginia, 5–10 April 1987; and subsequently updated
4 *Report of the Committee of Inquiry into Human Fertilisation and Embryology* (Warnock Report), London, 1984, 7.4, 4.25, 6.8, 7.7
5 American Fertility Society (AFS) Ethics Committee, 'Ethical Considerations of the New Reproductive Technologies', *Fertility and Sterility* Supplement, Vol 46 No 3, September 1986, p83
6 Policy Statement of the Californian Medical Association's

Committee on Evolving Trends in Society Affecting Life, November 1986
7 Lori Andrews, 'Legal Aspects of Assisted Reproduction', presentation to 5th World Congress on IVF, Norfolk, Virginia, 5–10 April 1987
8 Ricardo Asch, 'Gamete Intra-fallopian Transfer', presentation to 9th Postgraduate Course on Fertility and Sterility, Florence, 21–23 May 1987
9 Reuter, reprinted *Straits Times* (Singapore), 7 August 1985
10 Zev Rosenwaks, Lucinda Veeck, Hung-Ching Liu, 'Pregnancy following transfer of IVF donated oocytes', *Fertility and Sterility*, Vol 45 No 3, March 1986, p417–20
11 Joseph Schenker, 'Ovum Donation—State of the Art', IVF, Norfolk
12 Peter Singer, 'Ethical Issues in Reproductive Technology: The View From 1987', presentation to Office of Technology Assessment, Washington DC, 27 April 1987
13 Warnock Report 6.6–6.8
14 John Leeton & Jayne Harman, 'Attitudes Toward Egg Donation of 34 Infertile Women Who Donated During Their IVF Treatment', *Journal of IVF and Embryo Transfer*, Vol 3 No 6, 1986, p374–8
15 Alan Trounson, presentation to 12th World Congress of Fertility and Sterility, Singapore, 26–31 October 1986
16 Walters; also Gallup Poll
17 *Weekly World News*, 26 May 1987
18 David Whittingham, 'Cryostorage: Gametes and Embryos', presentation to Fertility Society of Australia 6th Annual Scientific Meeting, Sydney, 11–14 November 1987
19 Mary Warnock in *Moral Dilemmas in Modern Medicine*, ed. Michael Lockwood, Oxford, 1985, p140
20 Warnock Report, 10.2
21 *Report on Human Artificial Reproduction and Related Matters*, Ontario Law Reform Commission, 1985, p173
22 *Human Procreation: Ethical Aspects of The New Techniques*, Report of a Working Party, Council for Science and Society, London, 1985, 4.8
23 Warnock Report, 10.10
24 Warnock Report, 10.8
25 CSS Report, 5.8
26 CSS Report, 7.9

## CHAPTER 11

1 Russell Scott, 'Experimenting and the New Biology: A Consummation Devoutly to Be Wished', presentation to 1st International Conference on Health Law & Ethics, Sydney, August 1986
2 Tor Sverne, 'The Legal Regulation of AID, IVF and Surrogacy', presentation and debate at Colloquium on the Legal Regulation of Reproductive Medicine, Cambridge, 15–17 September 1987
3 *Report on Human Artificial Reproduction and Related Matters*, Ontario Law Reform Commission, 1985, p36
4 C. Broda, presentation to the Austrian Official Enquiry 'Family Policy and Medically Aided Reproduction', Vienna, 4 December 1985
5 AFS Ethics Committee, 'Ethical Considerations of the New Reproductive Technologies', *Fertility and Sterility* Supplement 1, Vol 46 No 3 September 1986
6 Nancy Gertner, Forum on Reproductive Laws for the 1990s, New York, 4 June 1987
7 John Robertson, 'The Legal Regulation of Reproductive Medicine', Regulation, Cambridge
8 Zelman Cowen, 'A View from the Clapham Omnibus', Ethics, Sydney
9 Lori Andrews, 1990s, New York
10 Infertility (Medical Procedures) Act 1984, Victoria
11 Cécile Ernst, 'Psychosocial Aspects of Artificial Procreation', Regulation, Cambridge
12 *IVF, Genome Analysis and Gene Therapy*, Working Group (Benda Committee), West Germany, 1985
13 George Miller, address, 1990s, New York
14 M.C. Horn & W.D. Mosher, 'Use of Services for Family Planning and Infertility', National Centre for Health Statistics, 1984
15 Sevgi Aral & Willard Cates, 'Increasing Concern With Infertility', *Journal of the American Medical Association* (JAMA) Vol 250 No 17, 4 November 1983
16 Glinda Cooper, 'An Analysis of the Costs of Infertility Treatment', *American Journal of Public Health*, Vol 76 No 8, August 1986
17 Shan Ratnam, 'The Ethics of IVF', *Singapore Journal of Obstetrics and Gynaecology*, Vol 16 No 2, July 1985, p95–102
18 Basil Tarlatzis & Alan DeCherney, 'IVF and Embryo Transfer: The Legal Status in Europe', *Journal of IVF and Embryo Transfer*, Vol 3 No 6, *1986*, p343–4
19 *New Straits Times* (Malaysia), editorial, 2 October 1986

20 Ian Kennedy, Reith Lectures, BBC, 1980 also *The Unmasking of Medicine*, Allen & Unwin, London, 1981, p61
21 *Issue* magazine of the National Association for the Childless (Britain), Autumn 1986
22 Robert Winston and Raul Margara, 'Effectiveness of the Treatment for Infertility', reply from Richard Ilford and Maureen Dalton, *British Medical Journal*, 5 September 1987.
23 G R Cunha et al, *Human Pathology*, November 1987, Vol 18 No 11, p1132–43; Gabor Kovacs et al, *Medical Journal of Australia*, 12 May 1984, p575–579; R H Gorwill et al, *American Journal of O&G*, 1982 Vol 144 No 5, p529–532
24 J. Boue & A. Boue, 'Retrospective and prospective epidemiological studies of 1500 karyotyped spontaneous human abortions', *Teratology*, Vol 12, 1975 p11–26
25 Hakan Wramsby et al, 'Chromosome Analysis of Human Oocytes Recovered from Preovulatory Follicles in Stimulated Cycles', *New England Journal of Medicine*, Vol 316 No 3, 15 January 1987
26 Robyn Rowland, article by, *The Age* (Melbourne), 30 March 1987
27 *Sunday Times*, 23 August 1987
28 Ian Craft, letter, 'A Testing Time for Test-Tube Babies', *The Lancet*, 16 May 1987
29 Editorial, *The Lancet*, 16 May 1987
30 *The Guardian* 23 July 1987
31 *Instruction on Respect for Human Life in its Origin and on the Dignity of Procreation. Replies to Certain Questions of the Day*, Congregation for the Doctrine of the Faith, Libreria Editrice Vaticana, 1987
32 Richard McCormick, 'The Importance of Naturalness and Conjugal Gametes', IVF, Norfolk
33 Peter Brady, article by, *Asiaweek*, 15 March 1987
34 *Weekend Australian*, editorial, 14–15 March 1987
35 *Newsweek*, 23 April 1987
36 *New Idea* (Australia) 6 April 1987
37 *Weekend Australian* 14–15 March 1987
38 Georgeanna Jones, 'Reply to the Vatican *Instruction*', letter to the editor, *The Ledger Star*, (Norfolk, Virginia), 10 May. 1987

## CHAPTER 12

1 Robert Edwards & Patrick Steptoe, *A Matter of Life*, Hutchinson, London, 1980, p91

2 Anne McLaren, 'Prelude to Embryogenesis', presentation to and reprinted in *Human Embryo Research: Yes or No?* Ciba Foundation, London, 1986, p12
3 *Report of the Committee of Inquiry into Human Fertilisation and Embryology* (Warnock Report), London, 1984, 11. 19
4 *Human Embryo Experimentation in Australia*, Report of the Senate Select Committee on the Human Embryo Experimentation Bill, Australian Government Publishing Service, Canberra, 1986, 3.15
5 Ian Donald, Introduction, *Test-Tube Babies: A Christian View*, Unity Press, London, 1985, p6
6 *Human Procreation: Ethical Aspects of the New Techniques*, Report of a Working Party, Council for Science and Society, London, 1985, 3.21 and 3.22
7 Royal Commission on Contraception, Sterilisation and Abortion, New Zealand, 1977, p184
8 Brian Harradine, 'From Animal Experimentation to Clinical Application', ANZAAS Congress, Melbourne, 28 August 1985
9 John Bowker, Ciba, p167
10 Bowker, Ciba, p175
11 Bowker, Ciba, p173–4
12 Senate Committee 3.18 and 3.23
13 Peter Singer, 'Ethical Issues in Reproductive Technologies: the View from 1987', presentation to Office of Technology Assessment, Washington, DC, 27 April 1987
14 Peter Singer, 'The Ethics of Embyro Research', presentation and debate at 1st International Conference on Health Law & Ethics, Sydney, August 1986
15 Gerard Wright, *Test-Tube Babies*, p51
16 Cecil Clothier, Ciba, p2
17 HEW *Support of Research Involving Human IVF and Embryo Transfer*, report of the US Department of Health, Education and Welfare, Ethics Advisory Board, released 4 May 1979
18 American Fertility Society (AFS) Ethics Committee, 'Ethical Considerations of the New Reproductive Technologies', *Fertility and Sterility* Supplement 1, Vol 46 No 3, September 1986, p30
19 *In Vitro Fertilisation, Discussion Paper 2*, New South Wales Law Reform Commission, Sydney, July 1987, 3.8
20 Warnock Report 11.16 & 11.17
21 Ruth Hubbard et al, 'GeneWatch Response to the Vatican Statement', *GeneWatch*, March–April 1987
22 *The Australian*, 27 June 1984
23 *Report on Human Artificial Reproduction and Related Matters*, Ontario Law Reform Commission, 1985, p216

24 John Loudon, presentation to 12th Congress of Fertility and Sterility, Singapore, 26–31 October 1986
25 Alan Trounson, *New Society*, reprinted *Weekend Australian*, 17–18 May 1986
26 Bowker, Ciba, p178
27 NSW LRC, 8.21
28 NHMRC, evidence to Senate Committee 26 February 1986
29 Patsy Littlejohn, 'IVF Patients and Their Attitudes to Ethical Issues: Replies to a Questionnaire', in Peter Singer and Deane Wells, *The Reproduction Revolution*, Oxford University Press, 1984, p234–243
30 E M Adler et al, 'Attitudes of Women of Reproductive Age to IVF and Embryo Transfer', discussed by Ciba, p195
31 Christian Unity poll on embryo experimentation, . . .
32 National Opinion Polls, 28–30 June 1985, in Ciba, p152
33 Lori Andrews, 'Legal Aspects of Assisted Reproduction', presention to 5th World Congress on IVF, Norfolk, Viginia, 5–10 April 1987
34 Robert Edwards, Ciba, p195
35 Bernard Williams, Ciba, p196
36 Cecil Clothier, Ciba, p215
37 Senate Report, 3.16
38 Brian Harradine, second reading speech, Human Embryo Experimentation Bill 1985, Senate, 23 April 1985
39 *Report on the Disposition of Embryos Produced by IVF*, The Committee to Consider the Social, Ethical and Legal Issues Arising from IVF (Waller Report), Melbourne, August 1984 3.27
40 Waller Report, Appendix A, p62
41 Senate Report, 3.28
42 David Baird, Ciba, p206
43 Antonia Gerard, Ciba, p210
44 Gordon Dunstan, Ciba, p209
45 Warnock Report 11.28
46 Senate Report, 3.33
47 Anne McLaren, Ciba, p206
48 *Instruction on Respect for Human Life in its Origin and on the Dignity of Procreation. Replies to Certain Questions of the Day*, Congregation for the Doctrine of the Faith, Libreria Editrice Vaticana, 1987.
49 Nicholas Tonti-Filippini, *Age* (Melbourne), 3 March 1987

## CHAPTER 13

1 Leviticus 12, 2
2 Talmud (Tractate Niddah, 31a)

3 Niddah 70B–71a

4 Gabor Kovacs & Kenneth Waldron, 'Sex Preselection—a Review', *Australian Family Physician*, Vol 16 No 5, May 1985

5 Viola Roggencamp, 'Abortion of a Special Kind: Male Sex Selection in India', in *Test-Tube Women*, Ed Rita Arditti, Renata Duelli Klein & Shelley Minden, Pandora Press, London, 1984 p272–274

6 quoted in Wendy Cooper, *The Fertile Years*, Hutchinson, London, 1987

7 *Sun-Herald* (Sydney) 7 March 1976

8 *Report of the Committee of Inquiry into Human Fertilisation and Embryology* (Warnock Report), London, 1984, 12.14

9 Peter Singer & Deane Wells, *The Reproduction Revolution* Oxford University Press, 1984, p159

10 William Walters in 'Cloning, Ectogenesis and Hybrids' *Test-Tube Babies*, Eds. William Walters & Peter Singer, Oxford University Press 1982, p114

11 Quoted in Paul Ramsay, *Fabricated Man*, Yale University Press, 1970

12 Singer & Wells, p158

13 Jerome Lejeune, 'Genetic Engineering: Test-Tube Babies are Babies', in *Test-Tube Babies: A Christian View*, Unity Press, London, 1985, p39

14 Peter Singer, 'Ethical Issues in Reproductive Technology: The View from 1987', presentation to the Office of Technology Assessment, Washington, DC, 27 April 1987

15 Peter Singer, 'The Ethics of Embryo Research', paper and debate, 1st International Conference on Health Law & Ethics, Sydney, August 1986

16 Warnock Report, 12.5 and 12.6

17 George Annas, 'The Ethics of Embyro Research: Not as Easy as it Sounds', Ethics, Sydney

18 Gary Anderson, 'Use of Chimeras to Study Development', in press

19 Warnock Report, 12.2 & 12.3

20 *The Australian*, 6 May 1987

21 *Courier-Mail* (Brisbane), 24 April 1987

22 *New York Times*, 17 April 1987

23 National Commission for the Protection of Human Subjects of Biomedical and Behavioural Research, Report and Recommendations: Research on the Fetus, p13

24 Carlo Bulletti et al, 'Extracorporeal Perfusion of the Human Uterus', *American Journal of Obstetrics and Gynaecology*, Vol 154, March 1986, p683–8

25 Carlo Bulletti et al, 'A 48-hour preservation of an isolated human uterus: endometrial responses to sex steroids', *Fertility and Sterility*, Vol 47 No 1, January 1987 p122–9
26 Questionnaire on reproductive technologies prepared by Judianne Densen-Gerber

## CHAPTER 14

1 *Straits Times* (Singapore), editorial 16 January 1985
2 Lori Andrews, 'Legal Aspects of Assisted Reproduction', presentation to 5th World Congress on IVF, Norfolk, Virginia, 5–10 April 1987
3 Patrick Steptoe, BBC TV, 14 October 1987
4 Denis Hawkins, University of London/Hammersmith Hospital, correspondence to a colleague, January 1985
5 Brian Harradine, 'From Animal Experimentation to Clinical Application', ANZAAS Congress, Melbourne, 28 August 1985
6 Ian Kennedy, 'The Moral Status of the Embryos', Chapter 6 in *Treat me Right: Essays in Medical Law and Politics*, Oxford University Press, 1988
7 *The Times*, editorial, 24 May 1984
8 *Science* Vol 223, 1983, p916
9 Hans Jochen quoted by C. Broda in presentation to Austria's Official Enquiry 'Family Policy and Medical Aided Reproduction', Vienna, 4 December 1985
10 Broda, Enquiry, Vienna
11 Russell Scott, 'Experimenting and the New Biology: A Consummation Devoutly to Be Wished', presentation to 1st International Conference on Health Law & Ethics, Sydney, August 1986
12 Michael Kirby, 'Medical Technology and New Frontiers of Family Law', *Ethics*, Sydney
13 Questionnaire on reproductive technologies prepared by Judianne Densen-Gerber

# INDEX